R. Baines

C000042146

DK GCSE MATHS

For Intermediate and Higher Levels

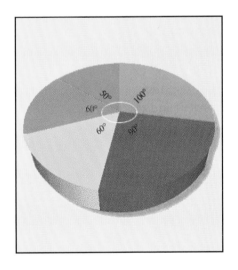

LONDON • NEW YORK • SYDNEY • DELHI

www.dk.com

Consultant Jim Miller

Jim Miller has over 30 years experience teaching GCSE and A Level Maths. He has been a GCSE examiner for over 20 years, and is currently Chair of Mathematics of a major UAB. He is also an Open University course tutor.

Editor Clare Pearson
Designer Suzanne Metcalfe-Megginson
Managing Editor Bridget Gibbs
Managing Art Editor Peter Bailey
Production Chris Avgherinos
Jacket Design John Dinsdale
Proof Reader Anna Hughes

Illustrators Kessia Beverley-Smith; Moises Chicharro; Matt Clifford; Christina Fairminer; Nathaniel Gale; Genny Haines; Sarah Harvey; Emma Humphries-Davies; Jon-Paul James; Steve Lewin; Jonathan Lord

First published in Great Britain in 1999 by Dorling Kindersley Limited, 9 Henrietta Street, London WC2E 8PS

2 4 6 8 10 9 7 5 3 1

Copyright © 1999 Dorling Kindersley Limited, London

All rights reserved. No part of this publication may be reproduced, stored in a retrieval system, or transmitted in any form or by any means, electronic, mechanical, photocopying, recording or otherwise, without the prior written permission of the copyright owner.

A CIP catalogue record for this book is available from the British Library.

ISBN: 0 7513 5934 3

Colour reproduction by First Impressions, UK

Printed and bound in Zrinski, Croatia

Contents

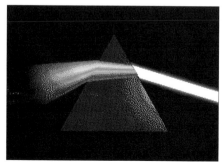
Index notation

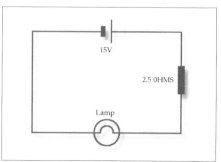
Construct and evaluate formulae

SHAPE, SPACE, AND MEASURES

HANDLING DATA

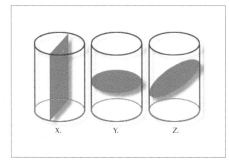

Symmetry

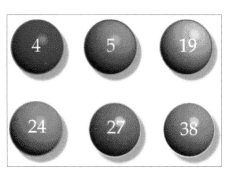

Probability

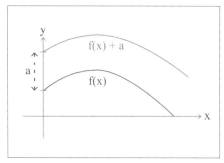

Transformation of functions

Introduction

This book will help you to study and revise for GCSE Maths. You can use it to test your knowledge of the mathematics covered in your syllabus.

Structure of this book

This book is divided into four sections, corresponding to the four areas of study at Key Stage 4: number; algebra; shape, space, and measures; and handling data. These sections are further broken down into sub-topics, each with key facts, followed by questions and answers.

Key facts

These provide a brief summary of the essential ideas that relate to specific topics within each section. You can use them as a quick reminder of useful information, and as a checklist of essential facts.

Questions

The first few questions in each topic are generally of the true/false type, which test basic mathematical understanding. The remaining questions are multiple choice, with only one right answer for each one. Some questions are easy, others are moderate, and some are much harder. There are higher level questions at the end of most topics. Make sure that you read the question carefully because it is often just one word that can make the difference between a right and a wrong answer. Even if you cannot pick the correct answer straight away, you may be able to work it out using your general mathematical understanding.

Answers

In many ways, this is the most important part of the book. Check whether your answer is correct or not. If it is – well done! Make sure you fully understand why the answer you chose was the right one. If your answer is incorrect – do not despair! Make sure that you understand where and why you went wrong by carefully reading the explanation given with each answer. These explanations will give you the information you need to consolidate your understanding.

Grades and levels at GCSE

There are three levels of entry for GCSE Maths: Foundation, Intermediate and Higher. The following grades can be achieved:
Foundation   D, E, F, G, and U (unclassified)
Intermediate   B, C, D, E, and U (unclassified)
Higher   A*, A, B, C, and U (unclassified)
There is an overlap, therefore, of two grades between adjacent levels. However, if you do not achieve the lowest pass grade available at any level, you will be unclassified.

Currently, a review of the "tiering" system in GCSE Maths is taking place. It is very unlikely that there will be any change until after the summer 2001 examination. From then, although the range of mathematical topics is likely to remain unchanged, the three level arrangement may alter. (For example, there may be a reduction to two levels, as in some other GCSE subjects.)

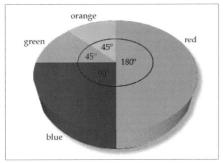

Representing data

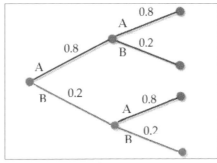

Probability: tree diagram

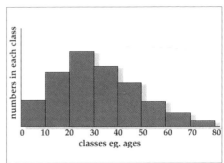

Analysing and interpreting data

Marking system

Use this marking system to discover your strengths and weaknesses. The marks are best worked out in percentages. You can convert your scores by using the following equation: (100 ÷ [maximum score]) × your score = % score. Use the key at the bottom of the page to assess your results.

SECTIONS		Intermediate Level		Higher Level	
NUMBER:	Place value, fractions, decimals and percentages	/12 =	%	/12 =	%
	Index notation	/25 =	%	/34 =	%
	Multiples and factors	/8 =	%	/16 =	%
	Mental computations	/23 =	%	/23 =	%
	Calculations	/39 =	%	/43 =	%
	Estimation, approximation, and significant figures	/29 =	%	/31 =	%
	Problems	/46 =	%	/61 =	%
ALGEBRA	Use of letters	/25 =	%	/28 =	%
	Number patterns	/19 =	%	/19 =	%
	Properties of functions	/9 =	%	/11 =	%
	Construct and evaluate formulae	/19 =	%	/21 =	%
	Manipulate algebraic expressions	/43 =	%	/55 =	%
	Solve linear, simultaneous, and quadratic expressions; and higher polynomials by trial and improvement	/34 =	%	/39 =	%
	Solve inequalities	/16 =	%	/18 =	%
	Construct and use tangents to curves/area under curves	/8 =	%	/11 =	%
	Transformation of functions			/10 =	%
SHAPE, SPACE, AND MEASURES	Representation of 2D and 3D shapes	/12 =	%	/12 =	%
	Classification of polygons	/30 =	%	/30 =	%
	Symmetry	/20 =	%	/20 =	%
	Angles	/48 =	%	/48 =	%
	Trigonometry and Pythagoras	/52 =	%	/52 =	%
	Co-ordinates and transformations	/32 =	%	/32 =	%
	Scale	/7 =	%	/7 =	%
	Loci	/9 =	%	/9 =	%
	Standard units of measure	/44 =	%	/52 =	%
	Discrete and continuous measure	/16 =	%	/22 =	%
	Compound measures	/21 =	%	/24 =	%
	Perimeter, area, and volume	/39 =	%	/47 =	%
HANDLING DATA	Collecting data	/17 =	%	/25 =	%
	Representing data	/38 =	%	/38 =	%
	Analysing and interpreting data	/40 =	%	/40 =	%
	Probability	/50 =	%	/56 =	%

				Average Score		
0–25 % Long way to go!	26–50 % Keep going!	51–75 % Nearly there!	76–100 % Excellent!	/840 =	%	/946 =	%

Revision tips

General tips

Set yourself a reasonable revision timetable and try to stick to it. When you're not revising, relax and do things that you enjoy.

Find a quiet area in which to revise. You will take in much more if you have no distractions, such as the television or music.

Try to revise at a regular time each day. For example, in the holidays you might decide to revise from 10:00 am to 12 noon and from 5:00 pm to 7:00 pm every day.

When you return to your revision after a break, spend a few minutes thinking about the material covered in the last session. This will help you to consolidate what you have already revised.

In an ideal world, you should aim to complete your revision two weeks before the exam. In the final two weeks you should try plenty of past exam questions.

Try to stay fit and healthy – this means you should get plenty of sleep, eat properly, and take regular exercise.

There are lots of people who want you to do well – friends, parents, relatives, and teachers. These people will always be happy to help you.

Your revision sessions

Try to make each revision session about 35 minutes long. A common mistake is to concentrate hard for the first five minutes, daydream for the next 25 minutes, and then to resume a high level of concentration for only the last five minutes. You think that you've done 35 minutes of hard work, but really you have done only ten! The secret of good revision is making the most of these 35 minute sessions. The following tips should help you do this.

• The sessions must be varied. In any one session you should aim to read, answer questions, and highlight key words. You may find it useful to write your notes onto revision cards to use as a reminder of important facts.

• Before you start, make sure that you have everything that you need.

• The first thing you must do is to make sure that you understand what you are revising. There is no point learning something that you don't understand. Do not be afraid to ask your teachers any questions that you might have – they are there to help you. Make sure you ask at a sensible time, and not at the very last minute.

• Once you understand a topic, make notes on it in your own words. If possible, draw a diagram. It is easier to remember things as pictures rather than as words.

• Test yourself at regular intervals by using the questions in this book. Start by looking at questions that address just one topic, and progress to those that address a wider range of topics.

• As you revise a topic, use a highlighter pen to pick out the key words and points. After going through your notes several times, you will be able to fit enough basic information on to one revision card to remind you of a whole topic. Remember to use these cards often to test yourself on the information you have already learnt.

• Keep your notes and cards organized! This is very important but often forgotten – you will lose much of the benefit of your revision if you lose your notes.

• As the exam gets closer, try past questions from your exam board. When you first start answering questions you may have to use your notes to produce a full answer. As your knowledge improves, you will need to refer to your notes less. If you cannot find an answer, ask your teacher. Don't just ignore it – a similar type of question may come up in your exam. Be aware of the time taken to answer a question; your answering speed will increase as your knowledge improves.

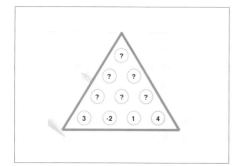

Multiples and factors

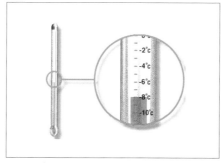

Mental computations

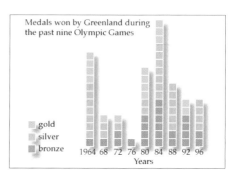

Calculations

The night before the exam

There are several different views as to what to do the night before the exam, ranging from working all night to having the afternoon off school the day before in order to relax. The best solution lies between these two.

We have consulted doctors and examiners to come up with this simple list. It is incredibly easy to follow and will give you the best chance of success in your exam.

• Have a good meal.

• Go over your revision cards for about an hour early in the evening.

• If you have any questions, ask someone rather than remain silent and worry about it.

• In the hour before your regular bedtime, try to relax. Many people relax by watching television or by listening to music.

• Go to bed at your regular bedtime and try to get a good night's sleep.

The exam

Arrive at least 15 minutes before the exam starts.

Make sure you have everything you need – pens, a pencil, a rubber, a watch, a ruler, compass, protractor, and a calculator.

Read all the instructions for the exam carefully and note the time allocated for the exam. Plan your time carefully. The marks available for each question give you a guide as to how much information the examiners are after. For example, a 2-mark question generally requires two separate points or one fully explained point as an answer.

Look out for key words in the question. For example, "calculate" means show your calculations.

Always read the question at least twice.

Exam presentation

Marks are awarded for correct steps as well as for the answer, so it is vital to **show all of your working**, however trivial it may appear.

• If a question requires a calculation, always show your working and use the correct units.

• In a calculation, work with more decimal places than the question requires and then reduce your final answer to the required number of decimal places. This will ensure that your answer is accurate. For example, if the question asks for your answer to 2 decimal places, do the calculation working to at least 3 decimal places. When you have your final answer reduce it to 2 decimal figures.

• If a diagram will aid your answer, use one. Make sure that it is neat, and properly labelled.

• Although units (cm^2 or kg) are given in many questions, there are likely to be some questions where you have to include the correct units.

• When you have answered everything that you can, and there is time remaining, check through as much of your work as possible. One useful method is to see whether your answer is a sensible one, in the context of the question. Another hint is to do the question "backwards", that is, use the answer you have obtained, and see if it gets you back to the initial information by following the steps in reverse order.

And finally...GOOD LUCK!

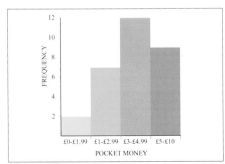

Representing data

Collecting data

Transformation of functions

Number

Having confidence in the behaviour of numbers is an essential skill, which can be developed by regular application of the rules that govern the way numbers interact with each other. Familiarity with decimals, fractions, percentages, the four rules of number, and a flexible range of computational techniques, is a pre-requisite for having a "feel" for numbers. Calculators and computers can be effectively used to enhance understanding of numbers.

Place value, fractions, decimals, and percentages

 KEY FACTS

• The "6" in the number 136.7 is 6 units, the "3" is 30 units, the "1" is 100 units, and the "7" is $\frac{7}{10}$ units (or 0.7 units).

• Multiplying by 10 moves each digit into the next column to the left. So, 209.31×10 is 2093.1 and 0.068×10 is 0.68.

• Similarly, dividing by 10 moves each digit into the next column to the right. So $86.03 \div 10 = 8.603$ and $0.027 \div 10 = 0.0027$ (the missing space needs to be filled with a "0").

• $0.35 = 35\%$ (i.e. multiply by 100).

• $0.35 = \frac{35}{100} = \frac{7}{20}$ (i.e. divide the decimal by 100).

• $42\% = 0.42$ (i.e. divide by 100).

• $42\% = \frac{42}{100} = \frac{21}{50}$ (i.e. divide by 100).

• $\frac{2}{5} = 2 \div 5 = 0.4$ (divide 2 by 5).

• $\frac{2}{5} = \frac{2}{5} \times 100 = \frac{200}{5} = 40\%$ (i.e. multiply by 100).

 QUESTIONS

1 How much money is shown on the following diagram?

☐ (a) £5.99
☐ (b) £6.01
☐ (c) £601
☐ (d) 610p
☐ (e) 591p

Q1

2 $\frac{3}{5}$ of a field is covered with daffodils. Which of the following fractions is this is equivalent to?

☐ (a) $\frac{14}{20}$
☐ (b) $\frac{6}{15}$
☐ (c) $\frac{7}{10}$
☐ (d) $\frac{15}{20}$
☐ (e) $\frac{9}{15}$

3 Which of the following fractions is $\frac{2}{3}$ equivalent to?

☐ (a) $\frac{18}{24}$
☐ (b) $\frac{10}{30}$
☐ (c) $\frac{12}{13}$
☐ (d) $\frac{10}{16}$
☐ (e) $\frac{16}{24}$

4 In a maternity hospital, $\frac{1}{6}$ of the babies are born on a Tuesday. Which of the fractions below is this equivalent to?

☐ (a) $\frac{11}{60}$
☐ (b) $\frac{1}{16}$
☐ (c) $\frac{3}{20}$
☐ (d) $\frac{5}{30}$
☐ (e) $\frac{6}{30}$

5 A double decker bus is $\frac{3}{4}$ full. Which of the fractions below is this not equivalent to?

☐ (a) $\frac{16}{24}$
☐ (b) $\frac{75}{100}$
☐ (c) $\frac{6}{8}$
☐ (d) $\frac{18}{24}$
☐ (e) $\frac{36}{48}$

6 A large cheese was bought by

Lou. She left it in the larder and when she returned only $\frac{3}{8}$ was left. Which of the fractions below is not equivalent to $\frac{3}{8}$?

☐ (a) $\frac{12}{32}$
☐ (b) $\frac{6}{16}$
☐ (c) $\frac{30}{80}$
☐ (d) $\frac{15}{40}$
☐ (e) $\frac{16}{40}$

7 At a basketball match $\frac{4}{5}$ of the spectators were men. Which of the fractions below is this not equivalent to?

☐ (a) $\frac{44}{55}$
☐ (b) $\frac{36}{45}$
☐ (c) $\frac{28}{35}$
☐ (d) $\frac{40}{45}$
☐ (e) $\frac{8}{10}$

8 Anne and Kate shared the driving on a long journey. Kate did $\frac{4}{10}$ of the journey. How is this written in decimal form?

☐ (a) 0.04
☐ (b) 0.4
☐ (c) 4.0
☐ (d) 0.410
☐ (e) 4.10

9 The fraction of boys in a class was $\frac{3}{4}$. How is this fraction written in decimal form?

☐ (a) 0.34
☐ (b) 0.75
☐ (c) 3.4
☐ (d) 0.6
☐ (e) 0.8

10 A recipe for toffee stated that $\frac{1}{3}$ of the ingredients must be milk. How can this fraction be written in decimal form?

☐ (a) 0.33
☐ (b) 0.3
☐ (c) 0.333 ...

☐ (d) 0.13
☐ (e) 3.13

11 ³⁄₂₀ of a lawn was covered in daisies. How can this fraction be written in decimal form?

☐ (a) 0.15
☐ (b) 0.20
☐ (c) 0.3
☐ (d) 0.320
☐ (e) 0.18

12 ⅑ of a 1 km race was downhill. Write this as a decimal, using a calculator.

☐ (a) 0.111 ...
☐ (b) 0.1
☐ (c) 0.9
☐ (d) 0.11
☐ (e) 0.19

Index notation

KEY FACTS

• $a \times a \times a$ can be written as a^3, and $4 \times p \times p \times p \times p \times p = 4p^5$.

• Hence, $2a^2 \times 4a^3 = 2 \times a \times a \times 4 \times a \times a \times a = 8a^5$.

• Also, $p^7 \div p^4 = (p \times p \times p \times p \times p \times p \times p) \div (p \times p \times p \times p) = p \times p \times p = p^3$.

• Also $(y^2)^5 = (y \times y) \times (y \times y) \times (y \times y) \times (y \times y) \times (y \times y) = y^{10}$.

• In general:
i) $a^m \times a^n = a^{m+n}$; $a^m \div a^n = a^{m-n}$; $(a^m)^k = a^{mk}$.
ii) $b^3 \div b^5 = \frac{b \times b \times b}{b \times b \times b \times b \times b} = \frac{1}{b^2}$. This can be written as b^{-2}. Hence, $a^{-m} = \frac{1}{a^m}$, in general.

• Large numbers can be written in a more concise and convenient way, using standard (index) form.
E.g. $5800 = 5.8$ (must be between 1 and 10) $\times 10^3$ (must be a whole number, either +, −, or 0).
$5800 = 580 \times 10 = 58 \times 100 = 5.8 \times 1000 = 5.8 \times 10^3$.

QUESTIONS

1 The velocity of light is about 300 000 km/s. Write this in standard form.

☐ (a) 3×10^5
☐ (b) 0.3×10^6
☐ (c) 30×10^4
☐ (d) 3×10^4
☐ (e) 3×10^6

2 The diameter of a molecule is about 0.000 000 000 1 mm. Write this in standard form.

☐ (a) 0.1×10^{-10}
☐ (b) 1×10^{-10}
☐ (c) 1×1010
☐ (d) 1×1011
☐ (e) 1×10^{-9}

3 The Sun is about 0.000 016 light years from the Earth. Write this in standard form.

☐ (a) 16×10^5
☐ (b) 1.6×10^4
☐ (c) 1.6×10^{-5}
☐ (d) 0.16×10^{-5}
☐ (e) 1.6×10^{-6}

4 The wavelength of visible light is about 5.0×10^{-5} cm. Write this in full decimal form.

☐ (a) 0.000 5 cm
☐ (b) 0.000 05 cm
☐ (c) 0.000 005 cm
☐ (d) 0.005 cm
☐ (e) 500 000 cm

Q4

5 The half-life of a chemical isotope is about 2.7×10^{-6} seconds. Write this in full decimal form.

☐ (a) 0.000 000 27
☐ (b) 0.000 027
☐ (c) 0.000 002 7
☐ (d) 27 000 000
☐ (e) 27.000 000

6 The hair on a spider's leg is 4×10^{-3} m long. Write this in full decimal form.

☐ (a) 0.000 4
☐ (b) 0.004
☐ (c) 0.04
☐ (d) 4.000
☐ (e) 4000

7 A colony of bacteria doubled in size every hour. After eight hours there were $2^3 \times 2^5$. What does this simplify to in index form?

☐ (a) 128
☐ (b) 64
☐ (c) 4
☐ (d) 2^{14}
☐ (e) 2^8

8 The number of flowers in a flowerbed is equivalent to $4^3 \times 4^4 \div 4^2$. How many flowers is this?

☐ (a) 4^5
☐ (b) 4^4
☐ (c) 4^6
☐ (d) 4
☐ (e) $12 \times 16 \div 8$

9 A seahorse had 25 spines on its back. Which of the following is not true about 25?

☐ (a) $25 = \sqrt{625}$
☐ (b) $25 = 125 \div 5$
☐ (c) $25 = {}^3\sqrt{625}$
☐ (d) $25 = 25^1$
☐ (e) $25 = 5^5 \div 5^3$

10 A new asteroid 5 000 000 000 light years away was discovered by American scientists. Write this in standard index form.

☐ (a) 5×10^9
☐ (b) 59
☐ (c) 5×10^8
☐ (d) 5^{10}
☐ (e) 0.5×10^{10}

11 The wavelength of radiation used in a microwave is 2450 Hz. Write this number in standard index form.

☐ (a) 2.45×10^4
☐ (b) 2.45×10^2
☐ (c) $2.45 \times 10\,000$
☐ (d) 2.45×10^0
☐ (e) 2.45×10^3

12 A space probe reached a speed of 4 560 000 mph. Write this in standard index form.

☐ (a) $4.56 \times 1\,000\,000$
☐ (b) 4.56×10^6
☐ (c) 4.65^5
☐ (d) 4.56×10^5
☐ (e) 5.56×10^6

13 The diameter of the Earth is about 12 680 km. Write this in standard index form.

☐ (a) $1.268 \times 10 \times 4$
☐ (b) 1.268×10^5
☐ (c) 1.268×10^3
☐ (d) 1.268×10^4
☐ (e) 1.268^5

14 The average human lives for 1 000 000 000 seconds. Write this in standard index form.

☐ (a) 10×10^9
☐ (b) 1×10^8
☐ (c) 1×10^9
☐ (d) 1×9
☐ (e) 1^9

15 The area of the Sahara desert is 8.6×10^6 km². Write this out in full.

☐ (a) 404 567 km²
☐ (b) 860 000 km²
☐ (c) 86 000 000 km²
☐ (d) 8 600 000 km²
☐ (e) 52 km²

16 There are about 1.83×10^5 species of butterfly. Write this out in full.

☐ (a) 1.83000
☐ (b) 183 000
☐ (c) 18 300
☐ (d) 1 830 000
☐ (e) 9.15

17 There are 5×10^9 red blood cells in 1 millilitre of blood. Write this out in full.

☐ (a) 500 000 000
☐ (b) 5 000 000 000
☐ (c) 1 953 125

☐ (d) 450
☐ (e) 5 999 999 999

18 A very popular newspaper sold 34 050 000 copies a day. Write this in standard index form.

☐ (a) 3.405×10^8
☐ (b) 3.405×10^6
☐ (c) 3.405×10^7
☐ (d) 3.405×10^6
☐ (e) $34.05 \times 10 \times 7$

19 Look at the calculator display shown below. What does this mean?

☐ (a) 9.36000
☐ (b) 9.365
☐ (c) 9.36×5
☐ (d) 93 600
☐ (e) 9.36×10^5

Q19

20 Look at the calculator display shown below. Which of the following is not true about it?

☐ (a) It equals 31 000
☐ (b) It equals 3.1^4
☐ (c) It equals 31 thousand
☐ (d) It equals 3.1×10^4
☐ (e) It equals 310×100

Q20

21 There are roughly 35 600 fans at a football match. Write this in standard index form.

☐ (a) $3.56 \times 10\,000$
☐ (b) 3.56^4
☐ (c) 3.56×10^4
☐ (d) 3.56
☐ (e) 0.356×10^5

22 There are 2.05×10^2 fishes in an area of the ocean. How many fish is this?

☐ (a) 205
☐ (b) 250
☐ (c) 2.05
☐ (d) 2050
☐ (e) 205^2

23 13 012 000 raindrops hit four window panes. How many raindrops is this per window pane? Write the answer in standard index form.

☐ (a) 3253×10^3
☐ (b) 3 253 000
☐ (c) 3.253×10^5
☐ (d) 3.253×10^3
☐ (e) 3.253×10^6

24 There are 4^6 raspberries on a bush. Use your calculator to work out 4^6.

☐ (a) 4 000 000
☐ (b) 24
☐ (c) 4096
☐ (d) 400 000
☐ (e) 48

25 There are 3^4 feathers on a peacock. Ensuring you choose the correct calculator sequence, determine how many feathers the peacock has.

☐ (a) 3000
☐ (b) 12
☐ (c) 81
☐ (d) 30 000
☐ (e) 64

● QUESTIONS

Higher Level only

26 Matt has the number 9 on his rugby shirt. Which of the following is not true about 9?

☐ (a) $9 = 3^2 \times 1$
☐ (b) $9 = {}^9/_3$
☐ (c) $9 = \sqrt{(3^2 \times 3^2)}$
☐ (d) $9 = 3^2 + 3^0$
☐ (e) $9 = 3^2/_1$

27 There are four relay runners in four teams. This equals $4^2 = 16$ runners. Which of the following is not true about 4^2?

☐ (a) $4^2 = 2^4$
☐ (b) $4^2 = 16^1$

☐ (c) $4^2 = \sqrt{256}$
☐ (d) $4^2 = 16^0$
☐ (e) $4^2 = (2^2)^2$

28 Simplify $\sqrt{(9^3 \times 9^5)}/9^{-1}$.

☐ (a) 9^8
☐ (b) 9^7
☐ (c) 9^6
☐ (d) 9^4
☐ (e) 9^5

29 Simplify $4^2 \times (4^{1/2})^4/4^3$.

☐ (a) 4
☐ (b) 16
☐ (c) 2
☐ (d) 45
☐ (e) 48

30 Simplify $3^5 \times 3^{-1}$.

☐ (a) 3^5
☐ (b) $(4^4)^{3/4}$
☐ (c) $(3^4)^{1/2}$
☐ (d) 27

☐ (e) 81

31 With a calculator work out $64^{1/3}$.

☐ (a) $\frac{1}{4}$
☐ (b) $\frac{1}{8}$
☐ (c) $\frac{1}{2}$
☐ (d) -4
☐ (e) $^{-1}\!/_4$

32 Without a calculator, work out $27^{2/3}$.

☐ (a) 81
☐ (b) 18
☐ (c) 6
☐ (d) 12
☐ (e) 9

33 Without a calculator work out $(\frac{1}{4})^{1/2}$.

☐ (a) $\frac{1}{8}$
☐ (b) 2
☐ (c) $\frac{1}{2}$

☐ (d) $\frac{1}{6}$
☐ (e) $\frac{1}{16}$

34 Simplify $\sqrt{3}/\sqrt{27}$.

☐ (a) $^3\!/_{27}$
☐ (b) $\frac{1}{3}$
☐ (c) $\frac{1}{9}$
☐ (d) 9
☐ (e) $\frac{1}{27}$

Multiples and factors

 KEY FACTS

• Multiples of a whole number, x, are numbers that x will divide into exactly (e.g. 4, 8, 12, 16, 20 are multiples of 4).

• Factors of a number, N, are any whole numbers that will divide exactly into N (e.g. 12 has factors 1, 2, 3, 4, 6 and 12).

• A prime number has two different factors only – these are 1 and itself. The first few prime numbers are 2, 3, 5, 7, 11, 13, 17, 19, 23, 29 … etc (1 is not considered prime, as it does not have two different factors).

 QUESTIONS

1 "The only common factor of 6, 12, and 15 is 3." Is this statement true or false?

☐ (a) True
☐ (b) False

2 Five cyclists in a race had the following numbers on their jerseys: 9, 43, 27, 57, 6. If the winner of the race had a prime number on his jersey, which number was this?

☐ (a) 27
☐ (b) 9
☐ (c) 43
☐ (d) 57
☐ (e) 6

3 Snow fell on the 7th, 9th, 13th, 29th, and 31st of December. Which of these numbers is not prime?

☐ (a) 29
☐ (b) 7
☐ (c) 13
☐ (d) 9
☐ (e) 31

4 Express 60 as the product of prime numbers.

☐ (a) $2 \times 2 \times 5 \times 3 \times 1 \times 1$
☐ (b) $6 \times 5 \times 2$
☐ (c) 20×3
☐ (d) $2 \times 3 \times 5$
☐ (e) $2 \times 3 \times 5 \times 2$

5 Express 126 as the product of prime numbers.

☐ (a) $2 \times 7 \times 3 \times 3$
☐ (b) $2 \times 21 \times 3$
☐ (c) 2×63
☐ (d) 6×21
☐ (e) $2 \times 31 \times 3$

6 The floor in Mike's bedroom is square. Each edge is 4.2 m long. What is the area of the floor?

☐ (a) 17.64 m²
☐ (b) 8.4 m²
☐ (c) 16.8 m²
☐ (d) 18.6 m²
☐ (e) 17.84 m²

7 A sea horse had 25 spines on its back. Which of the following statements is not true?

☐ (a) 25 is odd
☐ (b) 25 squared is 625
☐ (c) 5 is the square root of 25
☐ (d) 25 is prime
☐ (e) 25 cubed is 15 625

8 Look at the following diagram. The numbers in the circles are found by multiplying the two numbers directly below. Find the number in the top circle of the pyramid.

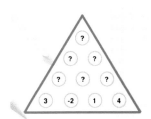

Q8

11

☐ (a) –80
☐ (b) –12
☐ (c) –84
☐ (d) –36
☐ (e) –96

QUESTIONS

Higher Level only

9 "The square root of 49 is irrational." Is this statement true or false?

☐ (a) True
☐ (b) False

10 What is the cube root of 64?

☐ (a) 1
☐ (b) 16
☐ (c) 4
☐ (d) 32
☐ (e) 8

11 Which one of the following numbers is rational?

☐ (a) $\sqrt{2}$
☐ (b) π
☐ (c) $\sqrt{5}$
☐ (d) $\sqrt{36}$
☐ (e) π^2

12 Which one of the following numbers is irrational?

☐ (a) 0.6
☐ (b) $\sqrt{8}$
☐ (c) 0.812
☐ (d) $\sqrt{16}$
☐ (e) $\sqrt{25}$

13 Which of the following is 0.121212 ... an example of?

☐ (a) An irrational number that can be written as a recurring decimal
☐ (b) A rational number that can be written as a recurring decimal
☐ (c) A rational number that can be written as a terminating decimal
☐ (d) An irrational number that can be written as a terminating decimal
☐ (e) A rational number that cannot be written as a recurring decimal

14 Write 0.777 ... as its simplest fraction.

☐ (a) $\frac{7}{90}$
☐ (b) $\frac{7}{10}$
☐ (c) $\frac{77}{99}$
☐ (d) $\frac{77}{90}$
☐ (e) $\frac{7}{9}$

15 Write 0.343434 ... as a fraction.

☐ (a) $\frac{34}{99}$
☐ (b) $\frac{34}{100}$
☐ (c) $\frac{34}{90}$
☐ (d) $\frac{34}{999}$
☐ (e) $\frac{34}{990}$

16 Which one of the following numbers is irrational?

☐ (a) $\sqrt{10}$
☐ (b) $\sqrt{100}$
☐ (c) $\sqrt{49}$
☐ (d) $\sqrt{1}$
☐ (e) 0.1

Mental computations

KEY FACTS

• These need to be practised regularly. Computations can be made easier by employing a few useful techniques:
i) When adding a list of numbers, see which make multiples of 10:
$17 + 25 + 3 + 2 + 18 = (17 + 3) + (2 + 18) + 25 = 20 + 20 + 25 = 65$.
ii) When subtracting a number with a units digit of 8 or 9, try this:
$52 – 18 = 53 – 19 = 54 – 20 = 34$.

• Learning tables is an invaluable help and will assist greatly in problems involving multiplying and dividing.

QUESTIONS

1 "A colony of bacteria doubled in size every hour. If there was one bacterium at the beginning, after seven hours there would be 14 bacteria." Is this statement true or false?

☐ (a) True
☐ (b) False

2 "Sita put £4 into a savings account. If the savings trebled every 10 years, she would have £24 after 20 years." Is this statement true or false?

☐ (a) True
☐ (b) False

3 *Do not use a calculator to answer this question.*
A ferry to Calais holds 326 people. How many people are there on 17 ferries that are full?

☐ (a) 5542
☐ (b) 5544
☐ (c) 5442
☐ (d) 2618
☐ (e) 5562

4 *Do not use a calculator to answer this question.*
Sunline minibuses can carry 17 passengers. There are 380 passengers wishing to travel, on the smallest number of minibuses possible. How many people are there on the last minibus, which is not full?

☐ (a) 4
☐ (b) 5
☐ (c) 6
☐ (d) 7
☐ (e) 8

5 *Do not use a calculator to answer this question.*
James set himself a target of doing 50 "press ups" each day and worked out how many "press ups" he would do in a 365-day year. How many was this?

☐ (a) 18 350
☐ (b) 18 300
☐ (c) 18 250
☐ (d) 19 250
☐ (e) 18 200

6 *Do not use a calculator to answer this question.*
In an orchard, the pickers placed their apples into containers. If each container had roughly 260 apples in it and there were 95 containers, estimate roughly how many apples there are altogether.

☐ (a) 20 600
☐ (b) 2600
☐ (c) 2060

☐ (d) 26 000
☐ (e) 20 000

7 *Do not use a calculator to answer this question.*
In an American Football stadium, 58 people could be seated in each row. Write down an estimate for the number of rows needed to seat a crowd of 3142.

☐ (a) 70
☐ (b) 500
☐ (c) 30
☐ (d) 40
☐ (e) 50

8 A set of traffic lights turns red after four minutes and another set after six minutes. If they are both red to begin with, when next will the lights both alter to red at the same time?

☐ (a) 12 minutes
☐ (b) 18 minutes
☐ (c) 10 minutes
☐ (d) 8 minutes
☐ (e) 30 minutes

9 Two lighthouses flash at different times. The first flashes every 9 seconds, the second flashes every 12 seconds. If they flash together at midnight exactly, after how many seconds will they next flash together?

☐ (a) 9 seconds
☐ (b) 12 seconds
☐ (c) 36 seconds
☐ (d) 108 seconds
☐ (e) 45 seconds

10 The temperature in Paris dropped overnight from 14°C to –6°C. What is the change in temperature in °C?

☐ (a) –16°C
☐ (b) 8°C
☐ (c) –8°C
☐ (d) –14°C
☐ (e) –20°C

11 The following table shows the maximum and minimum temperatures recorded during the year in six different towns in Great Britain. Which town had the greatest range between the maximum and minimum temperatures?

☐ (a) Southampton
☐ (b) Blackpool
☐ (c) Plymouth
☐ (d) Manchester
☐ (e) Aberdeen

Town	Max	Min
Blackpool	30	-10
Southampton	25	-8
Manchester	30	-8
Plymouth	32	2
Aberdeen	20	-15
London	28	-8

Q11

12 On the following map of Scotland, what is the lowest temperature of the six places?

☐ (a) –2°C
☐ (b) –5°C
☐ (c) –3°C
☐ (d) 4°C
☐ (e) 3°C

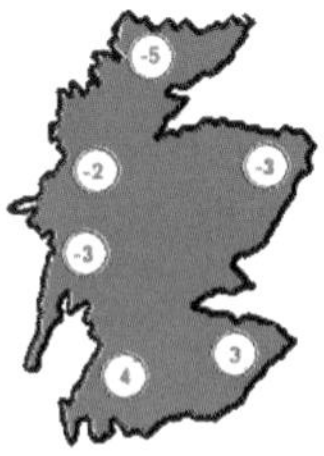

Q12

13 If the temperature on the thermometer shown below drops by 13°C, what will the new reading be?

☐ (a) –21°C
☐ (b) –20°C
☐ (c) –22°C
☐ (d) –19°C
☐ (e) 5°C

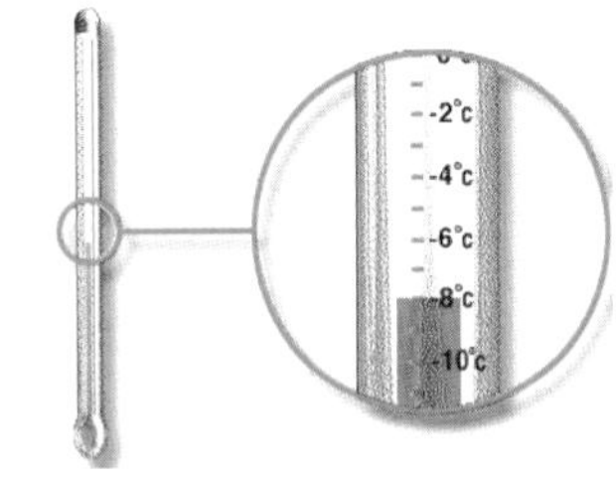

Q13

14 Fill in the magic square below to find the starred value. Remember each row, column, and the two diagonals should add up to 45.

Q14

☐ (a) 15

☐ (b) 17
☐ (c) 13
☐ (d) 11
☐ (e) 19

15 In a skating competition, both positive and negative scores are allowed. The judges award –2, –1, +9, –7, +8 to one contestant. What is the final score?

☐ (a) 9
☐ (b) 6
☐ (c) 8
☐ (d) 7
☐ (e) 10

16 A thermometer is put in a test tube of liquid. The temperature on it falls 12°C from 10°C. What is the new temperature reading?

☐ (a) 22°C
☐ (b) –4°C
☐ (c) 4°C
☐ (d) –22°C
☐ (e) –2°C

17 The temperature in a freezer is –13°C. If the temperature increases by 3°C when the door is left open for a minute, after how many minutes will the temperature be –4°C?

☐ (a) 2.5 minutes
☐ (b) 2 minutes
☐ (c) 3 minutes
☐ (d) 3.5 minutes
☐ (e) 4 minutes

18 If the temperature at the top of Mount Everest is –35°C, raise the temperature by 5°C to find the temperature 100 m further down.

☐ (a) –32°C
☐ (b) –30°C
☐ (c) –40°C
☐ (d) –35°C
☐ (e) –5°C

19 The temperature in Death Valley was 35°C during the day, then dropped by 40°C at night. What was the temperature at night?

☐ (a) 5°C
☐ (b) –5°C
☐ (c) 15°C
☐ (d) –35°C
☐ (e) –15°C

20 How many paving stones are there in a square paved area made up of seven rows of seven slabs?

☐ (a) 28
☐ (b) 14
☐ (c) 49
☐ (d) 63
☐ (e) 54

21 The perimeter of a square school playground is 320 m. What is the area of the playground?

☐ (a) 1280 m²
☐ (b) 6400 m²
☐ (c) 2560 m²
☐ (d) 10 204 m²
☐ (e) 12 400 m²

22 Two chemicals were mixed together in a test tube. The temperature of the mixture was equivalent to $(-4 - 7) \times -5°C$. What was the temperature?

☐ (a) 16°C
☐ (b) –55°C
☐ (c) 15°C
☐ (d) –15°C
☐ (e) 55°C

23 Mike played some holes of golf. He calculated his final score by adding the number of strokes he took under and over six per hole. Sum the following to calculate his

score: –3, –5, –2, +3, +6, +1, –1, +6.

☐ (a) 5
☐ (b) 6
☐ (c) 4
☐ (d) –6
☐ (e) –1

Calculations

 KEY FACTS

Calculations
• (a) With negative numbers:
　i) $-3 - 5 = -8$
　ii) $4 - (-3) = 4 + 3 = 7$
　iii) $3(-2) + 2(4) = -6 + 8 = 2$

• (b) With decimals:
　$4.37 \times 0.8 = 4.37 \times {}^{8}/_{10} =$
　${}^{34.96}/_{10} = 3.496$

• (c) With fractions:
　i) $3\frac{1}{4} + \frac{1}{3} = 3\frac{3}{12} + \frac{4}{12}$
　$= 3\frac{7}{12}$
　ii) $1\frac{2}{3} \times 2\frac{1}{2} = \frac{5}{3} \times \frac{5}{2} =$
　${}^{25}/_{6} = 4\frac{1}{6}$
　iii) $2\frac{2}{3} - 1\frac{1}{6} = (2 + \frac{4}{6}) -$
　$(1 + \frac{1}{6}) = 1 + \frac{4}{6} - \frac{1}{6} =$
　$1\frac{3}{6} = 1\frac{1}{2}$
　iv) $\frac{3}{4} \div \frac{2}{3} = \frac{9}{12} \div \frac{8}{12} =$
　$9 \div 8 = 1\frac{1}{8}$

• (d) With ratio:
If $2:3 = 10:c$, then work out the scale factor to get from 2 to 10 (i.e. × "5"), then multiply 3 by this scale factor (i.e. "5"), to give $c = 15$.

• For numbers between 0 and 1:
Squaring will give a smaller answer (e.g. $(0.2)^2 = 0.04$).
Multiplying gives a smaller answer (e.g. $30 \times 0.6 = 18$).
Dividing gives a larger answer (e.g. $30 \div 0.6 = 300 \div 6 = 50$).

 QUESTIONS

1 "If Maria and Fran delivered papers in the ratio 3:4, and Maria delivered 600 papers, Fran delivered 400." Is this statement true or false?

☐ (a) True
☐ (b) False

2 "A large jar of pickles cost £3.75, a small jar cost £1.50. Expressing these prices as a ratio in its lowest terms gives 5:2." Is this statement true or false?

☐ (a) True
☐ (b) False

Q2

3 "A 40 g bag of sweets costs 50p, so a 100 g bag will cost £1.25 if the prices are directly proportional." Is this statement true or false?

☐ (a) True
☐ (b) False

4 "If 4 kg of potatoes cost £1.10, 7 kg will cost £1.95 to the nearest penny." Is this statement true or false?

☐ (a) True
☐ (b) False

5 "A shop offered a 15% discount on any sofa. If a sofa normally cost £500, the discount would be £75." Is this statement true or false?

☐ (a) True
☐ (b) False

Q5

6 "The temperature at midnight on Mount Everest was –42°C. If it rose 23°C on the following day, then the temperature would be –19°C." Is this statement true or false?

☐ (a) True
☐ (b) False

7 "The following map of Sweden shows the various temperatures at different places at midnight on a night in January. The range of temperatures is 7°C." Is this statement true or false?

-15°C
-14°C
SWEDEN -10°C
-8°C
-3°C
-8°C

Q7

- ☐ (a) True
- ☐ (b) False

8 "A cashier worked 25 hours a week at £3.55 per hour for seven weeks. He should have earned £621.25 before tax." Is this statement true or false?

- ☐ (a) True
- ☐ (b) False

9 Derek bought a sailing boat costing £12 200, excluding VAT. If the VAT is 17.5%, how much did the boat cost including VAT?

- ☐ (a) £21 472
- ☐ (b) £12 200
- ☐ (c) £21 350
- ☐ (d) £10 065
- ☐ (e) £14 335

10 Work out the difference between the length ($17\frac{1}{4}$ cm) and width ($12\frac{3}{8}$ cm) of the famous painting shown below.

- ☐ (a) $29\frac{5}{8}$ cm
- ☐ (b) $27\frac{3}{8}$ cm
- ☐ (c) $4\frac{7}{8}$ cm
- ☐ (d) $4\frac{6}{8}$ cm
- ☐ (e) $27\frac{5}{8}$ cm

Q10

11 Two nails were driven into a wall. One nail was $1\frac{7}{10}$ cm long and another was $2\frac{3}{5}$ cm long. Work out the difference in length between the two nails.

- ☐ (a) $\frac{3}{10}$ cm
- ☐ (b) $2\frac{9}{10}$ cm
- ☐ (c) $2\frac{3}{10}$ cm
- ☐ (d) $\frac{9}{10}$ cm
- ☐ (e) $\frac{4}{10}$ cm

12 Maria sat her first piano exam after 35 lessons, each lasting $1\frac{1}{4}$ hours. Work out how many hours this was in total.

- ☐ (a) $43\frac{3}{4}$
- ☐ (b) $96\frac{1}{4}$
- ☐ (c) $8\frac{3}{4}$
- ☐ (d) $433\frac{1}{4}$
- ☐ (e) 28

13 A butterfly has a square on one of its wings. If the length of the square is 0.92 cm, which of the following most accurately represents the area of the square?

- ☐ (a) 0.84 cm^2
- ☐ (b) 0.85 cm^2
- ☐ (c) 0.9 cm^2
- ☐ (d) 1.84 cm^2
- ☐ (e) 0.96 cm^2

14 A beetle guards his square patch of garden carefully. The area of the patch is 25.6 cm^2. Calculate the length of the patch, rounded to 1 d.p.

- ☐ (a) 2.56 cm
- ☐ (b) 5.2 cm
- ☐ (c) 655.4 cm
- ☐ (d) 12.8 cm
- ☐ (e) 5.1 cm

15 A small business bought a computer worth £2500. The rate of depreciation was 15% per year. What was the value of the computer after two years?

- ☐ (a) £1806.25
- ☐ (b) £3306.25
- ☐ (c) £806.25
- ☐ (d) £2200
- ☐ (e) £1750

16 If $\frac{1}{4}$ of a class wear glasses, what is the ratio of children who wear glasses to children who don't wear glasses?

- ☐ (a) 1:5
- ☐ (b) 1:4
- ☐ (c) 1:3
- ☐ (d) 3:1
- ☐ (e) 4:1

17 If $\frac{3}{7}$ of a class go on a rollercoaster, what is the ratio of pupils on the rollercoaster to those not?

- ☐ (a) 3:7
- ☐ (b) 3:4
- ☐ (c) 4:7
- ☐ (d) 4:3
- ☐ (e) 3:10

18 If, on average, ash rises from a volcano $\frac{1}{5}$ of the days in a month, on how many days in September would you expect ash to rise?

- ☐ (a) 6
- ☐ (b) 5
- ☐ (c) 15
- ☐ (d) 4
- ☐ (e) 1

19 The probability of a tornado happening in any given year in a particular state in the U.S.A. is $\frac{3}{14}$. How many tornadoes would you expect in a typical lifespan of 70 years?

- ☐ (a) 12
- ☐ (b) 3
- ☐ (c) 14
- ☐ (d) 15
- ☐ (e) 9

20 The probability of a freak storm happening in a given year off the Cornish coast is thought to be $\frac{4}{5}$. How many storms would you expect in 20 years?

- ☐ (a) 15
- ☐ (b) 16
- ☐ (c) 8
- ☐ (d) 4
- ☐ (e) 18

21 If $\frac{2}{3}$ of the boats on a lake are sailing boats and the rest are motorboats, what is the ratio of sailing boats to motorboats?

- ☐ (a) 2:5
- ☐ (b) 1:2
- ☐ (c) 3:2
- ☐ (d) 2:1
- ☐ (e) 2:3

22 The number of spectators at a pop concert increased by $\frac{1}{5}$ from Friday to Saturday night. If there were 5500 people watching on Friday, how many were there on Saturday?

- ☐ (a) 6005
- ☐ (b) 1100
- ☐ (c) 6000
- ☐ (d) 5555
- ☐ (e) 6600

23 Jerry drove from Bristol to Birmingham along the M5 one afternoon. He stopped $\frac{5}{8}$ of the way along to refill with petrol. If the journey was 160 miles, after how many miles did he stop?

- ☐ (a) 90 miles
- ☐ (b) 50 miles
- ☐ (c) 80 miles
- ☐ (d) 100 miles
- ☐ (e) 60 miles

24 A rower wished to reduce his time for a 5000 m race. If it stood at 18 minutes, and he wanted to reduce it by one minute, what fraction was this of the original time?

- ☐ (a) 1
- ☐ (b) $\frac{1}{18}$
- ☐ (c) $\frac{1}{5000}$
- ☐ (d) $\frac{18}{5000}$
- ☐ (e) $\frac{18}{5}$

25 A canoeist canoed a gorge in the South of France, which took him 8 hours. If the second time he did it, his time was reduced by ¼, what was his new time?

- ☐ (a) 6 hours
- ☐ (b) 4 hours
- ☐ (c) 2 hours
- ☐ (d) 7 hours
- ☐ (e) 10 hours

26 It took a man 20 minutes to put together his sailboard. He wished to decrease this time by at least ⅗. What was the maximum time he could take on his second attempt to achieve this target?

- ☐ (a) 8 minutes
- ☐ (b) 12 minutes
- ☐ (c) 32 minutes
- ☐ (d) 11 minutes
- ☐ (e) 17 minutes

27 Kevin baked a pie. ⅖ of it went to Tanya, ⅗ of it went to Julie, and the rest was for Kevin. What fraction of the pie did Kevin end up with?

- ☐ (a) $\frac{5}{9}$
- ☐ (b) $\frac{2}{9}$
- ☐ (c) $\frac{3}{9}$
- ☐ (d) $\frac{6}{9}$
- ☐ (e) $\frac{4}{9}$

28 20% of Nurse Gladys's time was spent doing administrative work. How much time was this if she worked a 40-hour week?

- ☐ (a) 4 hours
- ☐ (b) 20 hours
- ☐ (c) 5 hours
- ☐ (d) 2 hours
- ☐ (e) 8 hours

29 A guitar had a reduction of £5 on the original price of £25. What was the percentage reduction?

- ☐ (a) 5%
- ☐ (b) 25%
- ☐ (c) 50%
- ☐ (d) 20%
- ☐ (e) 40%

30 A lawnmower was reduced by £40. Its old price was £240. What percentage reduction was this (to 1 d.p.)?

- ☐ (a) 40%
- ☐ (b) 16%
- ☐ (c) 16.7%
- ☐ (d) 20%
- ☐ (e) 6%

31 Calculate the percentage profit on an ice cream that has a cost price of 40p and is sold for 80p.

- ☐ (a) 200%
- ☐ (b) 100%
- ☐ (c) 40%
- ☐ (d) 80%
- ☐ (e) 10%

32 Calculate the profit on a camera that was bought for £80 and then sold at 10% more.

- ☐ (a) £10
- ☐ (b) £8
- ☐ (c) £16
- ☐ (d) £80
- ☐ (e) £18

33 Henry scored 14 out of 20 in a test. What percentage is this?

- ☐ (a) 70%
- ☐ (b) 14%
- ☐ (c) 28%
- ☐ (d) 280%
- ☐ (e) 7%

34 In a survey of car insurance companies, it was found that the most common claim was for one car running into the back of another. Out of 25 000 claims, 6350 were for this type of accident. What % is this?

- ☐ (a) 0.254%
- ☐ (b) 2.54%
- ☐ (c) 25.4%
- ☐ (d) 254%
- ☐ (e) 63.5%

35 In a survey of dog owners, it was found that 205 out of 312 used WOOF dog food. What % of owners used a dog food other than WOOF? Give the answer correct to 1 d.p.

- ☐ (a) 66%
- ☐ (b) 65.7%
- ☐ (c) 34%

- ☐ (d) 35%
- ☐ (e) 34.3%

36 The Murphys went to a restaurant to celebrate their son's 21st birthday. The bill came to £46.65, but a service charge of 10% had still to be added. What was the cost of the service charge? (Give the answer to the nearest penny.)

- ☐ (a) £0.47
- ☐ (b) £10
- ☐ (c) £21
- ☐ (d) £4.67
- ☐ (e) £5

37 The following diagram shows the medals won by Greenland over the past nine Olympics. What was the % of gold medals won in 1980 out of the medals won altogether in 1980?

- ☐ (a) 0.04%
- ☐ (b) 4%
- ☐ (c) 10%
- ☐ (d) 0.4%
- ☐ (e) 40%

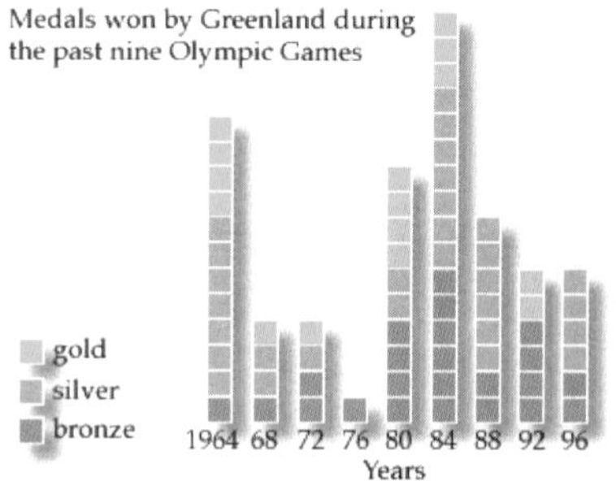

Medals won by Greenland during the past nine Olympic Games

gold
silver
bronze

1964 68 72 76 80 84 88 92 96
Years

Q37

38 A table and set of four chairs were on sale at 64% of their previous price. Write this as a fraction in its simplest form.

- ☐ (a) 0.64
- ☐ (b) $\frac{64}{100}$
- ☐ (c) $\frac{32}{50}$
- ☐ (d) 64%
- ☐ (e) $\frac{16}{25}$

39 What is the ratio of blue to yellow in the shape shown below, given in its lowest terms?

Q39

- ☐ (a) 3:5
- ☐ (b) 6:15
- ☐ (c) 6:21
- ☐ (d) 15:21
- ☐ (e) 2:5

QUESTIONS

Higher Level only

40 A building society offered a rate of 7.1%. The interest was paid into the account each year. How much would the account hold after five years if there was £1000 deposited initially?

- ☐ (a) £1355
- ☐ (b) £1035.50
- ☐ (c) £1409.12
- ☐ (d) £1455
- ☐ (e) £1904.12

41 £5000 was invested into an account where the interest was paid at 6% every six months. What would the total interest earned after two years be?

- ☐ (a) £24
- ☐ (b) £240
- ☐ (c) £1312.38
- ☐ (d) £1200
- ☐ (e) £2400

42 A child's tennis racquet cost £36.50 inclusive of VAT at 17.5%. What was its price without VAT?

- ☐ (a) £19
- ☐ (b) £31.06
- ☐ (c) £30.11
- ☐ (d) £30
- ☐ (e) £42.89

43 Philippa bought herself a hair dryer for £28.99 inclusive of VAT at 17.5%. How much was the hair dryer without VAT?

- ☐ (a) £34.06
- ☐ (b) £23.92
- ☐ (c) £11.49
- ☐ (d) £24.67
- ☐ (e) £26.49

Estimation, approximation, and significant figures

KEY FACTS

• To 1 significant figure (1 s.f.) – e.g. $19 \times 4.2 = 20 \times 4 = 80$ (useful to give a rough idea of an answer).

• To round 38.47 to 1 decimal place (1 d.p.) then, covering up the "7", the answer will be 38.4 or 38.5. As "7" is 5 or over, the answer is 38.5 (to 1 d.p.).

• If the accuracy of the measurements in a problem are given to 3 significant figures, then the degree of accuracy in your answer should not be to any more significant figures. For example, the area of a rectangle 3.27 cm by 2.16 cm should not be given as 7.0632 cm², but 7.06 cm² (3 s.f.). It is also worth checking that, in a problem, your answers are sensible.

QUESTIONS

1 A runner ran a marathon in 187.49 minutes. Round this to 1 d.p.

- ☐ (a) 187.4 minutes
- ☐ (b) 187.5 minutes
- ☐ (c) 187.9 minutes
- ☐ (d) 187.99 minutes
- ☐ (e) 187 minutes

2 The odometer reading on a school bus was136.06 km. Round this to 1 d.p.

- ☐ (a) 136.1 km
- ☐ (b) 136.0 km
- ☐ (c) 136 km
- ☐ (d) 136.2 km
- ☐ (e) 136.6 km

3 A racing car did five laps of a circuit in 59.58 s, 59.91 s, 58.07 s, 58.91 s, and 58.91 s. Estimate the total time for all five laps, to the nearest minute.

- ☐ (a) 6 minutes
- ☐ (b) 4 minutes
- ☐ (c) 5 minutes
- ☐ (d) 56 minutes
- ☐ (e) 60 minutes

4 The size of the petrol tank of a Rolls Royce is 42 litres, If it is filled 97 times, estimate how much petrol it has used altogether.

- ☐ (a) 4000 litres
- ☐ (b) 3000 litres
- ☐ (c) 400 litres
- ☐ (d) 5000 litres
- ☐ (e) 3600 litres

5 A train travels from London to Edinburgh 1007 times a year. If the one-way journey is 632 miles, estimate how many miles it has travelled in total.

- ☐ (a) 600 000 miles
- ☐ (b) 632 000 miles
- ☐ (c) 6000 miles
- ☐ (d) 700 miles
- ☐ (e) 63 200 miles

6 If there were 32 giraffes in a safari park, each with 28 spots, estimate how many spots there were in total on all the giraffes.

- ☐ (a) 60
- ☐ (b) 9000
- ☐ (c) 900
- ☐ (d) 600
- ☐ (e) 90

7 The length of a wasp sting was 1.969 mm. Round this to 2 d.p.

- ☐ (a) 2.97 mm
- ☐ (b) 1.96 mm
- ☐ (c) 1.7 mm
- ☐ (d) 2.0 mm
- ☐ (e) 1.97 mm

8 If Cinderella swept 67 stairs 789 times in a year, estimate how many stairs she swept in the year.

- ☐ (a) 49 000
- ☐ (b) 5600
- ☐ (c) 56 000
- ☐ (d) 4900
- ☐ (e) 42 000

9 Amanda wanted to split her lottery winnings between herself, her parents, and her four sisters. She won £25. When she divided £25 by 7 on her calculator, she got 3.57142857. What is this answer, correct to the nearest penny?

☐ (a) £3.571
☐ (b) £3.60
☐ (c) £3.57
☐ (d) £3.56
☐ (e) £3.58

10 If a disc jockey played 61 records that lasted 178 minutes, estimate the average length of each record.

☐ (a) 2.5 minutes
☐ (b) 1 minute
☐ (c) 2 minutes
☐ (d) 3 minutes
☐ (e) 3.5 minutes

11 Ed measured the radius of his frisbee to be 11.6 cm. Using his calculator he worked out that the area of the frisbee was 422.7327075 cm². What number of decimal places should he use in a reasonable value for the area?

☐ (a) 0
☐ (b) 2
☐ (c) 3
☐ (d) 1
☐ (e) 4

12 Mount Snowdon is 3561.56 ft high. Round this to 2 s.f.

☐ (a) 3500
☐ (b) 3600
☐ (c) 3560
☐ (d) 3562
☐ (e) 3561.56

13 The population of Scotland is given as 4 601 859. Round this to 3 s.f.

☐ (a) 4 601 000
☐ (b) 4 610 000
☐ (c) 4 600 000
☐ (d) 4 602 000
☐ (e) 4 601 900

14 If there were 31 680 sunflower seeds and 310 sunflowers, estimate how many seeds would be produced on average per sunflower.

☐ (a) 300
☐ (b) 30
☐ (c) 1000
☐ (d) 200
☐ (e) 100

15 496 parrots migrated from Mexico to Peru. Round 496 to 2 s.f.

☐ (a) 450
☐ (b) 490
☐ (c) 495
☐ (d) 400
☐ (e) 500

16 2999 flamingos migrated from Kenya to a lake in Tanzania. Round 2999 to 2 s.f.

☐ (a) 3000
☐ (b) 2900
☐ (c) 2990
☐ (d) 2995
☐ (e) 2991

17 An elephant weighed 4508.98 kg. Round this to 3 s.f.

☐ (a) 4509 kg
☐ (b) 4500 kg
☐ (c) 4600 kg
☐ (d) 4510 kg
☐ (e) 4508 kg

18 At a particular time, the distance of the Earth from the Sun was 93 567 543 miles. Round this to 3 s.f.

☐ (a) 93 500 000
☐ (b) 936
☐ (c) 936 000 000
☐ (d) 93 600 000
☐ (e) 93 060 000

19 One nautical mile is approximately 1.853 km. Estimate how many kilometres there are in 212 nautical miles, to 1 s.f.

☐ (a) 564 km
☐ (b) 106 km
☐ (c) 400 km
☐ (d) 460 km
☐ (e) 480 km

20 The calculation 2.56 × 1.8 was keyed into a calculator incorrectly, giving an answer of 0.4608 instead of 4.608. Which of the following mistakes could have been made?

Q20

☐ (a) Keyed 0.0256 instead of 2.56

☐ (b) Keyed ÷ instead of ×
☐ (c) Keyed + instead of ×
☐ (d) Keyed 2.65 instead of 2.56
☐ (e) Keyed 0.18 instead of 1.8

21 Sarah took an average of 43.5 seconds, to the nearest tenth of a second, to read a page. What is the minimum number of seconds this time could be?

☐ (a) 43
☐ (b) 43.45
☐ (c) –0.05
☐ (d) 44
☐ (e) 40

22 A plane flew from Barcelona to London. On five separate journeys of the same distance it took 121 minutes, 124 minutes, 119 minutes, 118 minutes, and 121 minutes. What journey time would a travel agency state in their brochure?

☐ (a) 120 minutes
☐ (b) 2 hours approximately
☐ (c) They work out the mean time
☐ (d) 120.6 minutes
☐ (e) Between 118 and 124 minutes

23 A pencil is measured as 17 cm to the nearest centimetre. Which of the following gives the range for the possible length of the pencil?

☐ (a) $16.5 \le L < 17.5$
☐ (b) $16.8 \le L < 17.2$
☐ (c) $16.5 \le L \le 17.5$
☐ (d) $16.9 \le L \le 17.1$
☐ (e) $17.25 \le L < 17.5$

24 A suitcase is weighed as 21 kg to the nearest ½ kilogram, What is the margin of error?

☐ (a) 2.5 kg each way
☐ (b) 1 kg each way
☐ (c) 0.5 kg each way
☐ (d) 0.5 g each way
☐ (e) 0.25 kg each way

25 An architect designed the plans for a house. The sitting room was rectangular with length 10.6 m and width 8.41 m, both to 3 s.f. Calculate the minimum possible area, to 3 s.f.

☐ (a) 89.6 m²
☐ (b) 89.1 m²
☐ (c) 88.7 m²
☐ (d) 88.2 m²
☐ (e) 88.3 m²

26 The front cover of a magazine is 31.5 cm long and 15.6 cm wide. If these are to the nearest millimetre, what is the maximum possible perimeter of the magazine?

- ☐ (a) 94.2 cm
- ☐ (b) 491.4 cm
- ☐ (c) 94.4 cm
- ☐ (d) 94.6 cm
- ☐ (e) 94.8 cm

27 The length of a garden bench is 130 cm to the nearest 10 cm. What is the minimum length it can be?

- ☐ (a) 129 cm
- ☐ (b) 120 cm
- ☐ (c) 125.1 cm
- ☐ (d) 125 cm
- ☐ (e) 129.5 cm

28 The height of a crane is 850 m. If this is to 2 s.f., what is the maximum height the crane can be?

- ☐ (a) 900 m

- ☐ (b) 854 m
- ☐ (c) 860 m
- ☐ (d) 855 m
- ☐ (e) 950 m

29 The weight of a rhino is 4800 kg. If this is given to 3 s.f., what is the least value the weight of the rhino can be?

- ☐ (a) 4895 kg
- ☐ (b) 4750 kg
- ☐ (c) 4795 kg
- ☐ (d) 4799 kg
- ☐ (e) 4796 kg

QUESTIONS

Higher Level only

30 "An engineer designs a rectangular landing pad for a helicopter. It has a minimum length

of 25 m and width of 20 m. Both dimensions are to 2 s.f. The lower bound for the area is 477.75 m². " Is this statement true or false?

- ☐ (a) True
- ☐ (b) False

31 "The depth of a pool is 10 m to 2 s.f. Hence the lower bound must be 9.95 m." Is this statement true or false?

- ☐ (a) True
- ☐ (b) False

Problems

KEY FACTS

• You need to be able to apply the rules and skills you have developed to practical problems. For example, if you mix 2 litres of red paint with 3 litres of yellow paint, then to find how much yellow is needed to mix with 10 litres of red (in order to make the same orange colour), you use 2:3 = 10:15 – i.e. 15 litres of yellow paint.

QUESTIONS

1 A supermarket cashier worked a basic 35-hour week at a rate of £3.55 per hour. He was paid overtime at time and a half. How much did he earn in a week with eight hours overtime?

- ☐ (a) £152.65
- ☐ (b) £124.25
- ☐ (c) £166.85
- ☐ (d) £181.05
- ☐ (e) £138.45

2 The hours worked by an employee can be calculated from a clock card like the one shown in the following diagram. Jim worked a basic eight-hour day, five days a week, and his

basic hourly rate was £4.05. Overtime was paid double on the weekend and time and a half on any other day. Calculate Jim's gross pay for this week.

- ☐ (a) £243
- ☐ (b) £162
- ☐ (c) £279.45
- ☐ (d) £198.45
- ☐ (e) £226.80

Day	In	Out	Basic hours	Overtime hours
Sat	10:00	16:00	0	6
Sun	08:00	12:00	0	4
Mon	08:00	17:00	8	1
Tue	08:00	18:00	8	2
Wed	08:00	16:00	8	0
Thu	08:00	19:00	8	3
Fri	09:00	17:00	8	0

Q2

3 The basic wage of employees in a factory was £144 for a 40-hour week. What was their hourly pay?

- ☐ (a) £5.76
- ☐ (b) £3.60
- ☐ (c) £104
- ☐ (d) £10.40
- ☐ (e) £2.77

4 A school bought a computer costing £899.90 excluding VAT. If

VAT is 17.5%, what was the price of the computer including VAT?

- ☐ (a) £1057.38
- ☐ (b) £765.87
- ☐ (c) £1305.70
- ☐ (d) £916.50
- ☐ (e) £882.40

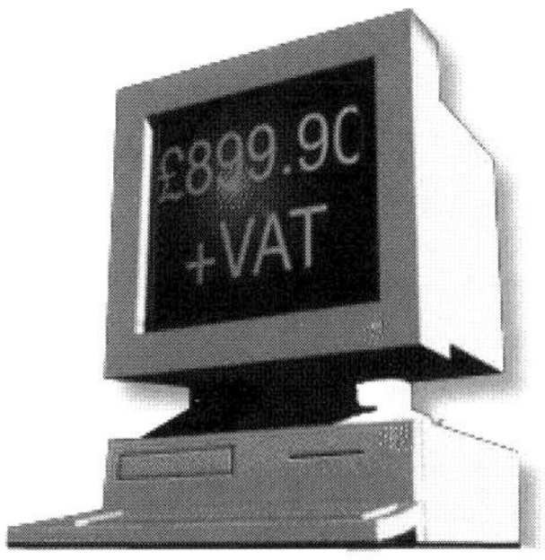

Q4

5 Mr Cartwright invested £10 000 in gold at a simple rate of interest of 15% p.a. How much interest did he gain after three years?

- ☐ (a) £1500
- ☐ (b) £4500
- ☐ (c) £3000
- ☐ (d) £300
- ☐ (e) £450

6 James sold his car for £1250 and put the money in a long term building society account that gained compound interest on the original

19

investment of 12% p.a. How much interest had he gained after two years?

☐ (a) £1568
☐ (b) £318
☐ (c) £636
☐ (d) £300
☐ (e) £1550

7 A department store offered a hi-fi system for sale at £529.00. A customer could also buy the hi-fi by paying a deposit of 10% and then paying the remainder with 10 monthly equal instalments. How much would each monthly instalment be?

☐ (a) £48.61
☐ (b) £52.90
☐ (c) £46.71
☐ (d) £47.61
☐ (e) £47.60

Q7

8 A television set could be bought for £205.55 cash or by credit purchase. The credit purchase terms were 24 monthly payments of £9.50 and included interest. Calculate the amount of interest paid.

☐ (a) £22.45
☐ (b) £28.00
☐ (c) £228.00
☐ (d) £9.50
☐ (e) £22.00

9 Bob enjoyed having margarine on his toast in the morning. He knew a 250 g tub of margarine sold for 45p and a 500 g tub sold for 88p. Bob worked out how much more expensive the smaller tub was per kilogram. What was his answer?

☐ (a) £0.40
☐ (b) 4p
☐ (c) £4
☐ (d) 2p
☐ (e) 43p

10 Compare the four advertisements below and decide which is the best value for money for two people.

☐ (a) Z
☐ (b) X
☐ (c) Y
☐ (d) W
☐ (e) All the same

Q10

11 Toby and Natasha ate a meal in a restaurant in Venice. The meal cost 90 680 lire. If there were 2205 lire to the pound, calculate the cost of the meal in pounds.

☐ (a) £19.99
☐ (b) £24.32
☐ (c) £41.12
☐ (d) £22.05
☐ (e) £40.00

12 Tim and Dave went on a skiing holiday to France. They took £350 worth of French francs with them. If there were 8.65 francs to the pound, calculate how much they took in French francs.

☐ (a) 3032.5 ff
☐ (b) 3030.5 ff
☐ (c) 3027.5 ff
☐ (d) 40.46 ff
☐ (e) 4046 ff

13 The Perrys spent a holiday touring the former Yugoslavia where petrol cost 1340 dinar per litre. The exchange rate was 4340 dinar to the pound. What was the price per litre of the petrol in pounds?

☐ (a) £0.30
☐ (b) £0.31
☐ (c) £0.58
☐ (d) £0.59
☐ (e) £0.32

14 A pizza restaurant added a service charge of 15% to a bill of £32.50. How much was the final bill?

☐ (a) £37.40
☐ (b) £37.38
☐ (c) £37.00
☐ (d) £15.00
☐ (e) £4.88

15 Matt invested £4000 in a computer firm. He received £600 interest from his shares in a year. What interest rate was this?

☐ (a) 16%
☐ (b) 5%
☐ (c) 60%
☐ (d) 66%
☐ (e) 15%

16 If there were 2.33 Australian $ to the pound and Pete spent $500.00 on a safari in the Australian bush, how much was this in pounds?

☐ (a) £215.49
☐ (b) £1165
☐ (c) £466
☐ (d) £46.60
☐ (e) £214.59

17 Greta visited the Parthenon in Athens. The entrance fee cost 800 drachma or £3.00. If there were 292 drachma to the pound, how much did she save by paying in drachma?

☐ (a) 50p
☐ (b) 876 Dr
☐ (c) £1
☐ (d) 76 Dr
☐ (e) 86 Dr

18 If there were 1.77 American $ to the pound and a trip to the Statue of Liberty cost $4, how much was this in pounds?

☐ (a) £2.26
☐ (b) £2.25
☐ (c) £7.08
☐ (d) £4.43
☐ (e) £2.62

19 A ladybird had a spot on its wing that had a radius of 0.75 mm. To work out a rough estimate of the area, square the radius and multiply by 3. Which of the below most accurately represents the area?

☐ (a) 1.69 mm^2
☐ (b) 4.5 mm^2
☐ (c) 1.68 mm^2
☐ (d) 1.6 mm^2
☐ (e) 5.1 mm^2

20 The diameter of Venus is 1.2×10^4. The diameter of Saturn is 1.2×10^5. How many times larger is Saturn's diameter than that of Venus?

☐ (a) 0
☐ (b) 2.5
☐ (c) 10

☐ (d) 100
☐ (e) 0.1

21 In a horse race there was $\frac{1}{4}$ of a length between the first and second horses and $\frac{2}{3}$ of a length between the first and third. What fraction of a length was there between the second and third horses?

☐ (a) $\frac{1}{7}$
☐ (b) 1
☐ (c) $\frac{5}{12}$
☐ (d) $\frac{3}{7}$
☐ (e) $\frac{5}{7}$

22 If a dress can be made from $1\frac{3}{4}$ m of fabric, how many of these dresses could be made from $22\frac{3}{4}$ m of fabric?

☐ (a) 54
☐ (b) 13
☐ (c) 21
☐ (d) 15
☐ (e) 17

23 $\frac{2}{5}$ of a garden was used to plant potatoes. $\frac{1}{3}$ of this area was used to plant King Edwards. What fraction of the whole garden was used to plant King Edward potatoes?

☐ (a) $\frac{2}{8}$
☐ (b) $\frac{3}{15}$
☐ (c) $\frac{3}{8}$
☐ (d) $\frac{2}{15}$
☐ (e) $\frac{1}{15}$

24 A spy had to cross two borders undetected. She paid $\frac{1}{2}$ her money to get over the first border and $\frac{1}{3}$ of her original money to get over the second. What fraction of the money she started with did the spy have left?

☐ (a) $\frac{1}{5}$
☐ (b) $\frac{1}{3}$
☐ (c) $\frac{2}{6}$
☐ (d) $\frac{1}{6}$
☐ (e) $\frac{2}{5}$

25 An ant travelled from its nest to a toaster to pick up crumbs 19 times. If the total distance travelled was 32.5 cm each time, how far did the ant travel altogether?

☐ (a) 616.5 cm
☐ (b) 617.5 cm
☐ (c) 607.5 cm
☐ (d) 325 cm
☐ (e) 585 cm

26 Calculate the cost of 125 telephone units at 4.4p each.

☐ (a) 550p
☐ (b) 528p
☐ (c) 545p
☐ (d) 548p
☐ (e) 450p

27 15% of Nurse Mary's time was spent doing administrative work. If this came to six hours, how long was her week?

☐ (a) 90 hours
☐ (b) 40 hours
☐ (c) 50 hours
☐ (d) 60 hours
☐ (e) 48 hours

28 A camera was bought for £80, having had an extra 10% added on. What was its previous price?

☐ (a) £72
☐ (b) £10
☐ (c) £8
☐ (d) £72.73
☐ (e) £88

29 Calculate the original cost of a car sold at £675 at a loss of 25%.

☐ (a) £700
☐ (b) £680
☐ (c) £900
☐ (d) £800
☐ (e) £850

30 Petrol prices rose by 15% one year. If they are now 53p a litre what were they before? Give your answer to the nearest penny.

☐ (a) 47p
☐ (b) 68p
☐ (c) 48p
☐ (d) 38p
☐ (e) 46p

31 Tom and Johnny delivered leaflets to a street in a ratio 2:3 respectively. If Tom delivered 400, how many leaflets did Johnny deliver?

☐ (a) 300
☐ (b) 500
☐ (c) 600
☐ (d) 1200
☐ (e) 3

32 A large jar of pickles cost £2.50 and a small jar cost £1.50. Express these prices as a ratio in its lowest terms.

☐ (a) 25:15
☐ (b) 2.50:1.50
☐ (c) 250:150
☐ (d) 5:3
☐ (e) 2:1

33 A pound of oranges cost £1.60 and a pound of apples cost £0.80. Write the ratio of the prices of oranges to apples in its lowest terms.

☐ (a) 1.6:0.8
☐ (b) 16:80
☐ (c) 16:8
☐ (d) 2:1
☐ (e) 0.2:0.1

34 A newsagent sold 45 copies of *The Daily News*, 30 copies of *The Daily Times*, and 40 copies of *The Morning Mirror*. Write this as a proportion in its lowest terms.

☐ (a) 4.5:3:4
☐ (b) 9:6:8
☐ (c) 45:30:40
☐ (d) 45:30
☐ (e) 9,6,8

35 A supermarket sold tins of baked beans and tins of noodles in the ratio 7:3 respectively. If 28 tins of baked beans are sold, how many tins of noodles are sold?

☐ (a) 12
☐ (b) 28
☐ (c) 3
☐ (d) 7
☐ (e) 21

36 An airforce base has Harrier Jets and Tomahawks garaged in the ratio 3:4 respectively. If there are 16 Tomahawks, how many Harrier Jets are there?

☐ (a) 3
☐ (b) 16
☐ (c) 12
☐ (d) 4
☐ (e) 6

37 Bulbs were planted in the proportion of three daffodils to two tulips to four crocuses. If 150 daffodils appeared, how many tulips would be expected?

☐ (a) 100
☐ (b) 2
☐ (c) 120
☐ (d) 200
☐ (e) 40

38 A farmer planted wheat, barley, and oats in the proportion 2:5:3

respectively. If he planted 1000 seeds altogether, how many of them were barley seeds?

- ☐ (a) 200
- ☐ (b) 50
- ☐ (c) 300
- ☐ (d) 500
- ☐ (e) 5

39 A Saxon Lord divided his 12 acres of land between his three sons in the proportion 4:5:3. What was the least amount of land he gave a son?

- ☐ (a) 4 acres
- ☐ (b) 10 acres
- ☐ (c) 3 acres
- ☐ (d) 5 acres
- ☐ (e) 12 acres

40 Gail's bungalow was 16 m long, 12 m wide, and 8 m high. She decided to make a miniature version of her home for her daughter Georgia. If the doll's house was 40 cm long, how high was it?

- ☐ (a) 8 cm
- ☐ (b) 20 cm
- ☐ (c) 30 cm
- ☐ (d) 80 cm
- ☐ (e) 40 cm

41 Phoebe was mixing concrete. The mix she used was one part cement to two parts sand to four parts aggregate. How much sand did she need to make 35 m^3 of concrete?

- ☐ (a) 20 m^3
- ☐ (b) 5 m^3
- ☐ (c) 10 m^3
- ☐ (d) 15 m^3
- ☐ (e) 2 m^3

42 If 3 kg of nectarines cost £3.60, how much would 5 kg cost?

- ☐ (a) £7.20
- ☐ (b) £1.20
- ☐ (c) 60p
- ☐ (d) £5.00
- ☐ (e) £6.00

43 If four lettuces cost £1.20, how much would seven lettuces cost?

- ☐ (a) £2.01
- ☐ (b) £2.40
- ☐ (c) £2.80
- ☐ (d) £2.10
- ☐ (e) £1.40

44 If 5 kg of carrots cost £1.25, how much would 2 kg cost?

- ☐ (a) £5
- ☐ (b) £0.50
- ☐ (c) £0.60
- ☐ (d) £0.75
- ☐ (e) £0.40

45 Karen can knit 400 stitches in five minutes. How long would it take her to knit 500 stitches?

- ☐ (a) 6 minutes 75 seconds
- ☐ (b) 6 minutes 15 seconds
- ☐ (c) 6 minutes 5 seconds
- ☐ (d) 6 minutes
- ☐ (e) 6 minutes 25 seconds

46 A 250 g jar of honey contains 1250 calories. How many calories are there in a 100 g jar?

- ☐ (a) 625
- ☐ (b) 250
- ☐ (c) 400
- ☐ (d) 600
- ☐ (e) 500

QUESTIONS

Higher Level only

47 A racing bike could be bought for £560 or on a hire purchase arrangement for a deposit of 25% of £560 and 10 monthly payments of £42. What was the interest charged on this hire purchase, if any?

- ☐ (a) No interest charged
- ☐ (b) £42
- ☐ (c) £56
- ☐ (d) £140
- ☐ (e) £14

48 An oxygen atom has a mass of about 2.7×10^{-23}. How heavy would 2000 oxygen atoms be?

- ☐ (a) 1.7×10^{-13}
- ☐ (b) 5.4×10^{-21}
- ☐ (c) 5.5×10^{-19}
- ☐ (d) 5.4×10^{-20}
- ☐ (e) 5.4^{-20}

49 A star was about 5.5×10^{16} km from the Earth. In a year, light travels about 9.46×10^{12} km. About how many light years (to the nearest light year) is this star from the Earth?

- ☐ (a) 5.203×10^{29}
- ☐ (b) 136
- ☐ (c) 5814
- ☐ (d) 52.03×10^{29}
- ☐ (e) 5.814^3

50 The Pacific Ocean covers an area of about $1.65 \times 10^8 km^2$. The Atlantic Ocean covers an area of about $8.22 \times 10^7 km^2$. How much of the Earth's surface do the two oceans cover together?

- ☐ (a) 2 472 000 000 km^2
- ☐ (b) 2 535 783 km^2
- ☐ (c) 2 4720 000 km^2
- ☐ (d) 247 200 000 km^2
- ☐ (e) 24 720 000 000 km^2

51 In a large American state, 8.416×10^6 people were on a hospital waiting list. Of these, 2.2×10^3 were waiting for plastic surgery. How many were waiting for other types of surgery?

- ☐ (a) 8 413 800
- ☐ (b) 8 431 800
- ☐ (c) 355 321
- ☐ (d) 3825
- ☐ (e) 8 418 200

52 One year about 5.35×10^4 tonnes of shellfish were caught and 6.24×10^5 tonnes of other fish. What was the total weight of fish caught in that year?

- ☐ (a) 10 280 tonnes
- ☐ (b) 677 500 tonnes
- ☐ (c) 66 768 tonnes
- ☐ (d) 687 500 tonnes
- ☐ (e) 66 876 tonnes

53 Find the area of a rectangular table that measures $1\frac{2}{3}$ m by $2\frac{3}{4}$ m.

- ☐ (a) $4\frac{7}{12} m^2$
- ☐ (b) $2\frac{1}{12} m^2$
- ☐ (c) $5\frac{5}{12} m^2$
- ☐ (d) $4\frac{1}{3} m^2$
- ☐ (e) $2\frac{1}{12} m^2$

54 The kitchen floor in Alan's house needed carpeting. Its dimensions were $3\frac{1}{4}$ m by $4\frac{1}{2}$ m. Work out the area.

- ☐ (a) $7\frac{3}{4} m^2$
- ☐ (b) $14\frac{5}{8} m^2$
- ☐ (c) $12\frac{7}{8} m^2$
- ☐ (d) $12\frac{2}{8} m^2$
- ☐ (e) $13\frac{1}{6} m^2$

55 Look at the following table. Given that y is proportional to x, find the missing value of y.

x	2	6	12
y	3	9	?

Q55

☐ (a) 12
☐ (b) 15
☐ (c) 24
☐ (d) 21
☐ (e) 18

56 The energy of a moving object is proportional to the square of its speed. If the object has 40 units of energy when it is moving at 8 m/s, how many units of energy does it have when it moves at 12 m/s?

☐ (a) 144
☐ (b) 100
☐ (c) 90
☐ (d) 1152
☐ (e) 15

57 When a ball is thrown up in the air, the height it reaches varies with the square of the speed at which it is thrown. A ball is thrown with speed 30.2 m/s and reaches a height of 46.2 m. What speed is needed to reach a height of 20 m?

☐ (a) 19.9 m/s
☐ (b) 20.1 m/s
☐ (c) 400 m/s
☐ (d) 4.5 m/s
☐ (e) 5.5 m/s

58 y is proportional to x^3. Examine the table below and find the missing value of y.

☐ (a) 32
☐ (b) 128
☐ (c) 108
☐ (d) 8
☐ (e) 162

x	10	20	40
y	2	16	?

Q58

59 The intensity of light on an object is inversely proportional to the square of the distance of the object from the light. If the intensity is 10 units at a distance of 2 m, what is the intensity at 4 m?

☐ (a) 0.1 units
☐ (b) 20 units
☐ (c) 5 units
☐ (d) 2.5 units
☐ (e) 0.5 units

60 The wavelength of sound waves is inversely proportional to the frequency. If the frequency of the note G is 390 cycles/s and wavelength 0.85 m, what wavelength does C have with frequency 256 cycles/s?

☐ (a) 1.92 m
☐ (b) 1.77 m
☐ (c) 1.66 m
☐ (d) 1.27 m
☐ (e) 1.29 m

61 The air pressure from a bicycle pump is inversely proportional to the square of the diameter of the pump. If a pressure of 10 units arises from a pump with diameter 20 mm, find the diameter of a pump giving a pressure of 15 units.

☐ (a) 25.5 mm
☐ (b) 30 mm
☐ (c) 16.3 mm
☐ (d) 60 mm
☐ (e) 33 mm

ANSWERS

Place value, fractions, decimals, and percentages

☐ 1 *(b)*
500p + 80p + 6p + 10p + 5p = 601p = £6.01.

☐ 2 *(e)*
⁹⁄₁₅ is the only equivalent fraction. If you multiply the denominator and numerator of ³⁄₅ by 3, you get ⁹⁄₁₅.

☐ 3 *(e)*
If you multiply the denominator and numerator of ²⁄₃ by 8, you get ¹⁶⁄₂₄.

☐ 4 *(d)*
⁵⁄₃₀ is the only equivalent fraction. If you multiply the denominator and numerator of ¹⁄₆ by 5, you get ⁵⁄₃₀.

☐ 5 *(a)*
¹⁶⁄₂₄ when simplified becomes ²⁄₃, not ³⁄₄. All the other fractions become ³⁄₄ when they are simplified.

☐ 6 *(e)*
When simplified, ¹⁶⁄₄₀ becomes ²⁄₅. All the other fractions become ³⁄₈.

☐ 7 *(d)*
⁴⁰⁄₄₅ when simplified becomes ⁸⁄₉, not ⁴⁄₅. All the other fractions become ⁴⁄₅ when they are simplified.

☐ 8 *(b)*
¹⁄₁₀ = 0.1. Therefore, ⁴⁄₁₀ = 0.4.

☐ 9 *(b)*
³⁄₄ = ⁷⁵⁄₁₀₀, so if you multiply top and bottom by 25, then ⁷⁵⁄₁₀₀ = 0.75.

☐ 10 *(c)*
Divide 1 by 3 on your calculator. The display will show 0.3333333. This can be written 0.333 ... i.e. 0.3 recurring.

☐ 11 *(a)*
³⁄₂₀ = ¹⁵⁄₁₀₀, so if you multiply top and bottom by 5, then ¹⁵⁄₁₀₀ = 0.15.

☐ 12 *(a)*
Divide 1 by 9 on your calculator and you will see 0.111111111. This can also be written 0.111 ... or 0.1 recurring.

Index notation

☐ 1 *(a)*
300 000 km/s can be written as 300 000 = 3×10^5.

☐ 2 *(b)*
0.000 000 000 1 mm = 1 ÷ 10 000 000 000 = 1 ÷ 10^{10} = 1×10^{-10}.

☐ 3 *(c)*
0.000 016 = 1.6 ÷ 100 000 = 1.6 ÷ 10^5 = 1.6×10^{-5}.

☐ 4 *(b)*
5.0×10^{-5} = 5 × 0.000 01 = 0.000 05 cm.

☐ 5 *(c)*
2.7×10^{-6} = 2.7 × 0.000 001 = 0.000 002 7.

☐ 6 *(b)*
4×10^{-3} = 4 × 0.001 = 0.004.

☐ 7 *(e)*
Rules of indices state that you can add the indices when two numbers are multiplied together, as long as the base number remains constant. Therefore, $2^3 \times 2^5 = 2^8$ in index form.

☐ 8 *(a)*
Rules of indices state that you can add the indices when two numbers are multiplied together and subtract when two numbers are divided as long as the base number remains constant. Therefore, $4^3 \times 4^4 \div 4^2 = 4^{(3 + 4 - 2)} = 4^5$.

☐ 9 *(c)*
25 × 25 × 25 = 15 625. Therefore, 25 is not $^3\sqrt{625}$.

☐ 10 *(a)*
5×10^9 = 5 × 1 000 000 000 = 5 000 000 000.

☐ 11 *(e)*
2.45×10^3 = 2.45 × 1000 = 2450.

☐ 12 *(b)*
4.56×10^6 = 4.56 × 1 000 000 = 4 560 000. *(a)* is incorrect because it is not written in standard index form.

☐ 13 *(d)*
1.268×10^4 = 1.268 × 10 000 = 12 680.

☐ 14 *(c)*
1×10^9 = 1 × 1 000 000 000 = 1 000 000 000.

☐ 15 *(d)*
8.6×10^6 km² = 8.6 × 1 000 000 = 8 600 000 km².

☐ 16 *(b)*
1.83×10^5 = 1.83 × 100 000 = 183 000.

☐ 17 *(b)*
5×10^9 = 5 × 1 000 000 000 = 5 000 000 000.

☐ 18 *(c)*
3.405×10^7 = 3.405 × 10 000 000 = 34 050 000.

☐ 19 *(e)*
It is the calculator's way of writing standard index form.

☐ 20 *(b)*
This is the calculator's way of writing standard index form. Therefore, it represents 3.1 multiplied by 10^4 rather than 3.1^4, which is 3.1 to the power of 4.

☐ 21 *(c)*
35 600 = 3.56 × 10 000 = 3.56×10^4.

☐ 22 *(a)*
2.05×10^2 = 2.05 × 100 = 205.

☐ 23 *(e)*
13 012 000 ÷ 4 = 3 253 000 = 3.253×10^6.

☐ 24 *(c)*
Type in your calculator: 4, x^y, 6, = 4096.

☐ 25 *(c)*
Type in your calculator: 3, x^y, 4 =, 81.

Index notation
Higher Levels

☐ 26 *(d)*
$3^2 + 3^0$ = 9 + 1 = 10. All the other solutions give 9.

☐ 27 *(d)*
16^0 = 1. Any number to the power of 0 is 1.

☐ 28 *(e)*
$\sqrt{(9^3 \times 9^5)}/9^{-1} = 9^8/9^{-1} = 9^4 \div 9^{-1} = 9^{4--1} = 9^5$.

☐ 29 *(a)*
$4^2 \times (4^{1/2})^4/4^3 = 4^2 \times 4^4/4^3 = 4^{2 + 2 - 3} = 4^1 = 4$.

☐ 30 *(e)*
$3^5 \times 3^{-1} = 3^{5-1} = 3^4 = 81$.

☐ 31 *(a)*
$64^{-1/3} = 1/64^{1/3} = 1/^3\sqrt{64} = ¼$ since 4 × 4 × 4 = 64.

☐ 32 *(e)*
$27^{2/3} = (^3\sqrt{27})^2 = (3)^2$ since 3 × 3 × 3 = 27. $(3)^2$ = 9.

☐ 33 *(c)*
$(¼)^{1/2} = \sqrt{¼} = \sqrt{1}/\sqrt{4} = ½$.

☐ 34 *(b)*
$^3\sqrt{27} = ^3\sqrt{(3 \times 9)} = 1/9 = ⅓$.

Multiples and factors

☐ 1 *(b)*
False. 1 is also a factor of each number. Remember, a factor is a number that will divide exactly into another number.

☐ 2 *(c)*
43 is the only number that is divisible by only itself and 1. Therefore it is prime.

☐ 3 *(d)*
9 has factors 1, 3, and 9. Prime numbers only have two factors: 1 and themselves. Since 9 can also be divided by 3 it has three factors: 1, 3, and 9. As all the other choices have two factors, this is the only non-prime number.

☐ 4 *(e)*
The diagram below shows a factor tree for 60. The numbers at the bottom of the branches are all prime: $5 \times 3 \times 2 \times 2 = 60$. (Note that 1 is not a prime number.)

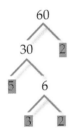

A4

☐ 5 *(a)*
The diagram below shows a factor tree for 126. The numbers at the bottom of the branches are all prime: $7 \times 3 \times 3 \times 2 = 126$.

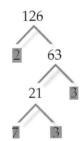

A5

☐ 6 *(a)*
The area is $4.2\text{ m} \times 4.2\text{ m} = 17.64\text{ m}^2$.

☐ 7 *(d)*
25 is not prime since 5 is a factor.

☐ 8 *(e)*
The following diagram shows that $(3) \times (-2) = -6$, $(-2) \times (1) = -2$, $(1) \times (4) = 4$, $(-6) \times (-2) = 12$, and so on.

A8

Multiples and factors
Higher Levels

☐ 9 *(b)*
False. The square root of $49 = 7$. This is an integer, or whole number, and is rational.

☐ 10 *(c)*
$4 \times 4 \times 4 = 64$. Therefore, the cube root of 64 is 4.

☐ 11 *(d)*
A number which can be written in the form $^m\!/_n$ is rational. $\sqrt{36} = 6 = ^6\!/_1$ and it is therefore rational.

☐ 12 *(b)*
$\sqrt{8}$ is a number that cannot be simplified to the form $^m\!/_n$ a rational number. As all the other solutions can, they are rational.

☐ 13 *(b)*
This is the only correct solution as 0.121212 ... is both recurring and rational.

☐ 14 *(e)*
Let $x = 0.777 ...$ Hence, $10x = 7.777 ...$ Subtracting, $9x = 7$ and so $x = ^7\!/_9$.

☐ 15 *(a)*
Let $x = 0.343434 ...$ Hence, $100x = 34.343434 ...$ Subtracting, $99x = 34$ and so $x = ^{34}\!/_{99}$.

☐ 16 *(a)*
$\sqrt{10}$ is a surd that cannot be simplified to the form $^m\!/_n$ a rational number. As all the other solutions can, they are rational.

Mental computations

☐ 1 *(b)*
False. After one hour there would be two bacteria, after two hours there would be four bacteria, after three hours there would be eight bacteria, and so on. By following this pattern, after seven hours there would be 128 bacteria.

☐ 2 *(b)*
False. After 10 years she has $£4 \times 3 = £12$. After another 10 years she has $£12 \times 3 = £36$.

☐ 3 *(a)*
Use long multiplication: $326 \times 7 = 2282$ and $326 \times 10 = 3260$. Add these together, giving $2282 + 3260 = 5542$.

☐ 4 *(c)*
$380 \div 17 = 22$, remainder 6.

☐ 5 *(c)*
$50 \times 365 = 18\,250$. To do this mentally, work out $100 \times 365 = 36\,500$. Then divide by 2, giving $36\,500 \div 2 = 18\,250$.

☐ 6 *(d)*
Estimate the answer to 260×95. Round 95 up to 100, and work out 260×100 in your head. This is $26\,000$.

☐ 7 *(e)*
Round 3142 to 3000. Round 58 to 60. $3000 \div 60 = 300 \div 6 = 50$.

☐ 8 *(a)*
The first set will be red after 4, 8, 12, 16, 20, 24, etc. minutes. The second set will be red after 6, 12, 18, 24, 30, etc. minutes. Hence, they are both red simultaneously after 12 minutes, as this is a common multiple.

☐ 9 *(c)*
The first flashes after 9 seconds, 18 seconds, 27 seconds, 36 seconds. The second flashes after 12 seconds, 24 seconds, 36 seconds. So they next coincide after 36 seconds.

☐ 10 *(e)*
$-6 - 14 = -20°C$. Therefore, 14°C down to $-6°C$ is a change of $-20°C$.

☐ 11 *(b)*
Blackpool's temperature range is 30°C to $-10°C = 40°C$. This is the greatest temperature difference.

☐ 12 *(b)*
$-5°C$ is the lowest of the temperatures.

☐ 13 *(a)*
The reading begins with $-8°C$. $-8 - 13 = -21°C$.

☐ 14 *(e)*
The rows, columns, and diagonals add to make 45. By calculating the missing numbers one by one, the starred value will be 19, as shown on the following, completed magic square.

18	13	14
11	15	19
16	17	12

A14

☐ **15** *(d)*
Adding the numbers together gives:
– 2 – 1 + 9 – 7 + 8 = 7.

☐ **16** *(e)*
The new reading is 10°C – 12°C = –2°C.

☐ **17** *(c)*
When the temperature changes from –13°C to –4°C, it has increased by 4°C – –13°C = 9°C. Since it takes 1 minute to increase by 3°C, then it will take 3 minutes to increase by 9°C.

☐ **18** *(b)*
Adding 5°C to the temperature gives –35 + 5 = –30°C.

☐ **19** *(b)*
The temperature at night fell to 35°C – 40°C = –5°C.

☐ **20** *(c)*
There are 7 × 7 = 49 paving stones.

☐ **21** *(b)*
If the perimeter is 320 m and the playground is square, the length of one side is 320 ÷ 4 = 80 m. Hence the area is 80 × 80 = 6400 m^2.

☐ **22** *(e)*
(–4 – 7) × –5 = –11 x –5 = 55°C.

☐ **23** *(a)*
– 3 – 5 – 2 + 3 + 6 + 1 – 1 + 6 = 5.

Calculations

☐ **1** *(b)*
False. 3:4 = 300:400 = 600:800. So, Fran delivered 800 papers.

☐ **2** *(a)*
True. 3.75:1.50 = 7.5:3 = 15:6 = 5:2.

☐ **3** *(a)*
True. If 40 g costs 50p, 20 g costs 25p, and therefore 100 g costs £1.25.

☐ **4** *(b)*
False.1 kg costs £1.10 ÷ 4 = 27.5p. So, 7 kg costs 7 × 27.5, which is equal to £1.93 to the nearest penny.

☐ **5** *(a)*
True. 15% of 500 = 0.15 × £500 = £75.

☐ **6** *(a)*
True. –42°C + 23°C = –19°C.

☐ **7** *(b)*
False. Highest temperature = –7°C. Lowest temperature = –15°C. Therefore, range of temperatures = –7°C – (–15°C) = 8°C.

☐ **8** *(a)*
True. 25 × £3.55 × 7 = £621.25.

☐ **9** *(e)*
117.5% of £12 200 = 1.175 × £12 200 = £14 335.

☐ **10** *(c)*
$17\frac{1}{4} - 12\frac{3}{8} = 4\frac{7}{8}$.

☐ **11** *(d)*
$2\frac{3}{5} - 1\frac{7}{10} = \frac{9}{10}$.

☐ **12** *(a)*
$35 \times 1\frac{1}{4} = 43\frac{3}{4}$.

☐ **13** *(b)*
Using a calculator, 0.92 × 0.92 = 0.85 cm^2 (to 2 d.p.).

☐ **14** *(e)*
The square root of 25.6 = 5.1 cm to 1 d.p.

☐ **15** *(a)*
15% depreciation on £2500 = 0.85 × £2500 after one year. After two years = 0.85 × 0.85 × £2500 = £1806.25.

☐ **16** *(c)*
If $\frac{1}{4}$ of a class wear glasses, this means out of every four pupils one wears glasses and three do not – i.e. the ratio is 1:3.

☐ **17** *(b)*
If $\frac{3}{7}$ of the class go on the rollercoaster, out of every seven pupils, three go on the rollercoaster and four do not – i.e. the ratio is 3:4.

☐ **18** *(a)*
There are 30 days in September. $\frac{1}{5}$ of 30 = $\frac{30}{5}$ = 6 days.

☐ **19** *(d)*
Work out $\frac{1}{14}$ of 70 = $\frac{70}{14}$ = 5. Therefore, $\frac{3}{14}$ of 70 = 3 × 5 = 15 times.

☐ **20** *(b)*
Work out $\frac{1}{5}$ of 20 = $\frac{20}{5}$ = 4. Therefore, $\frac{4}{5}$ of 20 = 4 × 4 = 16.

☐ **21** *(d)*
$\frac{2}{3}$ of the boats are sailing boats, which means that two out of three boats are sailing boats, and so one out of three is a motor boat. The ratio of sailing boats to motor boats is, therefore, 2:1.

☐ **22** *(e)*
$\frac{1}{5}$ of 5500 = $\frac{5500}{5}$ = 1100. On Saturday, there were 5500 + 1100 = 6600 spectators.

☐ **23** *(d)*
$\frac{1}{8}$ of 160 = 20. $\frac{5}{8}$ of 160 = 5 × 20 = 100 miles.

☐ **24** *(b)*
One minute out of 18 minutes is $\frac{1}{18}$ as a fraction.

☐ **25** *(a)*
$\frac{1}{4}$ of 8 = 2 hours. Therefore, 8 – 2 = 6 hours.

☐ **26** *(a)*
$\frac{1}{5}$ of 20 minutes = 4. $\frac{3}{5}$ of 20 = 3 × 4 = 12. Therefore, 20 – 12 = 8 minutes.

☐ **27** *(e)*
1 – ($\frac{2}{9}$ + $\frac{3}{9}$) = 1 – $\frac{5}{9}$ = $\frac{4}{9}$.

☐ **28** *(e)*
20% of 40 = $\frac{20}{100}$ × 40 = 0.2 × 40 = 8 hours.

☐ **29** *(d)*
Percentage reduction = $\frac{\text{reduction}}{\text{original price}}$ × 100 = $\frac{5}{25}$ × 100 = 20%.

☐ **30** *(c)*
Percentage reduction = $\frac{\text{reduction}}{\text{original price}}$ × 100 = $\frac{400}{240}$ × 100 = 16.7% (to 1 d.p.).

☐ **31** *(b)*
Percentage profit = $\frac{\text{profit}}{\text{cost price}}$ × 100 = $\frac{40}{40}$ × 100 = 100%.

☐ **32** *(b)*
Profit = 10% of 80 = $\frac{10}{100}$ × 80 = 0.1 × 80 = £8.

☐ **33** *(a)*
$\frac{14}{20}$ × 100 = 0.7 × 100 = 70%.

☐ **34** *(c)*
$\frac{6350}{25\,000}$ × 100 = 0.254 × 100 = 25.4%.

☐ **35** *(e)*
If 205 owners did, 107 didn't. $\frac{107}{312}$ × 100 = 0.343 × 100 = 34.3%.

☐ **36** *(d)*
10% of 46.65 = $\frac{10}{100}$ × 46.65 = 0.1 × 46.65 = 4.665, which is £4.67 rounded to the nearest penny.

☐ **37** *(e)*
Total medals won = 10. Number of gold = 4. Therefore, % of gold = $\frac{4}{10}$ × 100 = 40%.

☐ **38** *(e)*
64% = $\frac{64}{100}$ = $\frac{32}{50}$ = $\frac{16}{25}$.

☐ **39** *(e)*
6 parts blue:15 parts yellow = 6:15 = 2:5.

Calculations
Higher Levels

☐ **40** *(c)*
7.1% rate = multiply by 1.071 each year. After five years, multiply by 1.071^5. 1000 × 1.701^5 = £1409.12.

☐ **41** *(c)*
6% rate = multiply by 1.06 every six months. After 24 months, multiply by 1.06^4. 5000 × 1.06^4 = 6312.38. Therefore, interest only = £6312.38 – £5000 = £1312.38.

☐ **42** *(b)*
Price with VAT = 117.5% = £36.50. Price without VAT = 100% = £36.50 ÷ 117.5 × 100 = £31.06.

☐ **43** *(d)*
Price with VAT = 117.5% = £28.99. Price without VAT = 100% = £28.99 ÷ 117.5 × 100 = £24.67.

Estimation, approximation, and significant figures

☐ **1** *(b)*
187.49 is closer to 187.5 than 187.4 to 1 d.p.

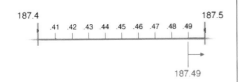

A1

☐ **2** *(a)*
136.06 is closer to 136.1 than 136.0.

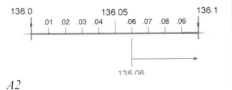

A2

☐ **3** *(c)*
Each of these laps round to 1 minute. There are five laps, so this is 5 minutes.

☐ **4** *(a)*
Rounding gives 40 × 100 = 4000 litres.

☐ **5** *(b)*
Rounding gives 1000 × 632 = 632 000 miles.

☐ **6** *(c)*
Rounding gives 30 × 30 = 900 spots.

☐ **7** *(e)*
1.969 is closer to 1.97 than 1.96 to 2 d.p.

☐ **8** *(c)*
67 rounds to 70 and 789 rounds to 800. 70 × 800 = 56 000.

☐ **9** *(c)*
To round to the nearest penny, look at the 100ths column. There is a 7 followed by a 1. The 7 remains a 7 and the full answer is £3.57.

☐ **10** *(d)*
61 rounds to 60, and 178 rounds to 180. Therefore, 180 ÷ 60 = 3 minutes.

☐ **11** *(d)*
The radius, 11.6 cm, is rounded to 1 d.p., so it is sensible to do the same for the area.

☐ **12** *(b)*
Rounding this to 2 s.f. = rounding to the nearest hundred. 3561.56 is nearer to 3600 than 3500 to the nearest hundred.

☐ **13** *(c)*
Rounding this to 3 s.f. = rounding to the nearest 10 000. 4 601 859 is closer to 4 600 000 than 4 610 000 to the nearest 10 000.

☐ **14** *(e)*
31 680 = 30 000 to 1 s.f. 310 = 300 to 1 s.f. 30 000 ÷ 300 = 100.

☐ **15** *(e)*
Rounding 496 to 2 s.f. = rounding to nearest 10 = 500.

☐ **16** *(a)*
Rounding 2999 to 2 s.f. = rounding to nearest 100 = 3000.

☐ **17** *(d)*
Rounding this to 3 s.f. = rounding to the nearest ten = 4510 kg.

☐ **18** *(d)*
Rounding this to 3 s.f. = rounding to nearest 100 000 = 93 600 000.

☐ **19** *(c)*
1.853 = 2 to 1 s.f. 212 = 200 to 1 s.f. 200 × 2 = 400 km.

☐ **20** *(e)*
2.56 × 0.18 = 0.4608.

☐ **21** *(b)*
The error is ± 0.05. Hence, the minimum number of seconds possible is 43.45 seconds.

☐ **22** *(b)*
All the other solutions are too precise or wrong for what will always be a variable journey time.

☐ **23** *(a)*
To the nearest centimetre means there is a margin error of 0.5 cm each way i.e. 16.5 ≤ L < 17.5. 17.5 is not included as it is an upper boundary, and rounds to 18 not 17.

☐ **24** *(e)*
To the nearest ½ kilogram means there is a margin of error by ¼ kg each way i.e. 0.25 kg each way.

☐ **25** *(c)*
Minimum length = 10.55 m, minimum width = 8.405 m. Area = length × width = 10.55 × 8.405 = 88.7 m² (to 3 s.f.).

☐ **26** *(c)*
Maximum length = 31.55 cm. Maximum width = 15.65 cm. Perimeter = (length × 2) + (width × 2) = (31.55 × 2) + (15.65 × 2) = 94.4 cm.

☐ **27** *(d)*
If it is rounded to the nearest 10, there is a margin of error of 5 each way. Minimum length = 130 – 5 = 125 cm.

☐ **28** *(d)*
If the rounding is to 2 s.f., then it is to the nearest 10 m, so there is a possible error of 5 m each way. Therefore, the maximum height = 850 + 5 = 855 m.

☐ **29** *(c)*
If the rounding is to 3 s.f., then it is to the nearest 10 kg, so there is a possible error of 5 kg each way. Therefore, the least value = 4800 – 5 = 4795 kg.

Estimation, approximation, and significant figures
Higher Levels

☐ **30** *(a)*
True. Lower bound for width = 19.5 m. Lower bound for length = 24.5 m.

Hence lower bound for area = 24.5 × 19.5 = 477.75 m².

□ **31** *(a)*
True. 9.95 m rounds to 10 m, to 2 s.f., whereas 9.94 m rounds to 9.9 m, to 2 s.f.

Problems

□ **1** *(c)*
(35 × 3.55) + [8 × (3.55 × 1.5)] = 124.25 + 42.60 = £166.85.

□ **2** *(c)*
He worked 40 basic hours: 40 × 4.05 = £162. He worked 10 hours overtime on Saturday and Sunday = 10 × (2 × 4.05) = £81. He worked six hours overtime on the other days = 6 × (1.5 × 4.05) = £36.45. Total = £279.45.

□ **3** *(b)*
£144 ÷ 40 = £3.60.

□ **4** *(a)*
An extra 17.5% onto £899.90 = 1.175 × £899.90 = £1057.38

□ **5** *(b)*
15% of £10 000 = £1500. £1500 × 3 = £4500.

□ **6** *(b)*
12% of £1250 = 0.12 × £1250 = £150. 12% of (£1250 + £150) = 12% of £1400 = 0.12 × 1400 = £168. Therefore, total interest = £150 + £168 = £318.

□ **7** *(d)*
The deposit was 10% of £529, which was £52.90. The remainder to pay was £529 – £52.90 = £476.10. So, each of the 10 monthly instalments was £476.10 ÷ 10 = £47.61.

□ **8** *(a)*
£9.50 × 24 = £228.00. Therefore, interest = £228.00 – £205.55 = £22.45.

□ **9** *(b)*
45p per 250 g = £1.80 per kg. 88p per 500 g = £1.76 per kg. Therefore, the difference = 4p per kilogram.

□ **10** *(d)*
W: £299 – £29.90 = £269.10 per person; X: £299 – £10 = £289 per person; Y: £600 ÷ £2 = £300 per person; Z: £270 per person. Hence W is the best value.

□ **11** *(c)*
90 680 ÷ 2205 = £41.12.

□ **12** *(c)*
350 × 8.65 = 3027.5 ff.

□ **13** *(b)*
1340 dinar per litre = 1340 ÷ 4340 pounds per litre = £0.31 per litre.

□ **14** *(b)*
115% of £32.50 = 1.15 × £32.5 = £37.375. Therefore, the final bill = £37.38 to the nearest penny.

□ **15** *(e)*
600 ÷ 4000 × 100 = 15%.

□ **16** *(e)*
500 ÷ 2.33 = £214.59.

□ **17** *(d)*
£3.00 = 3 × 292 = 876 drachma. Therefore, saving = 876 – 800 = 76 drachma.

□ **18** *(a)*
4 ÷ 1.77 = £2.26.

□ **19** *(a)*
0.75^2 × 3 = 1.69 mm² (to 2 d.p.).

□ **20** *(c)*
Diameter of Saturn ÷ diameter of Venus = $(1.2 \times 10^5) \div (1.2 \times 10^4)$ = 10.

□ **21** *(c)*
⅔ – ¼ = ⁸⁄₁₂ – ³⁄₁₂ = ⁵⁄₁₂.

□ **22** *(b)*
22¾ ÷ 1¾ = ⁹¹⁄₄ ÷ ⁷⁄₄ = ⁹¹⁄₄ × ⁴⁄₇ = ⁹¹⁄₇ = 13.

□ **23** *(d)*
⅓ of ⅖ = ⅓ × ⅖ = ²⁄₁₅.

□ **24** *(d)*
She paid ½, then ⅓, giving a total of ½ + ⅓ = ³⁄₆ + ²⁄₆ = ⁵⁄₆. Therefore, she had 1– ⁵⁄₆ = ⅙ of her money left.

□ **25** *(b)*
19 × 32.5 = 617.5 cm.

□ **26** *(a)*
125 × 4.4p = 550p.

□ **27** *(b)*
Consider the week to be 100%. 15% = 6 hours. 5% = 2 hours so 100% = 40 hours.

□ **28** *(d)*
The original price was 100%, and the latest price is 10% more, which makes 110%. 110% = 80, 1% = ⁸⁰⁄₁₁₀% = ⁸⁰⁄₁₁₀ × 100 = £72.73.

□ **29** *(c)*
The original price is 100%, the selling price is 25% less – i.e. 75%. 75% = 675, 1% = ⁶⁷⁵⁄₇₅, 100% = ⁶⁷⁵⁄₇₅ × 100 = £900.

□ **30** *(e)*
115% = 53p. So, 1% = ⁵³⁄₁₁₅. Therefore 100% = ⁵³⁄₁₁₅ × 100 = 46p to the nearest penny.

□ **31** *(c)*
Ratio = 2:3 = 200:300 = 400:600 Therefore, Johnny delivered 600 if Tom delivered 400.

□ **32** *(d)*
Ratio = 2.50:1.50. Decimals are not appropriate in ratios, so multiply by 2. Therefore, the ratio = 5:3.

□ **33** *(d)*
Ratio = 1.60:0.8. Multiply by 10 and divide by 8, and the ratio works out as 2:1.

□ **34** *(b)*
Proportion = 45:30:40 = 9:6:8 (divide by 5).

□ **35** *(a)*
Ratio = 7:3 = 14:6 = 28:12. Therefore, if 28 tins of baked beans are sold, 12 tins of noodles are sold.

□ **36** *(c)*
Ratio = 3:4 = 12:16. Therefore, there are 12 Harrier Jets if there are 16 Tomahawks.

□ **37** *(a)*
Daffodils:tulips = 3:2 = 15:10 = 150:100. Therefore, 100 tulips would be expected if 150 daffodils appeared.

□ **38** *(d)*
Proportion = 2:5:3. 2 + 5 + 3 = 10 parts altogether = 1000 seeds. One part = 100 seeds, so if barley = 5 parts = 500 seeds.

□ **39** *(c)*
Proportion = 4:5:3. 4 + 5 + 3 = 12 parts = 12 acres. Therefore, 1 part = 1 acre. The smallest portion = 3 parts = 3 acres.

□ **40** *(b)*
Gail's bungalow was 16 m long, and 8 m high. Ratio of length:height = 16:8 = 2:1 = 40:20 (if you multiply by 20). Therefore, if the length was 40 cm the height was 20 cm.

□ **41** *(c)*
Proportion = 1:2:4 and 1 + 2 + 4 = 7 parts = 35 m³. Therefore, 1 part = 5 m³. Sand = 2 parts = 10 m³.

☐ **42** *(e)*
3 kg cost £3.60. 1 kg cost £1.20 (divide by 3). Therefore, 5 kg cost £6.00 (multiply by 5).

☐ **43** *(d)*
Four lettuces cost £1.20. One lettuce costs £0.30 (divide by 4). Therefore, seven lettuces cost £2.10 (multiply by 7).

☐ **44** *(b)*
5 kg of carrots cost £1.25. 1 kg of carrots costs £0.25 (divide by 5). 2 kg of carrots cost £0.50 (multiply by 2).

☐ **45** *(b)*
400 stitches in five minutes = 100 stitches in 1.25 minutes. Therefore, she could knit 500 stitches in 6.25 minutes = 6 minutes 15 seconds.

☐ **46** *(e)*
A 250 g jar of honey contains 1250 calories. A 50 g jar of honey contains 250 calories, (divide by 5). Therefore, a 100 g jar of honey contains 500 calories, (multiply by 2).

Problems
Higher Levels

☐ **47** *(a)*
25% of £560 = 0.25 × 3560 = £140. Monthly payments total = 10 × £42 = £420. Total = £140 + £420 = £560. Therefore, there was no interest charged.

☐ **48** *(d)*
Using your calculator, 2000 × 2.7 × 10^{-23} = 5.4 × 10^{-20}.

☐ **49** *(c)*
Number of light years = distance of star from Earth ÷ distance light travels in a year. $(5.5 \times 10^{16}) \div (9.42 \times 10^{12})$ = 5814 (to the nearest whole number).

☐ **50** *(d)*
Total area = $(1.65 \times 10^8) + (8.22 \times 10^7)$ km². Total area = $16.5 \times 10^7 + 8.22 \times 10^7$. Total area = 24.72×10^7 = 247 200 000 km².

☐ **51** *(a)*
Waiting for surgery = $(8.416 \times 10^6) - (2.2 \times 10^3)$ = $8416 \times 10^3 - 2.2 \times 10^3$ = 8413.8×10^3 = 8 413 800.

☐ **52** *(b)*
Total weight of fish = $(5.35 \times 10^4) + (6.24 \times 10^5)$ = $5.35 \times 10^4 + 62.4 \times 10^4$. Total weight of fish = 67.75×10^4 = 677 500 tonnes.

☐ **53** *(a)*
$1\frac{2}{3} \times 2\frac{3}{4} = \frac{5}{3} \times \frac{11}{4} = \frac{55}{12} = 4\frac{7}{12}$ m².

☐ **54** *(b)*
$3\frac{1}{4} \times 4\frac{1}{2} = \frac{13}{4} \times \frac{9}{2} = \frac{117}{8} = 14\frac{5}{8}$ m².

☐ **55** *(e)*
y is proportional to x, so y = kx. From the table below, when x = 6, y = 9. Hence 9 = k × 6. k =1.5 and y =1.5x. Therefore, if x = 12, y = 1.5 × 12 = 18.

x	2	6	12
y	3	9	18

A55

☐ **56** *(c)*
E α v². Therefore, E = kv^2. When E = 40, v = 8. Hence, $40 = k \times 8^2$. $k = \frac{40}{8^2} = 0.625$. When v = 12, E = 0.625 × 12² = 90 units.

☐ **57** *(a)*
h α v². Therefore, h = kv^2. When h = 46.2, v = 30.2, so $46.2 = k(30.2)^2$. Hence, $k = \frac{46.2}{30.2^2} = 0.0507$. So, when h = 20, 20 = 0.0507 x v². Therefore, $v = \sqrt{(\frac{20}{0.0507})}$ = 19. 9m/s.

☐ **58** *(b)*
$y = kx^3$. $2 = k \times 10^3$. k = 0.002. When x = 40, y = 0.002 × 40³. Therefore, y = 128.

x	10	20	40
y	2	16	128

A58

☐ **59** *(d)*
I α $\frac{1}{d^2}$. Therefore, I = $\frac{k}{d^2}$. When I = 10, d = 2, so $10 = \frac{k}{2^2}$. Hence, k = 40. When d = 4, I = $\frac{40}{d^2}$. So, I = $\frac{40}{4^2}$ = 2.5 units.

☐ **60** *(e)*
w α $\frac{1}{f}$. Therefore, w = $\frac{k}{f}$. When f = 390, w = 0.85. Hence, $0.85 = \frac{k}{390}$. Therefore, k = 331.5. When f = 256, w = $\frac{331.5}{256}$. So, w = 1.29 m (2 d.p.).

☐ **61** *(c)*
P α $\frac{1}{d^2}$. Therefore, P = $\frac{k}{d^2}$. When p = 10, d = 20. Hence, $10 = \frac{k}{20^2}$. Therefore, k = 4000. When P = 15, $15 = \frac{4000}{d^2}$. So, d = 16.3 mm.

Algebra

Algebra enables us to explore a variety of situations that can lead us to express relationships between variables in a general way, by using symbols (usually letters) to represent these variables. Performing the usual number operations on these symbols helps us to see how we can manipulate these variables to model real-life situations, often enabling us to solve problems in a general way, rather than in a particular case.

Use of letters

KEY FACTS

• Algebra involves using letters to represent a value that can change (i.e. a variable). For example, we can let A stand for a person's age. Then, in two years' time, the person's age will be "A + 2", whatever their age is now.

QUESTIONS

1 "5a stands for 5 + a." Is this statement true or false?

- ☐ (a) True
- ☐ (b) False

2 If I am 16 years old today, what age will I be in x years time?

- ☐ (a) 16 − x
- ☐ (b) 16 + x
- ☐ (c) 16x
- ☐ (d) x − 16
- ☐ (e) 20

3 If I am x years old and my sister is y years younger than me, what is my sister's age?

- ☐ (a) x − y
- ☐ (b) y − x
- ☐ (c) x + y
- ☐ (d) y ÷ x
- ☐ (e) x ÷ y

4 If I spend £4a how much change will I get from a £50 note?

- ☐ (a) £46 − a
- ☐ (b) £4a − 50
- ☐ (c) £50 − £4a
- ☐ (d) £46a
- ☐ (e) £54a

5 Simplify $a^2 \times a^3$.

- ☐ (a) a^9
- ☐ (b) a^6
- ☐ (c) 6a
- ☐ (d) a^8
- ☐ (e) a^5

6 Simplify $a^5 \times a^7$.

- ☐ (a) $12a^2$
- ☐ (b) a^{35}
- ☐ (c) 35a
- ☐ (d) 12a
- ☐ (e) a^{12}

7 Simplify a^7/a^4.

- ☐ (a) $^7\!/_4$
- ☐ (b) a^{11}
- ☐ (c) a^3
- ☐ (d) $a^{7/4}$
- ☐ (e) 3

8 Simplify $(a^2)^3$.

- ☐ (a) a^6
- ☐ (b) a^5
- ☐ (c) a^8
- ☐ (d) $3a^2$
- ☐ (e) a^9

9 Simplify $(a^2)^4$.

- ☐ (a) a^6
- ☐ (b) a^8
- ☐ (c) $4a^2$
- ☐ (d) a^{24}
- ☐ (e) a^{16}

10 Simplify $3a^2 \times 2a$.

- ☐ (a) $6a^2$
- ☐ (b) $6a^3$
- ☐ (c) $5a^3$
- ☐ (d) $3a^3$
- ☐ (e) $9a^2$

11 Simplify $2a^3 \times 2a^2$.

- ☐ (a) $4a^6$
- ☐ (b) $2a^5$
- ☐ (c) a^{13}
- ☐ (d) $4a^5$
- ☐ (e) $4a^9$

12 Simplify $4a \times 3a^4$.

- ☐ (a) a^{48}
- ☐ (b) $12a^4$
- ☐ (c) $7a^5$
- ☐ (d) $4a^{13}$
- ☐ (e) $12a^5$

13 Simplify $6a^6/3a^4$.

- ☐ (a) $3a^2$
- ☐ (b) $2a^2$
- ☐ (c) $2a^{15}$
- ☐ (d) a^{24}
- ☐ (e) 4

14 Simplify $5a^5/3a^3$.

- ☐ (a) $5a^5/3$
- ☐ (b) $2a^2$
- ☐ (c) $5a^2/3$
- ☐ (d) $25/9$
- ☐ (e) $25/3$

15 Simplify $(5x)^3$.

- ☐ (a) $15x^3$
- ☐ (b) $5x^3$
- ☐ (c) $15x^3$
- ☐ (d) $125x^4$
- ☐ (e) $125x^3$

16 Simplify $(2x^3)^4$.

- ☐ (a) $16x^{12}$
- ☐ (b) $8x^7$
- ☐ (c) $8x^{12}$
- ☐ (d) $2x^{12}$
- ☐ (e) $16x^7$

17 Simplify, leaving the answer with a positive index, $a^{-7} \times a^2$.

- ☐ (a) a^5
- ☐ (b) $1/a^{14}$
- ☐ (c) $1/a^5$
- ☐ (d) a^{-5}
- ☐ (e) a^{-49}

18 Simplify $a^3 \times a^{-3}$.

- ☐ (a) a^{-1}
- ☐ (b) 0
- ☐ (c) $1/a^9$
- ☐ (d) 1
- ☐ (e) a^2

19 Simplify, leaving the answer with a positive index, $(x^{-2})^3$.

- ☐ (a) −6x
- ☐ (b) $1/x$
- ☐ (c) $1/x^6$
- ☐ (d) x^6

□ (e) $\frac{1}{x^6}$

20 Simplify, leaving the answer with a positive index, $7x^{-3} \times 4x^4$.

□ (a) $28x$
□ (b) $\frac{28}{x}$
□ (c) $\frac{28}{x^{12}}$
□ (d) $\frac{28}{x^{-1}}$
□ (e) $21x$

21 Simplify $5x^4 \times 3x^{-4}$.

□ (a) 0
□ (b) $15x$
□ (c) 15
□ (d) $\frac{15}{x}$
□ (e) $\frac{15}{x^{16}}$

22 Simplify, leaving the answer with a positive index, $\frac{7x^4}{2x^2}$.

□ (a) $\frac{7x^6}{2}$
□ (b) $\frac{-7}{2x^6}$
□ (c) $\frac{-7x^6}{2}$
□ (d) $\frac{7}{2x^6}$
□ (e) $\frac{7x}{2}$

23 Simplify, leaving the answer with a positive index, and evaluating numbers as fractions if necessary, $(4x)^{-2}$.

□ (a) $\frac{-16}{x^2}$
□ (b) $\frac{-8}{x^2}$
□ (c) $4^{-2}x^{-2}$
□ (d) $\frac{1}{16x^2}$
□ (e) $\frac{1}{16x}$

24 Simplify $3pq^2 \times 2p^2q^2$.

□ (a) $6p^2q^4$
□ (b) $6p^3q^4$
□ (c) $5p^3q^4$
□ (d) $6pq^4$
□ (e) $5pq^6$

25 Simplify $(5p^3q)^2$.

□ (a) $10p^5q^2$
□ (b) $25p^5q^2$
□ (c) $10p^6q^2$
□ (d) $25p^6q^2$
□ (e) $25p^5q^3$

QUESTIONS

Higher Level only

26 Simplify, leaving the answer with a positive index, $\frac{36x^{-3}}{24x^{-5}}$.

□ (a) $\frac{1.5}{x^4}$

□ (b) $\frac{3}{2x^8}$
□ (c) $\frac{9}{10}$
□ (d) $\frac{3}{2x^2}$
□ (e) $\frac{3x^2}{2}$

27 Simplify $\frac{15p^2q^3}{3pq}$.

□ (a) $5p^2q^5$
□ (b) $5pq^2$
□ (c) 3^5
□ (d) 5^6
□ (e) 5^3

28 Simplify $\frac{42p^3 \times q^6}{7p^3q^2}$.

□ (a) $6pq^4$
□ (b) 6^4
□ (c) $6q^4$
□ (d) $6pq^3$
□ (e) q^{24}

Number patterns

KEY FACTS

• "2, 4, 8, 16, 32 …" and "5, 8, 11, 14, 17 …" are examples of sequences of numbers following an easily recognisable pattern. To find the next term, double the previous term in the first sequence and add 3 to the previous term in the second sequence.

• The first sequence can also be written as $2, 2^2, 2^3, 2^4, 2^5$ …. Hence, the 4th term is 2^4, the 5th term is 2^5, and therefore the nth term will be 2^n.

• In the second sequence 3 is being added each time, so the nth term will be $3n + c$, where c is a constant for this sequence. By taking $n = 4$, for example, the 4th term is $(3 \times 4) + c$. But the 4th term is actually 14, so $(3 \times 4) + c = 14$, and hence $c = 2$. So, the nth term is $3n + 2$. (To check, 5th term is $(3 \times 5) + 2 = 15 + 2 = 17$).

QUESTIONS

1 Find the next term in the sequence 3, 7, 11, 15, 19, …

□ (a) 23
□ (b) 25
□ (c) 21
□ (d) 27
□ (e) 26

2 Find the next term in the sequence 2, 6, 10, 14, 18, …

□ (a) 24
□ (b) 22
□ (c) 20
□ (d) 21
□ (e) 23

3 Find the next term in the sequence 5, 8, 11, 14, 17, …

□ (a) 24
□ (b) 26
□ (c) 20
□ (d) 23
□ (e) 21

4 Find the next term in the sequence 27, 22, 17, 12, 7, …

□ (a) 12
□ (b) 3
□ (c) 5
□ (d) 2
□ (e) –2

5 Find the next term in the sequence 13, 10, 7, 4, 1, …

□ (a) –3
□ (b) –1
□ (c) 0
□ (d) 4
□ (e) –2

6 Find the next term in the sequence 100, 70, 40, 10, –20, …

□ (a) –50
□ (b) 10
□ (c) –80
□ (d) –40
□ (e) –30

7 Find the next term in the sequence 63, 56, 49, 42, 35, …

☐ (a) 41
☐ (b) 21
☐ (c) 28
☐ (d) 27
☐ (e) 26

8 Find the next term in the sequence 3, 7, 12, 18, 25, ...

☐ (a) 30
☐ (b) 33
☐ (c) 32
☐ (d) 34
☐ (e) 37

9 Find the next term in the sequence 1, 3, 6, 10, 15, 21, ...

☐ (a) 20
☐ (b) 25
☐ (c) 24
☐ (d) 19
☐ (e) 28

10 Find the next term in the sequence 2, 4, 8, 16, 32, ...

☐ (a) 52
☐ (b) 60
☐ (c) 58
☐ (d) 64
☐ (e) 48

11 Find the next term in the sequence 1, 4, 9, 16, 25, ...

☐ (a) 37
☐ (b) 50
☐ (c) 36
☐ (d) 34
☐ (e) 27

12 Find the nth term in the sequence 7, 11, 15, 19, 23, ...

☐ (a) 4n + 3
☐ (b) 4n
☐ (c) 4 + n
☐ (d) 7 + 3n
☐ (e) 7 + 4n

13 Find the nth term in the sequence 4, 6, 8, 10, 12, ...

☐ (a) 2n + 4
☐ (b) +2
☐ (c) 2n + 2
☐ (d) 2n
☐ (e) n + 2

14 Find the nth term in the sequence 20, 18, 16, 14, 12, ...

☐ (a) 24 – 2n
☐ (b) 22 – 2n
☐ (c) n – 2
☐ (d) –2
☐ (e) 20 – 2n

15 Find the nth term in the sequence 3, 8, 13, 18, 23, ...

☐ (a) 3n + 2
☐ (b) n + 5
☐ (c) 3 + 5n
☐ (d) –3 + 5n
☐ (e) 5n – 2

16 Find the nth term in the series 2.5, 5, 7.5, 10, 12.5, ...

☐ (a) $\frac{5n}{2}$ + 2.5
☐ (b) $\frac{5n}{2}$ ÷ 2.5

☐ (c) $\frac{5n}{2}$ – 2.5
☐ (d) $\frac{5n}{2}$
☐ (e) 2n – 25

17 Find the nth term in the series –3, –1, 1, 3, 5, ...

☐ (a) n – 1
☐ (b) 2n – 5
☐ (c) 2n – 3
☐ (d) 2n – 1
☐ (e) n + 2

18 Find the nth term in the series 8, 15, 22, 29, 36, ...

☐ (a) 7n
☐ (b) 7n – 6
☐ (c) 7n + 1
☐ (d) 7n + 8
☐ (e) n + 7

19 Find the nth term in the series 17, 26, 35, 44, 53, ...

☐ (a) 9n + 8
☐ (b) 17n + 8
☐ (c) n + 9
☐ (d) 9n – 1
☐ (e) 9n + 17

Properties of functions

 KEY FACTS

• A linear function can be arranged into the form $y = mx + c$.

• A quadratic function is of the form $y = ax^2 + bx + c$. For example, $y = 3x^2 + x – 2$, or $y = 4x^2 + 5$.

• A cubic function is of the form $y = ax^3 + bx^2 + cx + d$.

• A reciprocal function is of the form $y = \frac{k}{x}$.

• Values of the functions can be found by making a table. For example, $y = 2x^2 + 3x – 2$.

x	-2	-1	0	1	2	3	4
$2x^2$	8	2	0	2	8	18	32
+3x	-6	-3	0	3	6	9	12
-2	-2	-2	-2	-2	-2	-2	-2
y	0	-3	-2	3	12	25	42

Values of functions

• A graph can then be drawn of the function. A linear function has a graph that is a straight line.

• A quadratic function is either

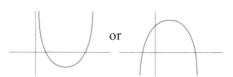

Quadratic functions

• A cubic function is

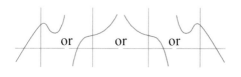

Cubic functions

• A reciprocal function is either

 or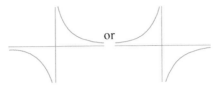

Reciprocal functions

QUESTIONS

1 "The equation of the line shown on the diagram below is y = 2x + 3." Is this statement true or false?

☐ (a) True
☐ (b) False

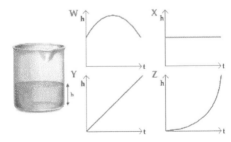

Q1

2 "Water is poured into the cylinder shown in the following diagram at a constant rate. Graph Y shows how the height of the water changes with time." Is this statement true or false?

☐ (a) True
☐ (b) False

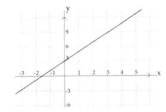

Q2

3 "The following diagram is a graph of y = x – 1." Is this statement true or false?

☐ (a) True
☐ (b) False

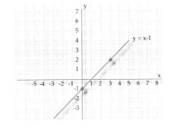

Q3

4 "The points (0, 0) and (100, 245) have been plotted on the following conversion graph. The x-axis represents £'s and the y-axis represents German DM. £100 = 245 DM. From the graph, the value in DM of £62 to the nearest DM is 152 and the value of 160 DM in £'s to the nearest £1 is £65." Is this statement true or false?

☐ (a) True
☐ (b) False

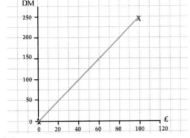

Q4

5 "The points (0, 0) and (10, 16) have been plotted on the following conversion graph. The x-axis represents £'s and the y-axis represents US$. £10 = $16. From the graph, the value of £4.20 to the nearest $0.1 is $6.70 and also the value of $11 in £'s to the nearest 10p is £6.80." Is this statement true or false?

☐ (a) True
☐ (b) False

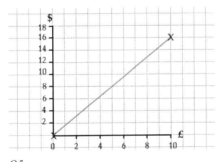

Q5

6 Using a scale of 1 cm = 1 unit on both axes, plot the points A (–4, –6) and B (6, 4), marking each clearly. Join the points with a straight line and give the co-ordinates of the points where the line cuts the x- and y-axes.

☐ (a) (–2, 0), (0, –2)
☐ (b) (2, 0), (0, –2)
☐ (c) (–2, 0), (0, 2)
☐ (d) (30, 0), (0, 5)
☐ (e) (2, 0), (0, 2)

7 Complete the table below, and then draw the graph, using 1 cm per unit on each axis. From your graph,

solve x² – 3x – 2 = 0. Give the answers correct to 1 d.p.

☐ (a) x = 0.6 or 3.6
☐ (b) x = –0.6 or 3.6
☐ (c) x = 3.6
☐ (d) x = –0.7 or 2.6
☐ (e) x = –2.0

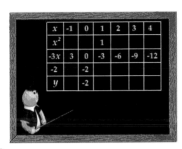

x	-1	0	1	2	3	4
x²			1			
-3x	3	0	-3	-6	-9	-12
-2		-2				
y		-2				

Q7

8 Using values of x from –1 to +5 draw the graph of y = x² – 4x – 2, using 1 cm for each unit on each axis. Use the graph to solve x² – 4x – 2 = 0. Give the answers correct to 1 d.p.

☐ (a) x = –0.4 or 4.4
☐ (b) x = 0.4 or 4.4
☐ (c) x = –0.7 or 3.6
☐ (d) x = 3.6
☐ (e) x = –2.0

9 Draw the graph of y = x² – 3x – 2, from x = –1 to 4 using a scale of 1 cm per unit on both the x- and y-axis, as shown on the diagram below. On your graph draw in the axis of symmetry. Write down the equation of the axis of symmetry.

☐ (a) x = 1.5
☐ (b) x = 1
☐ (c) x = 2
☐ (d) y = –3.25
☐ (e) y = 1.5, –3.25

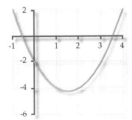

Q9

QUESTIONS

Higher Level only

10 Draw the graphs of y = x² and y = 2x + 5 on the same grid, with values of x from –2 to +4 and a scale of 1 cm per unit on both axes.

Use your graphs to solve $x^2 = 2x + 5$. Give the answers correct to 1 d.p.

☐ (a) x = –1.4 or 3.4
☐ (b) x = 2.5
☐ (c) x = –1.2 or 4.2
☐ (d) x = 0 or 5
☐ (e) x = –1.6 or 1.6

☐ (a) x = –2.6 or 1.6
☐ (b) x = 2.6
☐ (c) x = 0 or –4
☐ (d) x = –1.6 or 2.6
☐ (e) x = –2.6

11 Draw the graphs of $y = x^2 – 4$ and $y = -x$ on the same grid, with values of x from –3 to +3 and a scale of 1 cm per unit on both axes. Use your graphs to find solutions for $x^2 – 4 = -x$. Give the answers correct to 1 d.p.

Construct and evaluate formulae

KEY FACTS

• If it costs £12 plus £4 per day to hire a hedge trimmer then the cost, £C, of hiring it for d days will be C = 12 + 4d. More generally, if it costs £A plus £B per day, then C = A + Bd. So, if A = 30, B = 5, and d = 4, C = 30 + (5 × 4) = £50.

• In evaluating formulae, care must be taken to i) substitute numbers in correctly without doing any calculations, and ii) do the evaluation step-by-step.

• E.g. i) Solve k = $^{12}\!/_{5-x}$, when x = 2. Therefore, k = $^{12}\!/_{5-2}$ = $^{12}\!/_3$ = 4.

• E.g. ii) Solve p = 14 – 3x, when x = 1.4. p = 14 – (3 × 1.4) = 14 – 4.2 [and not (14 – 3) × 1.4 – remember BODMAS]. Therefore, p = 9.8.

• E.g. iii) Solve A = $3.14r^2$, when r = 3. A = 3.14 × 3^2 [not $(3.14 × 3)^2$ – the power refers only to the term immediately before it. We would need to write $(3.14r)^2$ if we meant $(3.14 × 3)^2 = (9.42)^2$]. Therefore, A = 3.14 × 9 = 28.26.

QUESTIONS

1 "y = mx + c. When m = 0.5, x = 3, and c = –1, y = 0.5." Is this statement true or false?

☐ (a) True
☐ (b) False

2 Distance = speed × time. If the speed is 30 km/h, what distance will be travelled in 7 hours?

☐ (a) 307 km
☐ (b) 220 km
☐ (c) 210 km
☐ (d) 37 km
☐ (e) 21 km

3 If the length of a candle in centimetres is given by the expression 16 – 6t, where t is the time in hours that the candle has been burning, what will be the length of the candle 2 hours after it has been lit?

☐ (a) 8 cm
☐ (b) 5 cm
☐ (c) 2 cm
☐ (d) 4 cm
☐ (e) 12 cm

4 If c = $^{a+b}\!/_5$, find the value of c when a = 6 and b = –4.

☐ (a) $4\frac{2}{3}$
☐ (b) –2
☐ (c) $3\frac{1}{3}$
☐ (d) –8
☐ (e) $\frac{2}{3}$

5 Cooking time in hours = $\frac{1}{3}$ × mass of meat in kilograms. If the mass of the meat is 4 kg, how long will it take to cook in hours and minutes?

☐ (a) 1 hour 20 minutes
☐ (b) 12 hours
☐ (c) 45 minutes
☐ (d) 4 hours 20 minutes
☐ (e) 3 hours 40 minutes

6 c = $a^2 + 2b$. Find the value of c when a = 6 and b = 4.

☐ (a) 20
☐ (b) 42
☐ (c) 52
☐ (d) 86
☐ (e) 44

7 H = 350 – 11t. Find H when t = 18.

☐ (a) 3729
☐ (b) 357
☐ (c) 321
☐ (d) 548
☐ (e) 152

8 If k = $d^2 + d + 2$, find k if d = 2.5.

☐ (a) 10
☐ (b) 25
☐ (c) 9.5
☐ (d) 10.75
☐ (e) 11.25

9 A square room has sides of length k. Find an expression for the area of the floor of the room.

☐ (a) $k^{(2)2}$
☐ (b) $2k^2$
☐ (c) k^2
☐ (d) 4k
☐ (e) $4k^2$

10 Find the perimeter of the shape shown in the following diagram.

☐ (a) 6ab
☐ (b) 2a + 6b
☐ (c) 2a + 7b
☐ (d) 2a + 5b
☐ (e) 5ab

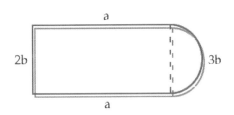

Q10

11 If I have x + y coins and my friend has six times as many, how many coins has he got?

- ☐ (a) 6 + x + y
- ☐ (b) 6xy
- ☐ (c) 36xy
- ☐ (d) 6x + 6y
- ☐ (e) 6x + y

12 The following is used by Professor Jenkins for his scientific calculations. T = (3t + 0.9) × 2.14. If t = –3.9, calculate T (to 3 d.p.).

- ☐ (a) 26.964
- ☐ (b) 23.112
- ☐ (c) –23.112
- ☐ (d) –26.964
- ☐ (e) 23.212

13 Ohm's Law gives the relationship between voltage V, current I, and resistance R: $R = \frac{V}{I}$. Find the current if the voltage is 15 V and the resistance is 2.5 ohms.

- ☐ (a) 37.5 amps
- ☐ (b) 6 amps
- ☐ (c) 1 amp 6
- ☐ (d) 2 amps 5
- ☐ (e) 1 amp 15

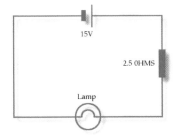

Q13

14 If a body is moving with uniform acceleration, this acceleration may be given by the formula $a = \frac{v - u}{t}$. If v = 20, u = 8.6, and t = 4, use your calculator to determine the value of a.

- ☐ (a) 2.85
- ☐ (b) 17.85
- ☐ (c) –16.5
- ☐ (d) 1.65
- ☐ (e) 1.25

15 The acceleration of the masses M and m in the diagram shown below is given by a = $\frac{mMg}{M(m + m)}$. If m = 0.6, M = 3, and g = 9.8, use a calculator to find a.

- ☐ (a) 3.24
- ☐ (b) 4.9
- ☐ (c) 2.71
- ☐ (d) 5.20
- ☐ (e) 3.92

Q15

16 $v^2 = u^2 + 2as$. Find v (to 2 d.p.), when s = 5.2 cm, a = 3.2 m/s, and u = 1.1 m/s.

- ☐ (a) 53.41 m/s
- ☐ (b) 34.49 m/s
- ☐ (c) 5.87 m/s
- ☐ (d) 5.78 m/s
- ☐ (e) 34.94 m/s

17 The extension, e, of a spring is proportional to the mass, m, hung from the spring. A mass of 2 kg gives an extension of 7 cm. What is the relationship between e and m?

- ☐ (a) e = m + 7
- ☐ (b) e = 7m
- ☐ (c) e = m + 5
- ☐ (d) e = 3.5m
- ☐ (e) e = m ÷ 7

18 The cost, C, of furnishing fabric to cover a sofa is proportional to the length, L, of the fabric bought. If 4 m of fabric cost £27, write down a formula linking C and L.

- ☐ (a) 27C = 4L
- ☐ (b) C = 27L
- ☐ (c) C = 23 + L
- ☐ (d) C = 4 + L
- ☐ (e) C = 6.75L

19 What is the relationship between r and v, using k as the constant of variation, if the air resistance (r) to a bullet varies with the square of the speed of the bullet (v).

- ☐ (a) $r = kv^2$
- ☐ (b) $r = k^2v^2$
- ☐ (c) $r = \sqrt{(kv)}$
- ☐ (d) $r = \frac{k}{v^2}$
- ☐ (e) $r = v^2$

QUESTIONS

Higher Level only

20 The formula $\frac{1}{t} = \frac{1}{h} + \frac{1}{c}$ gives the time taken for a sink to fill when both taps are running. h stands for the time it takes with only the hot tap on, c stands for the time it takes with only the cold tap on, and t when both are on. Find t (in minutes) when h = 4 and c = 6.

- ☐ (a) 10 minutes
- ☐ (b) 0.42 minutes
- ☐ (c) 24 minutes
- ☐ (d) 2.4 minutes
- ☐ (e) 2 minutes 40 seconds

21 Two balls are projected upwards vertically, the second ball going t seconds after the first. The balls meet at height h, where $h = \frac{4u^2 - g^2t^2}{8g}$. Find h (to 1 d.p.), when u = 25, t = 4, and g = 9.8

- ☐ (a) 15.3 m
- ☐ (b) 963.4 m
- ☐ (c) 108.0 m
- ☐ (d) 12.3 m
- ☐ (e) 12.6 m

35

Manipulate algebraic expressions

 KEY FACTS

• We often need to make algebraic expressions simpler in order to proceed to solve equations or inequalities. The rules used are the same as the rules for numbers, but brackets are often used in algebra. For instance, the perimeter of a rectangle measuring 8 cm by 5 cm is $2 \times (8 + 5) = 2(13) = 26$ cm. If the rectangle measures l cm by b cm, the perimeter is $2(l + b)$, or $2l + 2b$. If we are given values for l and b, it is easier to use $2(l + b)$ than $2l + 2b$, although both give the same answer. It is useful, in more complicated expressions, to be able to manipulate them into the most suitable form.

• Rules:
i) $3a + 5a - 2a = (a + a + a) + (a + a + a + a + a) - (a + a) = 8a - 2a = 6a$.
ii) $6(a - 3b) = 6a - 6(3b) = 6a - 18b$.
iii) $x(2y + z) = x(2y) + x(z) = 2xy + xz$.
iv) $p(8p^2 - p + 4) = p(8p^2) - p(p) + p(4) = 8p^3 - p^2 + 4p$. (N.B. You cannot add "$p^2$" to "$p^3$" terms. It is rather like trying to add a volume to an area – meaningless.)
v) $a^2 \times a^3 = (a \times a) \times (a \times a \times a) = a^5$.
vi) $12p^5 \div 4p^3 = (12 \times p \times p \times p \times p \times p) \div (4 \times p \times p \times p) = 3p^2$.
vii) $8a + 12b = 4(2a + 3b)$.
viii) $9x^2y - 3xy^2 = 3xy(3x - y)$.

QUESTIONS

1 "The product of $(x + 1)(x + 2)$ is $x^2 + 2$." Is this statement true or false?

☐ (a) True
☐ (b) False

2 "The equation $v^2 = 2gh$ may be rearranged to $h = v^2 \div 2g$." Is this statement true or false?

☐ (a) True
☐ (b) False

3 "The equation $v = u + at$ may be rearranged to $t = (v - u) \div a$." Is this statement true or false?

☐ (a) True

☐ (b) False

4 Simplify $a + 2a + 3a$.

☐ (a) 6a
☐ (b) $5a^2$
☐ (c) $6a^2$
☐ (d) 5
☐ (e) 5a

5 Simplify $a + (- 2a)$.

☐ (a) 2
☐ (b) –a
☐ (c) $-2a^2$
☐ (d) 3a
☐ (e) –3a

6 Simplify $4b - (-2b)$.

☐ (a) $-8b^2$
☐ (b) –2b
☐ (c) 6b
☐ (d) 2b
☐ (e) $8b^2$

7 Simplify $a \times a \times 3 \times a \times a$.

☐ (a) $3a\frac{3}{4}$
☐ (b) a^6
☐ (c) 7a
☐ (d) $3a^4$
☐ (e) 12a

8 Simplify $a + 2b - 4a + 2b$.

☐ (a) –4a + 2b
☐ (b) –3a
☐ (c) –3a + 4b
☐ (d) –5ab
☐ (e) ab

9 Simplify $-3c - 2(-4c)$.

☐ (a) –9c
☐ (b) –11c
☐ (c) 2c
☐ (d) 20c
☐ (e) 5c

10 Simplify $a + 2a^2 + 7a$.

☐ (a) $2a^2 + 7a$
☐ (b) $a + 14a^2$
☐ (c) $10a^4$
☐ (d) $8a + 2a^2$
☐ (e) $9a^2$

11 Simplify $a - 10a + 9a$.

☐ (a) 0
☐ (b) –18a
☐ (c) 18a
☐ (d) $-90a^2$

☐ (e) a

12 Simplify $9\frac{3}{4}a + 6\frac{b}{2}b$.

☐ (a) 12
☐ (b) 9a + 3b
☐ (c) 7.5
☐ (d) 12ab
☐ (e) 5

13 A coin has seven sides, each of length 3x. What is the length of the perimeter of the coin?

☐ (a) 7 + 3x
☐ (b) 1050x
☐ (c) 21x
☐ (d) 57 + 3x
☐ (e) 10x

14 Find the perimeter of a triangle whose sides measure 2y, 5y, and 4y.

☐ (a) 22y
☐ (b) 11y
☐ (c) $4y^2$
☐ (d) 40y
☐ (e) $45y^2$

15 Multiply out $6(2x + 1)$

☐ (a) 12x + 1
☐ (b) 12x
☐ (c) 8x + 7
☐ (d) 18x
☐ (e) 12x + 6

16 Multiply out $4(3 - x)$.

☐ (a) 12 – 4x
☐ (b) 12 – x
☐ (c) 12 – 3x
☐ (d) –12x
☐ (e) 7 – 4x

17 Multiply out $-5(2 + x)$.

☐ (a) –10 + 5x
☐ (b) –10 – 5x
☐ (c) –10 + x
☐ (d) –10x
☐ (e) 3 – 5x

18 Multiply out $-7(2x - 6)$.

☐ (a) –5x – 13
☐ (b) –5x + 13
☐ (c) –14x + 42
☐ (d) –14x – 6
☐ (e) –14x – 42

19 Factorize $14a - 16b$.

☐ (a) –2ab

☐ (b) 14(a − 2b)
☐ (c) 2(7a − 8b)
☐ (d) 2a(7 − 8b)
☐ (e) 2(7a + 8b)

20 Factorize 3x +12y.

☐ (a) 4xy
☐ (b) 3(x +9y)
☐ (c) 3(x + 4y)
☐ (d) 3(x4y)
☐ (e) 3(x +5y)

21 Factorize 15x + 5y.

☐ (a) 5(10x +y)
☐ (b) 5(3x +4y)
☐ (c) 12xy
☐ (d) 5(3x + y)
☐ (e) 5(11x + y)

22 Factorize 2x − 8y.

☐ (a) 2(x − 3y)
☐ (b) 2(x − 6y)
☐ (c) −6xy
☐ (d) 2(−4xy)
☐ (e) 2(x − 4y)

23 Factorize 3ab + 5ac.

☐ (a) a(3b + 5c)
☐ (b) 8bc
☐ (c) a(15bc)
☐ (d) 15a^{2bc}
☐ (e) a(b³+c⁵)

24 Factorize 7ax + x².

☐ (a) x(7a + 2x)
☐ (b) x(7a + 2)
☐ (c) x(7a + x)
☐ (d) 2x(5a +x)
☐ (e) 2x(5a +2)

25 Factorize 3xy − 15y².

☐ (a) 3(xy − 5y²)
☐ (b) 3y(x −10)
☐ (c) 3y(x − 75y)
☐ (d) y(3x − 15y)
☐ (e) 3y(x − 5y)

26 Factorize 3y − 9xy.

☐ (a) 3y(1 − 3x)
☐ (b) 3y(−3y)
☐ (c) 3(y − 3x)
☐ (d) y(3 − 9x)
☐ (e) 3y(1 − 6x)

27 Factorize 24p²r² − 16r³q.

☐ (a) 16r²(8p² − rq)
☐ (b) 8r²(3p² − 2rq)
☐ (c) 4r²(6p² − 4rq)
☐ (d) 8r²(3p²r − 2rq)

☐ (e) 2r(12p²r² − 8r²q)

28 Expand and simplify the terms (x + 3)(x + 1).

☐ (a) x² + 3x + 3
☐ (b) x² + x + 4
☐ (c) x² + 4x + 3
☐ (d) x² + 4x + 4
☐ (e) x² + 3

29 Expand and simplify the terms (x + 7)(x + 5).

☐ (a) x² + 5x + 35
☐ (b) x² + 12x + 35
☐ (c) x² + 12x − 35
☐ (d) x² + 35x + 12
☐ (e) x² + 12

30 Expand and simplify the terms (x − 4)(x − 1).

☐ (a) x² − 4
☐ (b) x² + 4
☐ (c) x² − 3x + 4
☐ (d) x² − 5x − 4
☐ (e) x² − 5x + 4

31 Expand and simplify the terms (x + 8)(x − 5).

☐ (a) x² + 3x − 40
☐ (b) x² − 3x − 40
☐ (c) x² − 40x + 3
☐ (d) x² − 40
☐ (e) x² + 8x − 3

32 Expand and simplify the terms (x − 6)(x + 3).

☐ (a) x² − 6x − 3
☐ (b) x² + 3x − 18
☐ (c) x² − 18
☐ (d) x² − 3x + 18
☐ (e) x² − 3x − 18

33 Expand and simplify the terms (2x + 3)(x + 5).

☐ (a) 2x² + 8x + 15
☐ (b) 2x² +15
☐ (c) 2x² + 13x + 15
☐ (d) 2x² + 5x + 15
☐ (e) 6x² + 13x + 15

34 Expand and simplify the terms (5x + 3)(3x + 5).

☐ (a) 15x² + 8x +15
☐ (b) 15x² + 34x + 15
☐ (c) 15x² +15
☐ (d) 25x² + 14x +15
☐ (e) 15x² +30x +15

35 Factorize x² + 8x + 15.

☐ (a) (x + 8)(x + 15)
☐ (b) (x + 2)(x + 4)
☐ (c) (x + 1)(x + 8)
☐ (d) (x + 1)(x + 15)
☐ (e) (x + 3)(x + 5)

36 Factorize x² + 9x +14.

☐ (a) (x + 9)(x + 14)
☐ (b) (x + 3)(x + 3)
☐ (c) (x + 1)(x + 9)
☐ (d) (x + 1)(x + 14)
☐ (e) (x + 2)(x + 7)

37 Factorize x² + 16x + 55.

☐ (a) (x + 4)(x + 4)
☐ (b) (x + 1)(x + 16)
☐ (c) (x + 2)(x + 8)
☐ (d) (x + 5)(x + 11)
☐ (e) (x + 1)(x + 55)

38 Factorize x² − 10x + 21.

☐ (a) (x − 1)(x − 21)
☐ (b) (x − 2)(x − 5)
☐ (c) (x − 1)(x − 10)
☐ (d) (x − 10)(x − 21)
☐ (e) (x − 3)(x − 7)

39 Factorize x² + 8x − 33.

☐ (a) (x − 3)(x − 11)
☐ (b) (x − 3)(x + 11)
☐ (c) (x − 1)(x + 8)
☐ (d) (x + 3)(x)
☐ (e) (x + 8)(x − 33)

40 Factorize x² + 3x − 10.

☐ (a) (x −2)(x + 5)
☐ (b) (x +2)(x − 5)
☐ (c) (x −2)(x − 5)
☐ (d) (x + 3)(x − 10)
☐ (e) (x + 1)(x − 10)

41 Factorize x² − 2x − 35.

☐ (a) (x − 5)(x − 7)
☐ (b) (x − 5)(x + 7)
☐ (c) (x + 5)(x + 7)
☐ (d) (x + 5)(x − 7)
☐ (e) (x − 2)(x + 7)

42 Rearrange the equation p = q + rt to make t the subject.

☐ (a) $^{p}/_{r}$ − q
☐ (b) $^{(p − q)}/_{r}$
☐ (c) q − $^{p}/_{r}$
☐ (d) p − q − r
☐ (e) $^{q − p}/_{r}$

43 Rearrange the equation y = mx + c to make x the subject.

☐ (a) y − c − m

□ (b) $\frac{y}{m} - c$
□ (c) $\frac{(y-c)}{m}$
□ (d) $\frac{c-y}{m}$
□ (e) $c - \frac{y}{m}$

 QUESTIONS

Higher Level only

44 Expand and simplify the terms $(x + 7a)(x + 2a)$.

□ (a) $x^2 + 9a^2x + 14a^2$
□ (b) $x^2 + 14ax + 9a^2$
□ (c) $x^2 + 9ax + 14a^2$
□ (d) $x^2 + 9a + 14a^2$
□ (e) $x^2 + 14a^2$

45 Expand and simplify the terms $(2x - y)(2x + y)$.

□ (a) $4x^2 - y^2$
□ (b) $4x^2 - xy$
□ (c) $4x$
□ (d) $4x - y^2$
□ (e) $4x^2 - 2xy + y - y^2$

46 Expand and simplify the terms $(x + 11y)(x - 11y)$.

□ (a) $x^2 - 22xy - y^2$
□ (b) $x^2 + 121y^2$
□ (c) $x^2 - 121y^2$
□ (d) $x^2 - 22xy - 121y^2$
□ (e) $x^2 - y^2$

47 Factorize $3x^2 + 4x + 1$.

□ (a) $(3x + 1)(x + 1)$
□ (b) $(3x + 1)(x + 4)$
□ (c) $(3x + 1)(4x + 1)$
□ (d) $(4x + 1)(-x + 1)$
□ (e) $(3x + 2)(x + 2)$

48 Factorize $2x^2 + 5x + 3$.

□ (a) $(2x - 1)(x + 3)$
□ (b) $(2x + 3)(x + 1)$
□ (c) $(2x + 3)(2x - 1)$
□ (d) $(2x + 1)(x + 4)$
□ (e) $(2x + 4)(x + 1)$

49 Factorize $5x^2 - 11x + 6$.

□ (a) $(5x - 11)(x + 6)$
□ (b) $(5x - 3)(x - 2)$
□ (c) $(5x + 6)(x + 1)$
□ (d) $(5x + 11)(x - 1)$
□ (e) $(5x - 6)(x - 1)$

50 Factorize $3x^2 - 10x + 7$.

□ (a) $(3x - 2)(x - 5)$
□ (b) $(3x - 1)(x - 7)$
□ (c) $(3x - 5)(x - 2)$
□ (d) $(3x - 7)(x - 1)$
□ (e) $(3x - 1)(x + 7)$

51 Factorize $10x^2 - 3x - 1$.

□ (a) $(5x - 3)(x + 1)$
□ (b) $(5x - 1)(x + 1)$
□ (c) $(10x + 1)(x - 1)$
□ (d) $(10x - 1)(x + 1)$
□ (e) $(5x + 1)(2x - 1)$

52 Factorize $21x^2 + 4x - 1$.

□ (a) $(21x + 1)(x - 1)$
□ (b) $(7x + 1)(3x - 1)$
□ (c) $(7x - 1)(3x + 1)$
□ (d) $(21x - 1)(x + 1)$
□ (e) $(7x + 2)(3x - 2)$

53 Factorize $x^2 - 4y^2$.

□ (a) $(x + y)(x - 4y)$
□ (b) $(x + 4y)(x - 4y)$
□ (c) $(x + 4y)(x - y)$
□ (d) $(x + 2y)(x - 2y)$
□ (e) $(x - 2y)^2$

54 Factorize $4x^2 - 9y^2$.

□ (a) $(2x + 3y)(2x - 3y)$
□ (b) $(4x + 3y)(x - 3y)$
□ (c) $(x + 3y)(4x - 3y)$
□ (d) $(2x + 9y)(2x - y)$
□ (e) $(2x + y)(2x - 9)$

55 Work out the following:
$(2 + \sqrt{3})(2 - \sqrt{3})$.

□ (a) $4 - 2\sqrt{3}$
□ (b) $3 + 2\sqrt{3}$
□ (c) 5
□ (d) -1
□ (e) 1

Solve linear, simultaneous, and quadratic equations; and higher polynomials by trial and improvement

KEY FACTS

• Solving an equation means finding the numerical value of the letter in the equation.
i) If $x - 5 = 2$, then by adding 5 to each side of the "balance", $x = 2 + 5 = 7$.
ii) If $3p + 2 = 17$, then taking 2 from each side gives $3p = 17 - 2 = 15$. Dividing each side by 3 will give $\frac{3p}{3} = \frac{15}{3}$ or $p = 5$.
iii) If $4(x - 2) = 28$, then $4x - 8 = 28$. Adding 8 gives $4x = 28 + 8 = 36$. Dividing each side by 4 will give $x = \frac{36}{4} = 9$.
iv) If $\frac{x+4}{3} = 7$, multiply by 3, so $x + 4 = 3 \times 7 = 21$. Subtract 4, so $x = 21 - 4 = 17$.

v) If $3x - 1 = x + 7$, subtracting an x from each side will maintain the "balance". $2x - 1 = 7$. Add 1, so $2x = 8$. Divide by 2, hence $x = 4$.

• When there are two unknowns, two equations are needed from which one is eliminated, to give a linear equation. Having solved this, substitute the value into the original equation to evaluate the other unknown. The equations are being solved simultaneously (together). E.g. $3x + y = 17$ and $x - y = 3$. First add the LHS of the equations to obtain $3x + y + x - y$, which is $4x$. Then, add the RHS of the equations, which gives $4x = 17 + 3 = 20$. Hence, dividing by 4, $x = 5$. From the second equation (the

simpler of the two), $x - y = 3$ will become $5 - y = 3$. Adding y, $5 = 3 + y$. Subtracting 3 gives $2 = y$ and therefore $y = 2$. Checking in the first equation: $3(5) + 2 = 15 + 2 = 17$.

• In solving quadratic equations, we need first to factorize the expression (if possible).
E.g. i) Solve $x^2 - 3x = 0$. $x(x - 3) = 0$. Hence $x = 0$ or $x - 3 = 0$. So, $x = 0$ or $x = 3$.
E.g. ii) Solve $x - 3x - 10 = 0$. $(x - 5)(x + 2) = 0$. Hence, $x - 5 = 0$ or $x + 2 = 0$. So $x = 5$ or $x = -2$.

• If the quadratic expression does not factorize, we can use the quadratic formula:
$x = \frac{-b \pm \sqrt{b^2 - 4ac}}{2a}$

in order to solve $ax^2 + bx + c = 0$.

• For more difficult equations, trial and improvement can be used. E.g. Solve $x^3 + x = 60$.
Try $x = 4$: $(4)^3 + 4 = 64 + 4 = 68$ (too high)
Try $x = 3.9$: $(3.9)^3 + 3.9 = 63.219$ (too low)
Try $x = 3.8$: $(3.8)^3 + 3.8 = 58.672$ (too low)
Try $x = 3.85$: $(3.85)^3 + 3.85 = 60.916625$ (just too high) etc.

○ QUESTIONS

1 "Draw a set of x- and y-axes with both ranges for x and y values being –3 to 8. Plot three points for each of the following graphs: $y = x + 4$ and $y = 2x + 2$. Then, use the three points to draw the two straight lines. The co-ordinates of the point where the two lines intersect = $(2, 6)$." Is this statement true or false?

- ☐ (a) True
- ☐ (b) False

2 "Draw a set of x- and y-axes with both ranges for x and y values being –3 to 8. Plot three points for each of the following graphs: $y = 5 – x$ and $y = x + 1$. Then use the three points to draw the two straight lines. The co-ordinates of the point where the two lines intersect = $(3, 2)$." Is this statement true or false?

- ☐ (a) True
- ☐ (b) False

3 "$2x + y = 10$. $x – y = 2$. The solutions to these simultaneous equations are $x = 4$, $y = 2$." Is this statement true or false?

- ☐ (a) True
- ☐ (b) False

4 "The solutions to the equation $(x + 2)(x + 5) = 0$ are $x = 2$ or $x = 5$." Is this statement true or false?

- ☐ (a) True
- ☐ (b) False

5 "$x + y = 12$. $x – y = 6$. The solutions to these simultaneous equations are $x = 3$, $y = 9$." Is this statement true or false?

- ☐ (a) True
- ☐ (b) False

6 "If the equation $2(x + 1) = 8$ is solved, the answer is $x = 3$." Is this statement true or false?

- ☐ (a) True
- ☐ (b) False

7 "If the equation $x + 2 = 7$ is solved, the answer is $x = 9$." Is this statement true or false?

- ☐ (a) True
- ☐ (b) False

8 "I buy six chocolate bars and six packets of crisps. I spend £3.54 and the crisps cost 35p per packet. Therefore, the chocolate bars must have cost 26p each." Is this statement true or false?

- ☐ (a) True
- ☐ (b) False

9 Solve the equation $3x + 4 = 13$.

- ☐ (a) $x = 3$
- ☐ (b) $x = 3\frac{1}{4}$
- ☐ (c) $x = \frac{1}{3}$
- ☐ (d) $x = 6$
- ☐ (e) $x = 9$

10 Solve the equation $2x – 5 = 10$.

- ☐ (a) $x = \frac{2}{15}$
- ☐ (b) $x = 7\frac{2}{3}$
- ☐ (c) $x = 7\frac{1}{2}$
- ☐ (d) $x = 2\frac{1}{2}$
- ☐ (e) $x = \frac{2}{5}$

11 Solve the equation $5x – 6 = –2$.

- ☐ (a) $x = 1\frac{3}{5}$
- ☐ (b) $x = \frac{-4}{5}$
- ☐ (c) $x = 2\frac{2}{5}$
- ☐ (d) $x = \frac{4}{5}$
- ☐ (e) $x = –1\frac{3}{5}$

12 Solve the equation $16 – 3x = 4$.

- ☐ (a) $x = 6\frac{2}{3}$
- ☐ (b) $x = \frac{1}{4}$
- ☐ (c) $x = \frac{-1}{4}$
- ☐ (d) $x = 4$
- ☐ (e) $x = –4$

13 Solve the equation $8x + 12 = 3x – 3$.

- ☐ (a) $x = \frac{1}{3}$
- ☐ (b) $x = \frac{9}{11}$
- ☐ (c) $x = –3$
- ☐ (d) $x = 3\frac{1}{3}$
- ☐ (e) $x = \frac{-1}{3}$

14 Solve the equation $6 + 3x = x + 16$.

- ☐ (a) $x = 5\frac{1}{2}$
- ☐ (b) $x = 5$
- ☐ (c) $x = –5$
- ☐ (d) $x = 2\frac{1}{2}$
- ☐ (e) $x = \frac{1}{5}$

15 Solve the equation $7 – 2x = x – 2$.

- ☐ (a) $x = 3$
- ☐ (b) $x = –3$
- ☐ (c) $x = 5$
- ☐ (d) $x = 1\frac{2}{3}$
- ☐ (e) $x = \frac{-1}{3}$

16 Solve the equation $x + 14 = 5x + 6$.

- ☐ (a) $x = \frac{1}{2}$
- ☐ (b) $x = 2$
- ☐ (c) $x = –2$
- ☐ (d) $x = 4$
- ☐ (e) $x = 5$

17 Solve the equation $4(x + 3) = 17$.

- ☐ (a) $x = \frac{4}{5}$
- ☐ (b) $x = 7\frac{1}{4}$
- ☐ (c) $x = 10$
- ☐ (d) $x = 3\frac{1}{2}$
- ☐ (e) $x = 1\frac{1}{4}$

18 Solve the equation $3(x – 6) = –14$.

- ☐ (a) $x = –6\frac{2}{3}$
- ☐ (b) $x = –10\frac{2}{3}$
- ☐ (c) $x = –2\frac{2}{3}$
- ☐ (d) $x = 5$
- ☐ (e) $x = 1\frac{1}{3}$

19 Solve the equation $7(x – 4) = 0$.

- ☐ (a) $x = \frac{4}{7}$
- ☐ (b) $x = \frac{-4}{7}$
- ☐ (c) $x = 4$
- ☐ (d) $x = 11$
- ☐ (e) $x = 21$

20 Solve the following simultaneous equations: $4x – 3y = 6$ and $3x + y = 11$.

- ☐ (a) $x = 3$, $y = 2$
- ☐ (b) $x = 2$, $y = 3$
- ☐ (c) $x = 3$, $y = –2$
- ☐ (d) $x = 1$, $y = 8$
- ☐ (e) $x = 2$, $y = 5$

21 Solve the following simultaneous equations: $3x + 2y = 9$ and $4x – y = 1$.

- ☐ (a) $x = 2$, $y = 5$
- ☐ (b) $x = 1$, $y = 3$
- ☐ (c) $x = 3$, $y = 1$
- ☐ (d) $x = 3$, $y = 0$
- ☐ (e) $x = –1$, $y = –5$

22 Solve the following simultaneous equations: $5x + 4y = 12$ and $7x - 4y = 12$.

- ☐ (a) $x = 4$, $y = -2$
- ☐ (b) $x = 2$, $y = \frac{1}{2}$
- ☐ (c) $x = 4$, $y = -4$
- ☐ (d) $x = 0$, $y = 3$
- ☐ (e) $x = 6$, $y = -4$

23 Solve the following simultaneous equations: $4x + y = 3$ and $3x - 5y = 31$.

- ☐ (a) $x = 15$, $y = 3$
- ☐ (b) $x = 1$, $y = -1$
- ☐ (c) $x = 3$, $y = -9$
- ☐ (d) $x = 10$, $y = -0.2$
- ☐ (e) $x = 2$, $y = -5$

24 Solve the following simultaneous equations: $3x + 2y = 13$ and $5x - 3y = 9$.

- ☐ (a) $x = 2$, $y = \frac{1}{3}$
- ☐ (b) $x = 5$, $y = -1$
- ☐ (c) $x = 7$, $y = -4$
- ☐ (d) $x = 3$, $y = 2$
- ☐ (e) $x = 1$, $y = -1$

25 Solve the following simultaneous equations: $3x + 2y = 16$ and $7x - 5y = -69$.

- ☐ (a) $x = -2$ $y = 11$
- ☐ (b) $x = 5$ $y = 0.5$
- ☐ (c) $x = 4$ $y = 2$
- ☐ (d) $x = 6$ $y = 0.2$
- ☐ (e) $x = 6$ $y = -1$

26 Solve, by factorizing, the quadratic equation $x^2 + 4x + 3 = 0$.

- ☐ (a) $x = -1$ or -3
- ☐ (b) $x = 1$ or 3
- ☐ (c) $x = 1$ or 4
- ☐ (d) $x = -1$ or -4
- ☐ (e) $x = -3$ or -4

27 Solve, by factorizing, the quadratic equation $x^2 + 10x + 21 = 0$.

- ☐ (a) $x = 3$ or 7
- ☐ (b) $x = -3$ or -7
- ☐ (c) $x = 11$ or -21
- ☐ (d) $x = -10$ or 21
- ☐ (e) $x = 3$ or -7

28 Solve, by factorizing, the quadratic equation $x^2 - 6x + 5 = 0$.

- ☐ (a) $x = -1$ or -5
- ☐ (b) $x = 1$ or 5
- ☐ (c) $x = -1$ or 6
- ☐ (d) $x = 1$ or 6
- ☐ (e) $x = -5$ or 6

29 Solve, by factorizing, the following quadratic equation: $x^2 - 10x + 21 = 0$.

- ☐ (a) $x = 3$ or 7
- ☐ (b) $x = -3$ or -7
- ☐ (c) $x = -11$ or 21
- ☐ (d) $x = -3$ or 7
- ☐ (e) $x = 3$ or -7

30 Solve, by factorizing, the following quadratic equation: $x^2 - 16x + 55 = 0$.

- ☐ (a) $x = -5$ or 11
- ☐ (b) $x = -5$ or -11
- ☐ (c) $x = 2$ or 8
- ☐ (d) $x = 5$ or -11
- ☐ (e) $x = 5$ or 11

31 Solve, by factorizing, the quadratic equation $x^2 + 2x - 24 = 0$.

- ☐ (a) $x = 2$ or 12
- ☐ (b) $x = -3$ or 8
- ☐ (c) $x = -4$ or 6
- ☐ (d) $x = -2$ or 12
- ☐ (e) $x = 4$ or -6

32 Use a trial and improvement method to find a positive solution to the equation $x^3 + 2x = 48$. Give the answer correct to 1 d.p.

- ☐ (a) $x = 3.8$
- ☐ (b) $x = 3.4$
- ☐ (c) $x = 3.5$
- ☐ (d) $x = 3.9$
- ☐ (e) $x = 9.6$

33 Use a trial and improvement method to find a positive solution to the equation $x^3 + 8x = 32$. Give the answer correct to 1 d.p.

- ☐ (a) $x = 2.5$
- ☐ (b) $x = 2.3$
- ☐ (c) $x = 2.4$
- ☐ (d) $x = 2.9$
- ☐ (e) $x = 3.0$

34 Solve the following equation: $x^2 - 8x + 16 = 0$.

- ☐ (a) $x = -4$ (twice)
- ☐ (b) $x = 4$ (twice)
- ☐ (c) $x = 2$ or 8
- ☐ (d) $x = -2$ or -8
- ☐ (e) $x = -4$ or 12

Higher Level only

35 Solve the equation $4(2x - 1) = 5x + 3$.

- ☐ (a) $x = 2\frac{1}{3}$
- ☐ (b) $x = 1\frac{1}{3}$
- ☐ (c) $x = \frac{7}{13}$
- ☐ (d) $x = \frac{4}{13}$
- ☐ (e) $x = -2\frac{1}{3}$

36 Solve the following equation, giving the answer correct to 2 d.p.: $x^2 + 7x + 3 = 0$.

- ☐ (a) $x = -0.92$ or -13.08
- ☐ (b) $x = 0.46$ or 6.54
- ☐ (c) $x = 0.41$ or -7.41
- ☐ (d) $x = -0.41$ or 7.41
- ☐ (e) $x = -0.46$ or -6.54

37 Solve the following equation, giving the answer correct to 2 d.p.: $x^2 + 5x + 1 = 0$.

- ☐ (a) $x = -0.21$ or -4.79
- ☐ (b) $x = 0.21$ or 4.79
- ☐ (c) $x = 0.19$ or -5.19
- ☐ (d) $x = -0.19$ or 5.19
- ☐ (e) $x = 2.08$ or -7.08

38 Solve the following equation, giving the answer correct to 2 d.p.: $x^2 + 4x - 2 = 0$.

- ☐ (a) $x = -0.59$ or -3.41
- ☐ (b) $x = -0.45$ or -4.45
- ☐ (c) $x = 0.45$ or -4.45
- ☐ (d) $x = 0.59$ or 3.41
- ☐ (e) $x = -0.83$ or 4.83

39 Solve the following equation, giving the answers correct to 2 d.p.: $2x^2 - 11x + 6 = 0$.

- ☐ (a) $x = -0.61$ or -4.89
- ☐ (b) $x = 0.61$ or 4.89
- ☐ (c) $x = -0.5$ or 6
- ☐ (d) $x = 0.5$ or -6
- ☐ (e) $x = 1.22$ or 9.78

Solve inequalities

KEY FACTS

• In solving inequalities, we can use most of the techniques used in solving equations.

• We can add and subtract to both sides, but multiply and divide by positive numbers only (otherwise we need to change the inequality around). To avoid this problem, make the unknown term positive. E.g. Solve $12 - x < 4$. Firstly, as the x-term is negative, add it to each side. $12 < 4 + x$. Then subtract 4, to give $8 < x$, which is the same as $x > 8$.

• With a quadratic inequality, we need to remember that a square root can be positive or negative. E.g. Solve $2x^2 \leq 32$. Firstly, divide by 2, to give $x^2 \leq 16$. Hence, $\pm x \leq 4$. Therefore, $x \leq -4$ or $-x \leq 4$. Adding x to each side, $0 \leq 4 + x$. Subtract 4, to give $-4 \leq x$ or $\{x \geq -4\}$. Hence, $-4 \leq x \leq 4$ (or x is numerically less than or equal to 4).

Useful notes:

1. $7 < x$ means the same as $x > 7$
2. If you have $-x$, it will become $+x$ when it is taken over the inequality sign
3. Use notes 1 and 2 and it is possible never to have to worry about changing the inequality

Useful rules for solving inequalities

QUESTIONS

1 Solve the inequality $x + 7 < 10$.

☐ (a) $x > 17$
☐ (b) $x = 3$
☐ (c) $x < 17$
☐ (d) $x < 3$
☐ (e) $x > 3$

2 Solve the inequality $x + 2 > 1$.

☐ (a) $x < -1$
☐ (b) $x > 3$
☐ (c) $x < 3$
☐ (d) $x > -1$
☐ (e) $x > 12$

3 Solve the inequality $3x + 7 \leq -5$.

☐ (a) $x \leq -4$
☐ (b) $x \leq -11\frac{2}{3}$
☐ (c) $x \leq -9$
☐ (d) $x \geq 9$
☐ (e) $x \leq 4$

4 Solve the inequality $4x + 7 \geq 9$.

☐ (a) $x \geq -15\frac{3}{4}$
☐ (b) $x \geq \frac{1}{2}$
☐ (c) $x \leq -\frac{1}{2}$
☐ (d) $x \geq -4$
☐ (e) $x \geq 4$

5 Solve the inequality $5x + 6 \geq 6$.

☐ (a) $x \leq 0$
☐ (b) $x \geq 0$
☐ (c) $x \geq 2\frac{2}{5}$
☐ (d) $x \leq -2\frac{2}{5}$
☐ (e) $x \geq 7\frac{1}{5}$

6 Solve the inequality $6 - x < 2$.

☐ (a) $x > 8$
☐ (b) $x < 4$
☐ (c) $x < 8$
☐ (d) $x > 4$
☐ (e) $x > 13$

7 Solve the inequality $6 - 3x > 12$.

☐ (a) $x < -3$
☐ (b) $x > -2$
☐ (c) $x < 2$
☐ (d) $x > -3$
☐ (e) $x < -2$

8 Solve the inequality $11 - 7x > -3$.

☐ (a) $x = -1\frac{1}{8}$
☐ (b) $x = 1\frac{1}{8}$
☐ (c) $x > 2$
☐ (d) $x > -2$
☐ (e) $x < 2$

9 Solve the inequality $14 - 5x < 1$.

☐ (a) $x > 2.6$
☐ (b) $x > 3$
☐ (c) $x < 3$
☐ (d) $x < 2.6$
☐ (e) $x < -2.6$

10 Solve the inequality $2x - 3 > x + 5$.

☐ (a) $x > 2$
☐ (b) $x > 8$
☐ (c) $x \geq \frac{2}{3}$
☐ (d) $x \geq 2\frac{2}{3}$
☐ (e) $x \leq \frac{2}{3}$

11 Solve the inequality $11x + 16 \leq 3x + 20$.

☐ (a) $x \geq \frac{1}{2}$
☐ (b) $x \leq \frac{2}{3}$
☐ (c) $x \leq \frac{1}{2}$
☐ (d) $x \leq 2\frac{4}{7}$
☐ (e) $x \leq -\frac{2}{3}$

12 Solve the inequality $3x + 7 > 2(x - 3)$.

☐ (a) $x < 15$
☐ (b) $x > -2$
☐ (c) $x > -1$
☐ (d) $x > -13$
☐ (e) $x > -10$

13 Solve the inequality $5x - 11 \leq 2(x + 2)$.

☐ (a) $x \geq 4\frac{1}{3}$
☐ (b) $x \leq 4\frac{1}{2}$
☐ (c) $x \leq 1\frac{6}{7}$
☐ (d) $x \geq 1\frac{2}{7}$
☐ (e) $x \leq 5$

14 Solve the inequality $23x + 5 \geq 4x + 43$.

☐ (a) $x \geq 2$
☐ (b) $x \geq 1\frac{21}{27}$
☐ (c) $x \leq 2$
☐ (d) $x \leq -2$
☐ (e) $x \geq -2$

15 Solve the inequality $12x - 14 > 7(2x - 3)$.

☐ (a) $x < -5\frac{1}{2}$
☐ (b) $x < 3\frac{1}{2}$
☐ (c) $x < -8\frac{1}{2}$
☐ (d) $x > -3\frac{1}{2}$
☐ (e) $x > -5\frac{1}{2}$

16 Solve the quadratic inequality $x^2 - 9 < 0$.

☐ (a) $-3 < x < 3$
☐ (b) $x < 3$
☐ (c) $x > 3$
☐ (d) $-4.5 < x < 4.5$
☐ (e) $0 < x < 3$

QUESTIONS

Higher Level only

17 How many number solutions (integers) are there for the inequality $60 \leq 5x + 11 < 121$?

☐ (a) 12
☐ (b) 13
☐ (c) 11
☐ (d) 16
☐ (e) 22

18 How many number solutions (integers) are there for the inequality $156 \leq 3x + 120 < 181$?

☐ (a) 10
☐ (b) 9
☐ (c) 8
☐ (d) 7
☐ (e) 6

Construct and use tangents to curves/areas under curves

KEY FACTS

• In a distance/time graph, the gradient of the tangent drawn at any point represents the velocity at that point.

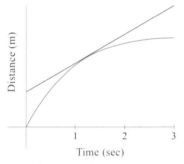

Distance/time graph

• In general, the gradient of the tangent to a curve at any point represents its rate of change at that point. It is therefore possible to estimate the rate of increase of a patient's temperature, at each hour, by finding the gradient of the tangent to the curve at 9:00 am, 10:00 am, 11:00 am etc.

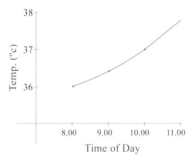

Graph of patient's temperature

• The area under a velocity/time graph represents the distance travelled. The shaded area will give the distance travelled in the first 3 seconds by a body moving with the velocity shown.

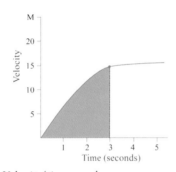

Velocity/time graph

QUESTIONS

1 "A tank is filled with water. The following graph shows how the depth of the water changes, during the first 4 minutes. The gradient of the tangent to the curve, after 2 minutes, is drawn. This shows that, 2 minutes after the start, the depth of the water is increasing at a rate of approximately 1.3 m/min." Is this statement true or false?

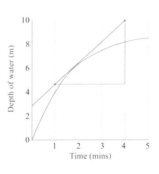

Q1

☐ (a) True
☐ (b) False

2 "A tank contains hot water at a temperature of 70°C. The heat is switched off and the water allowed to cool. The following graph shows how the temperature drops, over a period of 5 hours. Using the tangent drawn on the graph, the rate at which the temperature is falling after 2½ hours is 6°C per hour." Is this statement true or false?

☐ (a) True
☐ (b) False

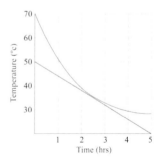

Q2

3 "A stone is thrown up and lands 3 seconds later. The following graph shows the velocity of the stone until it lands. The area under the graph represents the distance travelled by the stone." Is this statement true or false?

☐ (a) True
☐ (b) False

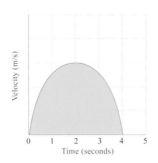

Q3

4 The following graph shows the distance from the starting point travelled by an object in its first 5 seconds of motion. What is its speed during this time?

- ☐ (a) 30 m/s
- ☐ (b) 10 m/s
- ☐ (c) 7.5 m/s
- ☐ (d) ²⁄₁₅ m/s
- ☐ (e) 4 m/s

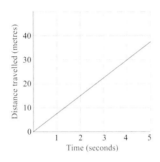

Q4

5 Oil is being pumped into a tank. The following graph shows the amount of oil – in litres – in the tank until it is filled, after 5 minutes. What is the rate at which the oil is pumped into the tank?

- ☐ (a) 300 l/min
- ☐ (b) 60 l/min
- ☐ (c) 0.00167 l/min
- ☐ (d) 100 l/min
- ☐ (e) 1500 l/min

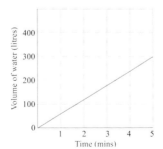

Q5

6 A goods train slowly accelerates until after an hour it reaches a speed of 90 km/h. After another 2 hours at this speed it begins to slow down

steadily and stops after another hour, as shown in the following graph. How far has it travelled?

- ☐ (a) 4 km
- ☐ (b) 90 km
- ☐ (c) 360 km
- ☐ (d) 45 km
- ☐ (e) 270 km

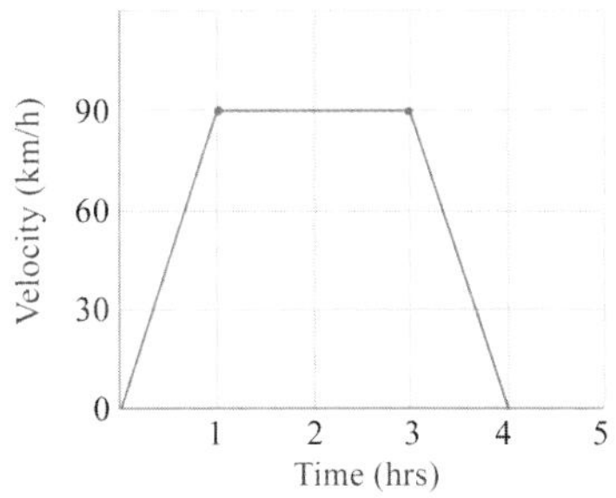

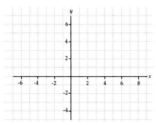

Q6

7 A ᵈⁱˢᵗᵃⁿᶜᵉ⁄ₜᵢₘₑ graph is drawn for a moving object, which starts at the point O, as shown on the following diagram. At the point P on the graph the tangent is found to be horizontal (parallel to the time axis). Which of the statements below describe the object at P?

- ☐ (a) Stopped moving
- ☐ (b) Accelerating
- ☐ (c) At its maximum distance from O
- ☐ (d) Moving towards O
- ☐ (e) Reached its maximum speed

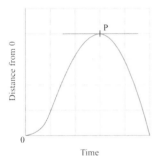

Q7

8 The speed v m/s of an object at the time t seconds is given by $v = 10t - t^2$. Draw a graph of this data from t = 0 to 5, using scales of 1 cm/s on the x-axis and 1 cm per 5 m/s on the y-axis. Use the graph to find the acceleration of the object at t = 3.5 seconds, by drawing a suitable line.

- ☐ (a) 3 m/s²
- ☐ (b) 3 m/s
- ☐ (c) 3 m
- ☐ (d) 6 m/s²
- ☐ (e) 7 m/s²

 QUESTIONS

Higher Level only

9 "Draw the graph of $y = x^2 - 2x - 3$, using x values from –6 to +8, and scales of 2 cm per unit on the x- axis and 1 cm per unit on the y-axis, as shown on the following diagram. If you draw a tangent at the point on the curve where x = –0.5 and measure its slope, it will be –3 (to the nearest whole number)." Is this statement true or false?

- ☐ (a) True
- ☐ (b) False

Q9, Q10, Q11

10 "Draw the graph of $y = x^3$, using x values from –6 to +8, and scales of 2 cm per unit on the x-axis and 1 cm per unit on the y-axis, as shown on the diagram above. If you draw a tangent at the point on the curve where x = 1 and measure its slope, the answer to the nearest whole number will be 3." Is this statement true or false?

- ☐ (a) True
- ☐ (b) False

11 "Draw the graph of $y = 3x - x^2$, using x values from –6 to +8, and scales of 2 cm per unit on the x-axis and 1 cm per unit on the y-axis, as shown on the previous diagram. If you draw a tangent at the point on the curve where x = 0 and measure its slope, the answer to the nearest whole number will be 3." Is this statement true or false?

- ☐ (a) True
- ☐ (b) False

43

Transformation of functions

• If the function $y = f(x)$ is transformed to $y = f(x + a)$, the transformation is a translation of $-a$ parallel to the x-axis.

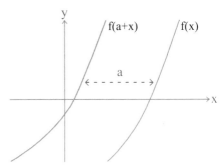

Graph of $f(x)$ and $f(a + x)$

• If the function $y = f(x)$ is transformed to $y = f(kx)$, the transformation is a one-way stretch parallel to the x-axis, of factor $\frac{1}{k}$.

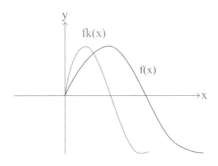

Graph of $f(x)$ and $fk(x)$

• If $y = f(x)$ is transformed to $y = af(x)$, then the transformation is a one-way stretch, parallel to the y-axis, of factor a.

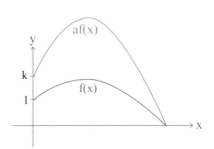

Graph of $f(x)$ and $af(x)$

• If $y = f(x)$ is transformed to $y = f(x) + a$, then the transformation is a translation of a parallel to the y-axis.

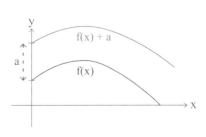

Graph of $f(x)$ and $f(x) + a$

QUESTIONS

Higher Level only

1 "The graph of $y = x^3 + 2$ is obtained from the graph of $y = x^3$ by translating it +2 units parallel to the x-axis." Is this statement true or false?

☐ (a) True
☐ (b) False

2 "The graph of $y = (x + 2)^3$ is obtained from the graph of $y = x^3$ by translating it +2 units parallel to the x-axis." Is this statement true or false?

☐ (a) True
☐ (b) False

3 "The graph of $y = 4x^3$ is obtained from the graph of $y = x^3$ by stretching it by a factor of +4 parallel to the y-axis, from the line $y = 0$." Is this statement true or false?

☐ (a) True
☐ (b) False

4 "The graph of $y = (2x)^3$ is obtained from the graph of $y = x^3$ by stretching it by a factor of +2 parallel to the x-axis, from the line $x = 0$." Is this statement true or false?

☐ (a) True
☐ (b) False

5 The dotted graph shown on the following diagram has equation $y = x^2$. Which of the equations below would transform it into the second graph shown?

☐ (a) $y = x^2 + 3$
☐ (b) $y = 3x^2$
☐ (c) $y = x^2 - 3$
☐ (d) $y = (x + 3)^2$
☐ (e) $y = \frac{x^2}{3}$

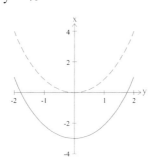

Q5

6 The dotted graph shown on the diagram below has equation $y = x^2$. Which of the equations below would transform it into the second graph shown?

☐ (a) $y = x^2 + 2$
☐ (b) $y = 2x^2$
☐ (c) $y = x^2 - 2$
☐ (d) $y = (x - 2)^2$
☐ (e) $y = \frac{x^2}{2}$

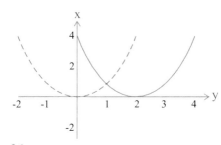

Q6

7 The dotted graph shown on the diagram below has equation $y = -x^2$. Which of the equations below would transform it into the second graph shown?

☐ (a) $y = 4 - x^2$
☐ (b) $y = 4x^2$
☐ (c) $y = x^2 + 4$
☐ (d) $y = (4 - x)^2$
☐ (e) $y = \frac{-x^2}{4}$

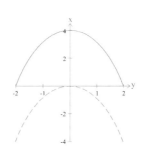

Q7

8 The dotted graph shown on the diagram below has equation y = sin x. Which of the equations below would transform it into the second graph shown?

☐ (a) y = 2 sin x
☐ (b) y = sin(½x)
☐ (c) y = sin 2x
☐ (d) y = sin x – 2
☐ (e) y = sin(x + 2)

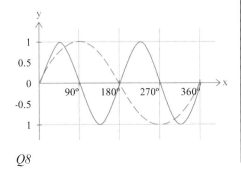

Q8

9 The dotted graph shown on the diagram below has equation y = sin x. Which of the equations below would transform it into the second graph shown?

☐ (a) y = 3 sin x
☐ (b) y = sin x⁄3
☐ (c) y = sin 3x
☐ (d) y = sin x – 3
☐ (e) y = sin(x + 3)

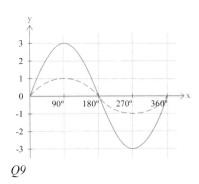

Q9

10 The dotted graph shown on the diagram below has equation y = sin x. Which of the equations below would transform it into the second graph shown?

☐ (a) y = sin 2x + 1
☐ (b) y = 2 sin x + 1
☐ (c) y = sin 2x – 1
☐ (d) y = sin(2x – 1)
☐ (e) y = 2 sin(x + 1)

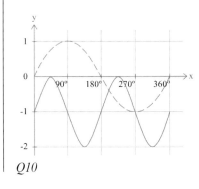

Q10

ANSWERS

Use of letters

1 *(b)*
False. 5a means "5 lots of a". So, 5a stands for $5 \times a$.

2 *(b)*
To obtain your age in x year's time the original age must be added by the number of years passed. The answer is therefore $16 + x$.

3 *(a)*
The difference in ages is y. As my sister is younger, we must subtract the difference from my age. Therefore, the answer is $x - y$.

4 *(c)*
£4a needs to be subtracted from £50, giving the answer £50 – £4a.

5 *(e)*
a^2 is shorthand for $a \times a$, and similarly $a^3 = a \times a \times a$. Therefore, $a^2 \times a^3 = a \times a \times a \times a \times a = a^5$. We add powers (or indices) when we multiply expressions of this sort.

6 *(e)*
a^5 is shorthand for $a \times a \times a \times a \times a$, and similarly $a^7 = a \times a \times a \times a \times a \times a \times a$. Therefore, $a^5 \times a^7 = a \times a \times a \times a \times a \times a \times a \times a \times a \times a \times a \times a = a^{12}$. We add powers (or indices) when we multiply expressions of this sort.

7 *(c)*
$\frac{a^7}{a^4} = \frac{a \times a \times a \times a \times a \times a \times a}{a \times a \times a \times a}$. Four a's in the numerator (top line) cancel four in the denominator (bottom), leaving $a \times a \times a = a^3$. We subtract power (index) of denominator from power of numerator to divide such expressions.

8 *(a)*
$(a^2)^3 = (a^2) \times (a^2) \times (a^2) = a \times a \times a \times a \times a \times a = a^6$. We multiply powers (or indices) in such expressions.

9 *(b)*
$(a^2)^4 = (a^2) \times (a^2) \times (a^2) \times (a^2) = a \times a \times a \times a \times a \times a \times a \times a = a^8$. We multiply powers (or indices) in such expressions.

10 *(b)*
As we can rearrange the order in multiplication, $3a^2 \times 2a = 3 \times 2 \times a^2 \times a$. Handle the numbers and letters separately. $3 \times 2 = 6$ and $a^2 \times a = a \times a \times a = a^3$ (add indices for multiplication).

11 *(d)*
As we can rearrange the order in multiplication, $2a^3 \times 2a^2 = 2 \times 2 \times a^3 \times a^2$. Handle the numbers and letters separately. $2 \times 2 = 4$ and $a^3 \times a^2 = a \times a \times a \times a \times a = a^5$ (add indices for multiplication).

12 *(e)*
As we can rearrange the order in multiplication, $4a \times 3a^4 = 4 \times 3 \times a \times a^4$. Handle the numbers and letters separately. $4 \times 3 = 12$ and $a \times a^4 = a^5$ (add indices for multiplication).

13 *(b)*
$\frac{6a^5}{3a^4} = \frac{6}{3} \times \frac{a^5}{a^4}$. Since $\frac{6}{3} = 2$ and $\frac{a^5}{a^4} = a^2$ (subtract indices when dividing), the answer is $2 \times a^2 = 2a^2$.

14 *(c)*
$\frac{5a^5}{3a^3} = \frac{5}{3} \times \frac{a^5}{a^3} = a^2$ (subtract indices when dividing). The answer is $\frac{5}{3} \times a^2 = \frac{5a^2}{3}$.

15 *(e)*
We can separate the numbers and the letters and handle them separately since we can change the order, so $(5x)^3 = 5x \times 5x \times 5x = 5^3 \times x^3 = 125 \times x^3 = 125x^3$.

16 *(a)*
We can separate the numbers and the letters and handle them separately since we can change the order, so $(2x^3)^4 = 2x^3 \times 2x^3 \times 2x^3 \times 2x^3 = 2^4 \times (x^3)^4 = 16 \times x^{12} = 16x^{12}$.

17 *(c)*
$a^{-7} \times a^2 = a^{(-7 + 2)} = a^{-5} = \frac{1}{a^5}$.

18 *(d)*
$a^3 \times a^{-3} = a^{(3 + -3)} = 1$ (since any number$^0 = 1$.

19 *(e)*
$(x^{-2})^3 = (\frac{1}{x^2})^3 = \frac{1^3}{(x^2)^3} = \frac{1}{x^6}$.

20 *(a)*
Rearrange into numbers and x's and handle each as a separate problem. $7 \times 4 \times x^{-3} \times x^4 = 28x^{(-3 + 4)} = 28x^1 = 28x$.

21 *(c)*
Rearrange into numbers and x's and handle each as a separate problem. $5 \times 3 \times x^4 \times x^{-4} = 15x^{(4 + -4)} = 15x^0 = 15$.

22 *(d)*
Rearrange into numbers and x's and handle each as a separate problem. $\frac{7}{2} \times x^{(-4 - 2)} = \frac{7}{2} \times x^{-6} = \frac{7}{2} \times \frac{1}{x^6} = \frac{7}{2x^6}$.

23 *(d)*
Rearrange into numbers and x's and handle each as a separate problem. $(4x)^{-2} = \frac{1}{(4x)^2} = \frac{1}{4x} \times \frac{1}{4x} = \frac{1}{4} \times \frac{1}{4} \times \frac{1}{x} \times \frac{1}{x} = \frac{1}{16x^2}$.

24 *(b)*
Rearrange into numbers, p's, and q's and handle each as a separate problem. $3pq^2 \times 2p^2q^2 = 3 \times 2 \times p \times p^2 \times q^2 \times q^2 = 6 \times p^3 \times q^4$.

25 *(d)*
Rearrange into numbers, p's, and q's and handle each as a separate problem. $(5p^3q)^2 = 5p^3q \times 5p^3q = 5 \times 5 \times p^3 \times p^3 \times q \times q = 25 \times p^6 \times q^2$.

Use of letters
Higher Levels

26 *(e)*
Rearrange into numbers and x's and handle each as a separate problem. $\frac{36}{24} \times \frac{x^3}{x^5} = \frac{3}{2} \times x^2 = \frac{3x^2}{2}$.

27 *(b)*
Rearrange into numbers, x's, and y's and handle each as a separate problem. $\frac{15p^3q^3}{3pq} = \frac{15}{3} \times \frac{p^3}{p} \times \frac{q^3}{q} = 5 \times p \times q^2$.

28 *(c)*
Rearrange into numbers, x's, and y's and handle each as a separate problem. $\frac{42p^3 \times q^6}{7p^3q^2} = \frac{42}{7} \times \frac{p^3}{p^3} \times \frac{q^6}{q^2} = 6 \times 1 \times q^4$.

Number patterns

1 *(a)*
Each number is 4 greater than the one before (remember to check them all). Therefore, the next number will be $19 + 4 = 23$.

2 *(b)*
Each number is 4 greater than the one before (remember to check them all). Therefore, the next number will be $18 + 4 = 22$.

3 *(c)*
Each number is 3 greater than the one before (remember to check them all). Therefore, the next number will be $17 + 3 = 20$.

4 *(d)*
Each number is 5 less than the one before (remember to check them all). Therefore, the next number will be $7 - 5 = 2$.

5 *(e)*
Each number is 3 less than the one before (remember to check them all). Therefore, the next number will be $1 - 3 = -2$.

□ **6** (a)
Each number is 30 less than the one before (remember to check them all). Therefore, the next number will be –20 – 30 = –50.

□ **7** (c)
Each number is 7 less than the one before (remember to check them all). Therefore, the next number will be 35 – 7 = 28.

□ **8** (b)
The changes between numbers are not constant; 3 to 7 is +4; 7 to 12 is +5; 12 to 18 is +6; 18 to 25 is +7. The change is increasing by +1 each operation. Therefore, the next term in the sequence will be 25 + 8 = 33.

□ **9** (e)
Work out the differences between the first and second numbers, then between the second and the third, and so on. This shows a change of 2, then 3, then 4, then 5, then 6, so the next change should be 7, giving 21 + 7 = 28.

□ **10** (d)
Each number is twice the previous one. Therefore, the next number in the series is 2 × 32 = 64.

□ **11** (c)
Work out the differences between the first and second numbers, then between the second and the third etc. This shows a change of 3, then 5, then 7, then 9, so the next change should be 11 (as the change is increasing by 2 at each stage), giving 25 + 11 = 36. (N.B. This is a sequence of square numbers.)

□ **12** (a)
Each number is 4 greater than the one before (remember to check them all). Therefore, the formula will be "nth number is 4n + a". Choose n = 1, giving first number = 7 = (4 × 1) + a. Solving, it is found that a = 7 – 4 = 3. The nth term is therefore 4n + a = 4n + 3.

□ **13** (c)
Each number is 2 greater than the one before (remember to check them all). Therefore, the formula will be "nth number is 2n + a". Choose n = 1, giving first number = 4 = (2 × 1) + a. Solving this, it is found that a = 4 – 2 = 2. The nth term is therefore 2n + a = 2n + 2.

□ **14** (b)
Each number is 2 less than the one before (remember to check them all). Therefore, the formula will be "nth number is –2n + a". Choose n = 1, giving first number = 20, 20 = (–2 × 1)

+ a. Solving, it is found that a = 20 + 2. So, the nth term is –2n + a = –2n + 22, or 22 – 2n.

□ **15** (e)
Each number is 5 greater than the one before (remember to check them all). Therefore the formula will be "nth number is 5n + a". Choose n = 1, giving first number = 3 = (5 × 1) + a. Solving, it is found that a = 3 – 5 = –2. The nth term is therefore 5n + a = 5n – 2.

□ **16** (d)
Each number is 2.5 (⁵⁄₂) greater than the one before (remember to check them all). The formula is "nth number is ⁵ⁿ⁄₂ + a". Choosing n = 1, first number = 2.5 = (2.5 × 1) + a. Therefore a = 2.5 – 2.5 = 0. The nth term is therefore ⁵ⁿ⁄₂ + 0 = ⁵ⁿ⁄₂.

□ **17** (b)
Each number is 2 greater than the one before (remember to check them all). Therefore the formula will be "nth number is 2n + a". Choose n = 1, giving first number = –3 = (2 × 1) + a. Solving, it is found that a = –3 – 2 = –5. The nth term is therefore 2n + a = 2n – 5.

□ **18** (c)
Each number is 7 greater than the one before (remember to check them all). Therefore the formula will be "nth number is 7n + a". Choose n = 1, giving first number = 8 = (7 × 1) + a. Solving, it is found that a = 8 – 7 = 1. The nth term is therefore 7n + a = 7n + 1.

□ **19** (a)
Each number is 9 greater than the one before (remember to check them all). Therefore the formula will be "nth number is 9n + a". Choose n = 1, giving first number = 17 = (9 × 1) + a. Solving, it is found that a = 17 – 9 = 8. The nth term is therefore 9n + a = 9n + 8.

Properties of functions

□ **1** (a)
True. In y = mx + c, "m" stands for the gradient and "c" stands for the intercept on the y-axis. The gradient has been found by using the two points (0, 3) and (2, 7), giving m = 2. The intercept is y = 3, so c = 3, as shown on the following diagram.

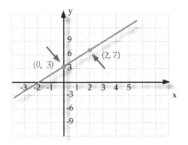

A1

□ **2** (a)
True. The height increases at a constant rate so the correct option will be a straight line graph, in this case, graph Y.

□ **3** (a)
True. Each y value is one less than the corresponding x value. For example, when x = 0, y = –1.

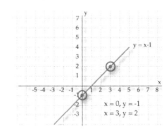

A3

□ **4** (a)
True. The x-axis is the horizontal one; remember to mark it clearly with the £ sign. The y-axis is the vertical one; remember to mark it with the foreign currency name. Take care when reading the scales.

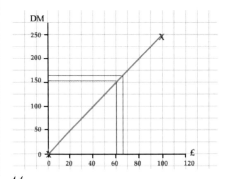

A4

□ **5** (b)
False. The x-axis is the horizontal one, remember to mark it clearly with the £ sign. The y-axis is the vertical one, remember to mark it with the foreign currency name. If both axes are marked with currency signs it is easier to avoid errors. In this case the value of £4.20 is $6.70 and the value of $11 is £6.90.

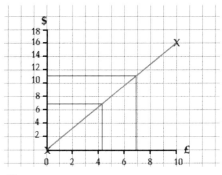

A5

☐ 6 *(b)*
The x-axis is horizontal and the y-axis is vertical. (6, 4) means that x is +6 and y is +4. The point (6, 4) is found by starting at the origin then going 6 units along the x-axis in the positive direction, followed by 4 units in the positive y direction. If the x (or y) value is negative we go to the left (or downwards).

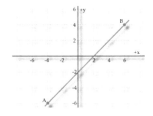

A6

☐ 7 *(b)*
The x^2 row is obtained by squaring each x value in turn: $\{(-1^2) = 1, 0^2 = 0, 1^2 = 1, 2^2 = 4, 3^2 = 9, 4^2 = 16\}$. The number –2 is not affected by changes in the value of x, so –2 can be entered right across the –2 row. The y row is obtained by adding each column. So, under x = –2, add together (4) + (–6) + (–2) = –4. Use these values to plot a graph to solve the equation.

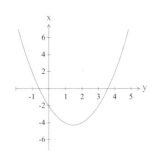

A7

☐ 8 *(a)*
The x^2 row is obtained by squaring each x value in turn: $\{(-1^2) = 1, 0^2 = 0, 1^2 = 1, 2^2 = 4, 3^2 = 9, 4^2 = 16, 5^2 = 25\}$. The –4x row is obtained by multiplying each x value by –4. The number –2 is not affected by changes in the value of x, so –2 can be entered right across the –2 row. The y row is obtained by adding each column. So, under x = 2, add together (4) + (–8) + (–2) = –6. Use

these values to plot a graph to solve the equation.

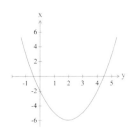

A8

☐ 9 *(a)*
The axis of symmetry is a mirror line and from the graph shown below it can be seen that this must be x = 1.5. Remember to draw a smooth curve between (1, –4) and (2, –4), not a straight line.

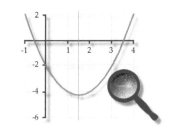

A9

Properties of functions

Higher Levels

☐ 10 *(a)*
The first row shows values of x^2 for each x value, from which the graph of $y = x^2$ can be drawn. The second row shows values of 2x + 5 for each x value, form which the graph of y = 2x + 5 can be drawn. The x values where these two graphs intersect are the solutions of the equation $x^2 = 2x + 5$.

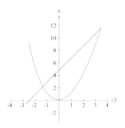

A10

☐ 11 *(a)*
The x^2 row is obtained by squaring each x value in turn: $\{(-3^2) = 9, (-2)^2 = 4, (-1)^2 = 1, 0^2 = 0, 1^2 = 1, 2^2 = 4, 3^2 = 9\}$. The number –4 is not affected by changes in the value of x, so –4 can be

entered right across the –4 row. The y row is obtained by adding each column and gives values of $y = x^2 - 4$. So, under x = 2, add together (4) + (–4) = 0. The bottom row shows –x, for each value of x, giving values for y = –x. The x values where these two graphs intersect are the solutions of the equation $x^2 - 4 = -x$.

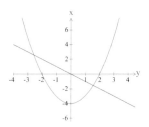

A11

Construct and evaluate formulae

☐ 1 *(a)*
True. $0.5 \times 3 = 1.5$. $1.5 + (-1) = 0.5$.

☐ 2 *(c)*
Multiply the numbers together: $30 \times 7 = 210$ km.

☐ 3 *(d)*
Work out $6t = 6 \times 2 = 12$. Now subtract this number from 16.

☐ 4 *(e)*
$\frac{a+b}{3} = \frac{6 + -4}{3} = \frac{6 - 4}{3} = \frac{2}{3}$.

☐ 5 *(a)*
$\frac{1}{3} \times 4 = \frac{4}{3} = 1 + \frac{1}{3}$. One third of an hour = $\frac{1}{3}$ of 60 minutes = 20 minutes. The cooking time, therefore, is 1 hour 20 minutes.

☐ 6 *(e)*
$a^2 = a \times a = 6 \times 6 = 36$. $2b = 2 \times b = 2 \times 4 = 8$. Therefore $a^2 + b = 36 + 8 = 44$.

☐ 7 *(e)*
$11t = 11 \times t = 11 \times 18 = 198$. Subtract this from 350.

☐ 8 *(d)*
$d^2 = d \times d = 2.5 \times 2.5 = 6.25$, and $6.25 + 2.5 + 2 = 10.75$.

☐ 9 *(c)*
Area is length times width. As width = length = k, area = $k \times k = k^2$.

☐ 10 *(d)*
$a + 2b + a + 3b = a + a + 2b + 3b = 2a + 5b$.

☐ **11** *(d)*
x + y is the same as (x+ y). Therefore the answer is 6 × (x + y) = 6(x + y) = 6x + 6y.

☐ **12** *(c)*
T = [(3 × –3.9) + 0.9] × 2.14. Therefore, using a calculator, T = –23.112 (to 3 d.p.).

☐ **13** *(b)*
R = V/I. I/R = V/I. V/R = I. I = $^{15}/_{2.5}$ = 6 amps .

☐ **14** *(a)*
a = $^{(20 – 8.6)}/_4$, = $^{11.4}/_4$ = 2.85.

☐ **15** *(b)*
a = $^{(0.6 × 3 × 9.8)}/_{3(0.6 + 0.6)}$, = $^{17.64}/_{3.6}$ = 4.9.

☐ **16** *(c)*
v^2 = $(1.1)^2$ + (2 × 3.2 × 5.2) = 34.49. Therefore v = $\sqrt{34.49}$ = 5.87 m/s (2.d.p.).

☐ **17** *(d)*
7 ÷ 2 = 3.5. This is the multiplier. Therefore, e = 3.5 × m = 3.5m.

☐ **18** *(e)*
If 4m of fabric cost £27, 1 m costs £6.75. Therefore, C = 6.75 × L= 6.75L.

☐ **19** *(a)*
r α v^2, i.e. r = kv^2.

Construct and evaluate formulae

Higher Levels

☐ **20** *(d)*
$^1/_t$ = $^1/_4$ + $^1/_6$ = $^6/_{24}$ + $^4/_{24}$ = $^{10}/_{24}$. So, t = $^{24}/_{10}$ = 2.4 minutes.

☐ **21** *(d)*
h = $^{4u^2 – g^2t^2}/_{8g}$. h = $^{\{4(25)^2 – (9.8)^2(4)^2\}}/_8$ × 9.8 = 12.3 (1 d.p.).

Manipulate algebraic expressions

☐ **1** *(b)*
False. Multiply the first term in each bracket together to get first term of answer. Multiply the second term in each bracket (including the signs) together to get last term of answer. Multiply out the two remaining pairs, including the signs, and add them together to get the middle term of answer. The correct answer, therefore, is x^2 + 3x + 2.

☐ **2** *(a)*
True. The right-hand side of the equation is divided by 2g to leave h. So, the left-hand side must be divided by 2g as well.

☐ **3** *(a)*
True. Firstly, "u" is subtracted from the right-hand side to leave "at". With an equation you must do the same to both sides. This leaves "v – u" on the left-hand side. The right-hand side of the equation is divided by "a" to leave "t". So, the left-hand side must be divided by "a" as well.

☐ **4** *(a)*
"a" might be an "ANIMAL", so it can be understood that we would have 1 "ANIMAL" + 2 "ANIMAL(S)" + 3 "ANIMAL(S)" = 6 "ANIMAL(S)", or 6a.

☐ **5** *(b)*
a + (–2a) = a – 2a = –a.

☐ **6** *(c)*
– (–2b) = –1 × –2 × b = +2b. Therefore, the answer is 4b + 2b = 6b.

☐ **7** *(d)*
Rearrange as 3 × a × a × a × a = 3 × a^4 = 3a^4.

☐ **8** *(c)*
Rearrange as a – 4a + 2b + 2b, and simplify each part = –3a + 4b.

☐ **9** *(e)*
–2(–4c) = –2 × –4 × c = +8c, so the answer is –3c + 8c = 8c – 3c = 5c.

☐ **10** *(d)*
Simplify a + 7a + 2a^2, which is 8a + 2a^2. No further simplification is possible since a and a^2 are not the same quantities.

☐ **11** *(a)*
Rearrange as a + 9a – 10a = 10a – 10a = 0.

☐ **12** *(a)*
First expression a's cancel, leaving 9. Second expression b's cancel leaving $^6/_2$ = 3. 9 + 3 = 12.

☐ **13** *(c)*
Seven lengths of 3x = 7 × 3x = 21x.

☐ **14** *(b)*
The perimeter is the sum of the sides = 2y + 5y + 4y = 11y.

☐ **15** *(e)*
(6 × 2x) + (6 × 1) = 12x + 6.

☐ **16** *(a)*
(4 × 3) + (4 × –x) = 12 – 4x.

☐ **17** *(b)*
(–5 × 2) – (5 × x) = –10 – 5x.

☐ **18** *(c)*
(–7 × 2x) – (7 × –6) = –14x + 42.

☐ **19** *(c)*
14a = 2 × 7 × a; 16b = 2 × 2 × 2 × 2 × b. 2 is common to both expressions and can therefore be taken outside the bracket. Inside the bracket we place the remaining values: 7 × a = 7a and 2 × 2 × 2 × b = 8b so that when each term is multiplied by 2, the answer is 14a – 16b.

☐ **20** *(c)*
3x = 3 × x; 12y = 2 × 2 × 3 × y. 3 is common to both expressions and can therefore be taken outside the bracket. Inside the bracket we place the remaining values: x and 2 × 2 × y = 4y so that when each term is multiplied by 3 the answer is 3x + 12y.

☐ **21** *(d)*
15x = 3 × 5 × x; 5y = 5 × y. 5 is common to both expressions and can therefore be taken outside the bracket. Inside the bracket we place the remaiing values: 3 × x = 3x and y so that when each term is multiplied by 5 the answer is 15x + 5y.

☐ **22** *(e)*
2x = 2 × x; 8y = 2 × 2 × 2 × y. 2 is common to both expressions and can therefore be taken outside the bracket. Inside the bracket we place the remaining values: x and 2 × 2 × y = 4y so that when each term is multiplied by 2 the answer is 2x – 8y.

☐ **23** *(a)*
3ab = 3 × a × b; 5ac = 5 × a × c. a is common to both expressions and can therefore be taken outside the bracket. Inside the bracket we place the remaining values: 3 × b = 3b and 5 × c = 5c so that when each term is multiplied by a the answer is 3ab + 5ac.

☐ **24** *(c)*
7ax = 7 × a × x; x^2 = x × x. x is common to both expressions and can therefore be taken outside the bracket. Inside the bracket we place the remaining values: 7 × a = 7a and x so that when each term is multiplied by x the answer is 7ax + x^2.

☐ **25** *(e)*
3xy = 3 × x × y; 15y^2 = 3 × 5 × y × y. 3 × y = 3y is common to both expressions and can therefore be taken outside

the bracket. Inside the bracket we place the remaining values: x and $5 \times y = 5y$ so that when each term is multiplied by 3y the answer is $3xy - 15y^2$.

26 (a)
$3y = 3 \times y$; $9xy = 3 \times 3 \times x \times y$. $3 \times y = 3y$ is common to both expressions and can therefore be taken outside the bracket. Inside the bracket we place the remaining values: 1 and $3 \times x = 3x$ so that when each term is multiplied by 3y the answer is $3y - 9xy$.

27 (b)
$24p^2r^2 = 2 \times 2 \times 2 \times 3 \times p \times p \times r \times r$; $16r^3q = 2 \times 2 \times 2 \times 2 \times r \times r \times r \times q$. $2 \times 2 \times 2 \times r \times r = 8r^2$ is common to both expressions and can therefore be taken outside the bracket. Inside the bracket we place the remaining values: $3 \times p \times p = 3p^2$ and $2 \times r \times q = 2rq$ so that when each term is multiplied by $8r^2$ the answer is $24p^2r^2 - 16r^3q$.

28 (c)
Multiply the first term in each bracket together to get the first term of the answer. Multiply the second term in each bracket (including the signs) together to get the last term of the answer. Multiply out the two remaining pairs, including the signs, and add them together to get the middle term of the answer.

29 (b)
Multiply the first term in each bracket together to get the first term of the answer. Multiply the second term in each bracket (including the signs) together to get the last term of the answer. Multiply out the two remaining pairs, including the signs, and add them together to get the middle term of the answer.

30 (e)
Multiply the first term in each bracket together to get the first term of the answer. Multiply the second term in each bracket (including the signs) together to get the last term of the answer. Multiply out the two remaining pairs, including the signs, and add them together to get the middle term of the answer.

31 (a)
Multiply the first term in each bracket together to get the first term of the answer. Multiply the second term in each bracket (including the signs) together to get the last term of the answer. Multiply out the two remaining pairs, including the signs, and add them together to get the middle term of the answer.

32 (e)
Multiply the first term in each bracket together to get the first term of the answer. Multiply the second term in each bracket (including the signs) together to get the last term of the answer. Multiply out the two remaining pairs, including the signs, and add them together to get the middle term of the answer.

33 (c)
Multiply the first term in each bracket together to get the first term of the answer. Multiply the second term in each bracket (including the signs) together to get the last term of the answer. Multiply out the two remaining pairs, including the signs, and add them together to get the middle term of the answer.

34 (b)
Multiply the first term in each bracket together to get the first term of the answer. Multiply the second term in each bracket (including the signs) together to get the last term of the answer. Multiply out the two remaining pairs, including the signs, and add them together to get the middle term of the answer.

35 (e)
+15 means both signs will be the same, +8x means they will both be +. So, the terms will be $(x + ?)(x + ?)$. +15 means we need factors of 15 that add to 8. Factors of 15 are 1 and 15 or 3 and 5. Trials show $15 + 1 = 16$ (no good) or $3 + 5 = 8$, which is correct. Therefore, the answer is $(x + 3)(x + 5)$.

36 (e)
+14 means both signs will be the same, +9x means they will both be +. So, the terms will be $(x + ?)(x + ?)$. +14 means we need factors of 14 that add to 9. Factors of 14 are 1 and 14 or 2 and 7. $2 + 7 = 9$, which is correct. Therefore, the answer is $(x + 2)(x + 7)$.

37 (d)
+55 means both signs will be the same, +16x means they will both be +. So, the terms will be $(x + ?)(x + ?)$. +55 means we need factors of 55 that add to 16. Factors of 55 are 1 and 55 or 5 and 11. $5 + 11 = 16$, which is correct. Therefore, the answer is $(x + 5)(x + 11)$.

38 (e)
+21 means both signs will be the same, -10x means they will both be -. So, the terms will be $(x - ?)(x - ?)$. +21 means we need factors of 21 that add to 10. Factors of 21 are 1 and 21 or 3 and 7.

Trial shows $3 + 7 = 10$, which is correct. Therefore, the answer is $(x - 3)(x - 7)$.

39 (b)
-33 means one + sign and one - sign, +8x means the larger number will be +, so the terms will be $(x - ?)(x + ?)$. -33 means we need factors of 33 that subtract to give 8. Factors of 33 are 1 and 33 or 3 and 11. Trial shows $11 - 3 = 8$, which is correct. Therefore, the answer is $(x - 3)(x + 11)$.

40 (a)
-10 means one + sign and one - sign, +3x means the larger number will be +, so the terms will be $(x - ?)(x + ?)$. -10 means we need factors of 10 that subtract to give 3. Factors of 10 are 1 and 10 or 2 and 5. Trial shows $5 - 2 = 3$, which is correct. Therefore, the answer is $(x - 2)(x + 5)$.

41 (d)
-35 means one + sign and one - sign, -2x means the larger number will be -, so the terms will be $(x + ?)(x - ?)$. -35 means we need factors of 35 that subtract to give 2. Factors of 35 are 1 and 35 or 5 and 7. Trial shows $7 - 5 = 2$, which is correct. Therefore, the answer is $(x + 5)(x - 7)$.

42 (b)
Rearrange with the term in t on one side of the equation and everything else on the other side, so $p - q = rt$. Divide both sides by r to get t by itself.

43 (c)
Rearrange with the term in x on one side of the equation and everything else on the other side, so $y - c = mx$. Divide both sides by m to get x by itself.

Manipulate algebraic expressions

Higher Levels

44 (c)
Multiply the first term in each bracket together to get the first term of the answer. Multiply the second term in each bracket (including the signs) together to get the last term of the answer. Multiply out the two remaining pairs, including the signs, and add them together to get the middle term of the answer.

45 (a)
Multiply the first term in each bracket together to get the first term of the answer. Multiply the second term in

each bracket (including the signs) together to get the last term of the answer. Multiply out the two remaining pairs, including the signs, and add them together to get the middle term of the answer.

□ 46 *(c)*
Multiply the first term in each bracket together to get the first term of the answer. Multiply the second term in each bracket (including the signs) together to get the last term of the answer. Multiply out the two remaining pairs, including the signs, and add them together to get the middle term of the answer.

□ 47 *(a)*
$3x^2$ can be split into $(3x.....)(x.....)$. The last term of the expression is 1. 1 can be factorized as 1×1. If you place 1 in each bracket and double check the answer, you can see that 4x is also obtainable. $(3x + 1)(x + 1)$.

□ 48 *(b)*
$2x^2$ can be split into $(2x.....)(x.....)$. The last term of the expression is 3. By placing factors of 3 in the brackets you must find numbers which add to make 5. Remembering the 2x in the first bracket, these numbers are 3 and 1. $(2x + 3)(x + 1)$.

□ 49 *(e)*
$5x^2$ can be split into $(5x.....)(x.....)$. The last term of the expression is 6. By placing factors of 6 in each bracket you must find numbers that add up to –11. Remembering the 5x in the first bracket, these numbers are –6 and –1. $(5x – 6)(x – 1)$.

□ 50 *(d)*
$3x^2$ can be split into $(3x.....)(x.....)$. The last term of the expression is 7. By placing factors of 7 in each bracket you must find numbers that add up to –10. Remembering the 3x in the first bracket, these numbers are –7 and –1. $(3x – 7)(x – 1)$.

□ 51 *(e)*
$10x^2$ can be split into $(5x....)(2x....)$. The last term of the expression is –1. By placing factors of –1 in each bracket you must find numbers that add to make –3. Remembering the coefficients of x in each bracket (5 and 2), these numbers are –1 and 1. $(2x – 1)(5x + 1)$.

□ 52 *(c)*
$21x^2$ can be split into $(7x.....)(3x....)$. The last term of the expression is –1. By placing factors of –1 in each bracket you must find numbers that add to

make 4. Remembering the coefficients of x in each bracket (7 and 3), these numbers are –1 and 1. $(7x – 1)(3x + 1)$.

□ 53 *(d)*
Any expression with two terms that factorize can only have either a common factor or, as in this case, "the difference of two perfect squares", $(x)^2 – (2y)^2$, which factorizes to $(x + 2y)(x – 2y)$.

□ 54 *(a)*
Any expression with two terms that can be factorized can only have either a common factor or, as in this case, "the difference of two perfect squares", $(2x)^2 – (3y)^2$, which factorizes to $(2x + 3y)(2x – 3y)$.

□ 55 *(e)*
$(2 + \sqrt{3})(2 – \sqrt{3}) = 4 – \sqrt{3}\sqrt{3} + 2\sqrt{3} – 2\sqrt{3}$
$= 4 – 3 = 1$.

Solve linear, simultaneous, and quadratic equations; and higher polynomials by trial and improvement

□ 1 *(a)*
True. This is solving two simultaneous equations using the graphical method.

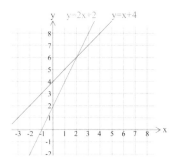

A1

□ 2 *(b)*
False. The correct answer is (2, 3). This is solving two simultaneous equations using the graphical method.

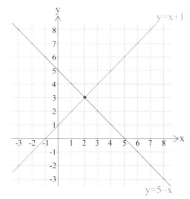

A2

□ 3 *(a)*
True. To eliminate y add both equations, giving 3x = 12, x = 4. Then, to find y, substitute x = 4 into the first equation, which gives 8 + y = 10 and therefore y = 2. You can check both the answers in the second equation.

□ 4 *(b)*
False. Either x + 2 = 0, which leads to x = –2, or x + 5 = 0, which leads to x = –5.

□ 5 *(b)*
False. To eliminate y, add both equations, giving 2x = 18, x = 9. Then substitute in the first equation: 9 + y = 12, y = 3. Check both answers in the second equation.

□ 6 *(a)*
True. Firstly, you need to multiply out the brackets on the left-hand side. This leads to 2x + 2 = 8. Then you need to subtract 2 from each side of the equation. 2x = 6, hence x = 3.

□ 7 *(b)*
False. You need to subtract 2 from the left-hand side of the equation to leave x. With an equation you must do the same to both sides. This means the right-hand side becomes 7 – 2 = 5, so x = 5.

□ 8 *(b)*
False. The total cost of crisps = £0.35 × 6 = £2.10. Therefore, the total cost of six bars of chocolate = £3.54 – £2.10 = £1.44. So, one bar of chocolate costs £1.44 ÷ 6 = £0.24 (24p).

□ 9 *(a)*
3x + 4 = 13; 3x = 13 – 4 = 9. Therefore, x = ⁹⁄₃, so x = 3.

□ 10 *(c)*
2x = 10 + 5; 2x = 15. Therefore, x = ¹⁵⁄₂ so x = 7½.

□ 11 *(d)*
5x = –2 + 6; 5x = 4. Therefore, x = ⅘.

□ 12 *(d)*
16 = 4 + 3x; 16 – 4 = 3x; 12 = 3x. Therefore, x = 4.

□ 13 *(c)*
8x = 3x – 3 – 12; 8x – 3x = –3 –12; 5x = –15. Therefore, x = ⁻¹⁵⁄₅ or –3.

□ 14 *(b)*
3x = x +16 – 6; 3x – x = 16 – 6; 2x = 10. Therefore, x = ¹⁰⁄₂ or 5.

□ 15 *(a)*
7 = x – 2 + 2x; 7 + 2 = x + 2x; 9 = 3x; 3x = 9. Therefore, x = ⁹⁄₃ or 3.

16 *(b)*
+14 = 5x +6 – x; 14 – 6 = 5x – x; 8 = 4x; 4x = 8. Therefore, x = $\frac{8}{4}$ or 2.

17 *(e)*
4(x+3) = 17; 4x+12 = 17; 4x = 17 – 12; 4x = 5. Therefore, x = $\frac{5}{4}$ or 1¼.

18 *(e)*
3x –18 = –14; 3x = –14 +18; 3x = 4. Therefore, x = $\frac{4}{3}$ or 1⅓.

19 *(c)*
7x – 28 = 0; 7x = 28. Therefore, x = $\frac{28}{7}$ = 4. Or x – 4 = $\frac{0}{7}$ = 0, so x = 4.

20 *(a)*
To eliminate y, multiply the second equation by 3 and add to the first equation, giving 4x + 9x = 6 + 33, 13x = 39, x = 3. Then substitute in the second equation: 3 × 3 + y = 11, 9 + y = 11, y = 2. Check both answers in the first equation.

21 *(b)*
To eliminate y, multiply the second equation by 2 and add to the first equation, giving 3x + 8x = 9 + 2, 11x = 11, x = 1. Then substitute in the first equation: 3 × 1 + 2y = 9, y = 3. Check both answers in the second equation.

22 *(b)*
To eliminate y, add the second equation to the first equation, giving 5x + 7x = 12 + 12, 12x = 24, x = 2. Then substitute in the first equation: (5 × 2) + 4y = 12, y = ½. Check both answers in the second equation.

23 *(e)*
To eliminate y, multiply the first equation by 5 and add to the second equation, giving 20x + 3x = 15 + 31, 23x = 46, x = 2. Then substitute in the first equation: (4 × 2) + y = 3, y = –5. Check both answers in the second equation.

24 *(d)*
To eliminate y, multiply the second equation by 2 and multiply the first equation by 3, then add both these new equations, giving 9x + 10x = 39 + 18, 19x = 57, x = 3. Then substitute in the first equation: (3 × 1) + 2y = 13, y = 2. Check both answers in the second equation.

25 *(a)*
To eliminate y, multiply the second equation by 2 and multiply the first equation by 5, then add both these new equations, giving 15x + 14x = 80 + (–138), 29x = –58, x = –2. Then substitute in the first equation: –6 + 2y = 16, 2y = 22, y = 11. Check both answers in the second equation.

26 *(a)*
Factorizing rules give (x + 1)(x + 3) = 0. Therefore, either x + 1 = 0, which leads to x = –1 or x + 3 = 0, which leads to x = –3.

27 *(b)*
Factorizing rules give (x + 3)(x + 7) = 0. Therefore, either x + 3 = 0, which leads to x = –3 or x + 7 = 0, which leads to x = –7.

28 *(b)*
Factorizing rules give (x – 1)(x – 5) = 0. Therefore, either x – 1 = 0, which leads to x = 1 or x – 5 = 0, which leads to x = 5.

29 *(a)*
Factorizing rules give (x – 3)(x – 7) = 0. Therefore, either x – 3 = 0, which leads to x = 3 or x – 7 = 0, which leads to x = 7.

30 *(e)*
Factorizing rules give (x – 5)(x – 11) = 0. Therefore, either x – 5 = 0, which leads to x = 5 or x – 11 = 0, which leads to x = 11.

31 *(e)*
Factorizing rules give (x – 4)(x + 6) = 0. Therefore, either x – 4 = 0, which leads to x = 4 or x + 6 = 0, which leads to x = –6.

32 *(c)*
x = 3 gives 33 (too small), x = 4 gives 72 (too large). The answer is closer to x = 3 than x = 4. x = 3.4 gives 46.104, x = 3.5 gives 49.875. Therefore, x = 3.5 is (just) the closest.

33 *(c)*
x = 2 gives 24 (too small), x = 3 gives 51 (too large). The answer is closer to x = 2 than x = 3. x = 2.3 gives 30.567, x = 2.4 gives 33.024, so x = 2.4 is the closest.

34 *(b)*
Firstly check whether factorization is possible – in this case the co-efficients are suitable. Hence, (x – 4)(x – 4) = 0, so x – 4 = 0 twice (the expression is a perfect square).

Solve linear, simultaneous, and quadratic equations; and higher polynomials by trial and improvement

Higher Levels

35 *(a)*
8x – 4 = 5x + 3; 8x = 5x + 3 + 4; 8x – 5x = 3 + 4; 3x = 7. Therefore, x = $\frac{7}{3}$ or 2⅓.

36 *(e)*
The formula gives x = –0.46 and x = –6.54.

37 *(a)*
The formula gives x = –0.21 and x = –4.79.

38 *(c)*
The formula gives x = 0.45 and x = –4.45.

39 *(b)*
The formula gives x = 0.61 and x = 4.89.

Solve inequalities

1 *(d)*
x < 10 – 7. Therefore, x < 3.

2 *(d)*
x > 1 – 2. Therefore x > –1.

3 *(a)*
3x ≤ – 5 – 7. 3x ≤ – 12. x ≤ –4.

4 *(b)*
4x ≥ 9 – 7. 4x ≥ 2. x ≥ ½.

5 *(b)*
5x ≥ 6 – 6. 5x ≥ 0. x ≥ 0.

6 *(d)*
6 < 2 + x. 6 – 2 < x. 4 < x and therefore x > 4.

7 *(e)*
6 > 12 + 3x. 6 – 12 > 3x. –6 > 3x. 3x < –6 and therefore x < –2.

8 *(e)*
11 > –3 + 7x. 11 + 3 > 7x. 14 > 7x. 7x < 14 and therefore x < 2.

9 *(a)*
14 < 1 + 5x. 14 – 1 < 5x. 13 < 5x. 5x > 13 and therefore x > 2.6.

10 *(b)*
2x – 3 – x > 5. 2x – x > 5 + 3 and

therefore x > 8.

☐ **11** *(c)*
11x – 3x + 16 ≤ 20. 11x – 3x ≤ 20 – 16.
8x ≤ 4 and therefore x ≤ ½.

☐ **12** *(d)*
3x + 7 > 2x – 6. 3x – 2x > –6 – 7 and
therefore x > –13.

☐ **13** *(e)*
5x – 11 ≤ 2x + 4. 5x – 11 – 2x ≤ 4.
5x – 2x ≤ 4 + 11. 3x ≤ 15
and therefore x ≤ 5.

☐ **14** *(a)*
23x + 5 – 4x ≥ 43. 23x – 4x ≥ 43 – 5.
19x ≥ 38 and therefore x ≥ 2.

☐ **15** *(b)*
12x – 14 > 14x – 21. 21 – 14 > 14x –
12x. 7 > 2x. 2x < 7 and therefore
x < 3½.

☐ **16** *(a)*
Either: Squaring maps all of the
numbers between –3 and +3 onto the
numbers between 0 and 9. Hence $x^2 <$
9 so –3 < x < 3.
Or: Sketch the graph of $y = x^2 – 9$ and
see for what values y is negative, as
shown on the following diagram.
Or: $x^2 – 9 < 0$. (x – 3)(x + 3) < 0. x – 3
< 0 and x + 3 < 0 so x < 3 and x > –3.

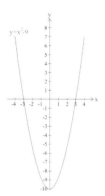

A16

Solve inequalities

Higher Levels

☐ **17** *(a)*
49 ≤ 5x < 110. 9.8 ≤ x <22. x = 10, 11,
12 ... to 21. Therefore, there are 12
whole number solutions.

☐ **18** *(b)*
156 ≤3 x + 120 < 181. 156 – 120 ≤ 3x
< 191 –120. 36 ≤ 3x <61. 12 ≤ x <
20⅓. Therefore, the integers 12 to 20
inclusive are solutions, 9 in total.

Construct and use tangents to curves/areas under curves

☐ **1** *(b)*
False. The gradient is $^{(10 – 4.8)}\!/\!_{(4 – 1)} = ^{5.2}\!/\!_3$
= 1.73 m/min.

☐ **2** *(a)*
True. The gradient of the graph is
$^{– (50 – 20)}\!/\!_{(5 – 0)} = ^{–30}\!/\!_5 = –6°C$.

☐ **3** *(a)*
True. The area under a $^{velocity}\!/\!_{time}$ graph
= distance travelled.

☐ **4** *(c)*
The object travelled 30 m in 4 seconds,
which is $^{30}\!/\!_4$ graph = 7.5 m/s.

☐ **5** *(b)*
300 litres in 5 minutes gives a rate of
$^{300}\!/\!_5$ = 60 l/min.

☐ **6** *(e)*
The area under a $^{velocity}\!/\!_{time}$ graph =
distance travelled. Area of the
trapezium = ½(4 + 2) × 90 = 270 km.

☐ **7** *(c)*
At P, the object is furthest away from
O – after which it starts to return
towards O.

☐ **8** *(a)*
The gradient of a speed/time graph at a
particular time is the acceleration at that
instant. Draw a long tangent at the
point on curve where x = 3.5, as it is
easier to measure the change in t and v
more accurately over a large distance.
Even so the accuracy may be poor as
tangents are difficult to estimate.

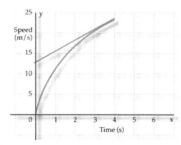

A8

Construct and use tangents to curves/areas under curves

Higher Levels

☐ **9** *(a)*
True. Draw a long tangent, as shown on
the following diagram, as it is easier to
measure the change in x and y over a
large distance. Even so, the accuracy

may be poor as the correct positioning
of the tangent is difficult to estimate.

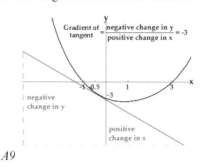

A9

☐ **10** *(a)*
True. Draw a long tangent, as shown on
the following diagram, as it is easier to
measure the change in x and y over a
large distance. Even so, the accuracy
may be poor as the correct positioning
of the tangent is difficult to estimate.

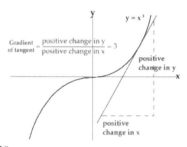

A10

☐ **11** *(a)*
True. Draw a long tangent, as shown in
the following diagram, as it is easier to
measure the change in x and y over a
large distance. Even so, the accuracy
may be poor as the correct positioning
of the tangent is difficult to estimate.

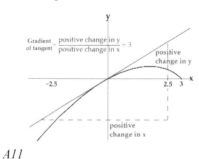

A11

Transformation of functions

Higher Levels

☐ **1** *(b)*
False. The translation is +2 units
parallel to the y-axis. In general,
f(x) + b is obtained from f(x) by
translation of b units parallel to the
y-axis.

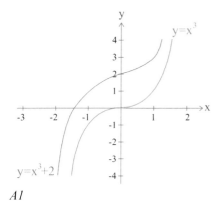

A1

2 *(b)*
False. The translation is –2 units parallel to the x-axis. In general, f(x + c) is obtained from f(x) by translation of –c units parallel to the x-axis.

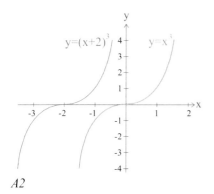

A2

3 *(a)*
True. In general, k × f(x) is obtained from f(x) by a stretch parallel to the y-axis, of stretch factor k from y = 0 (i.e. the x-axis).

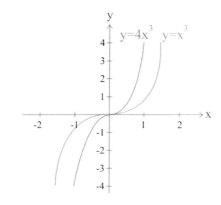

A3

4 *(b)*
False. The stretch factor is ½. In general, f(px) is obtained from f(x) by a stretch parallel to the x-axis, of stretch factor ⅟ₚ from x = 0 (i.e. the y-axis).

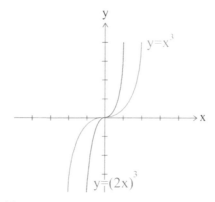

A4

5 *(c)*
The curve has been moved 3 units vertically down.

6 *(d)*
The curve has been moved +2 units horizontally across.

7 *(a)*
The curve has been moved 4 units vertically up.

8 *(c)*
The curve has been stretched by a factor of ½ (i.e. it has been "squashed") in the x-direction.

9 *(a)*
The curve has been stretched by a factor of 3 in the y-direction.

10 *(c)*
The curve has been stretched by a factor of ½ (i.e. it has been "squashed") in the x-direction, then moved vertically down by 1 unit.

Shape, Space, and Measures

Simple and complex shapes are all around us and to make sense of some of these, it is helpful to have a knowledge of the properties of some simple shapes, plane and solid, and how they relate to the space they occupy. Measuring these shapes helps us to understand their properties. Other measures – such as mass and time – enable us to understand some of the more complex aspects of, say, density and velocity, which can give us a clearer picture of the world around us.

Representation of 2D and 3D shapes

 KEY FACTS

• A line has only length – so it is one-dimensional (1D).

• A plane surface has area – so it is two-dimensional (2D). Examples of 2D shapes are triangles, quadrilaterals, circles, and polygons. 2D shapes can be represented by drawing them on a piece of paper.

• A solid shape has volume – so it is three-dimensional (3D). Examples of 3D shapes are cubes, spheres, pyramids, and cylinders. 3D shapes can be represented on a (2D) piece of paper in two ways:
i) by a perspective drawing, often on triangular "spotty" paper.
ii) a "net", where the faces of the shape are drawn flat, so that they can be cut out and folded along the edges in order to make the 3D shape.

 QUESTIONS

1 "The following diagram shows the net of a triangular prism." Is this statement true or false?

☐ (a) True
☐ (b) False

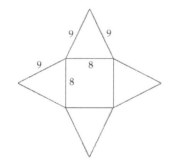

Q1

2 "The following diagram could be the net of a pyramid." Is this statement true or false?

☐ (a) True
☐ (b) False

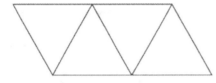

Q2

3 "The figure in the following diagram could be the net of an open rectangular box." Is this statement true or false?

☐ (a) True
☐ (b) False

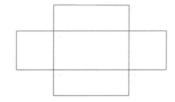

Q3

4 Which of the solids shown in the following diagram are prisms?

☐ (a) V and W
☐ (b) V and X
☐ (c) V, X, and Z
☐ (d) W, Y, and Z
☐ (e) X, Y, and Z

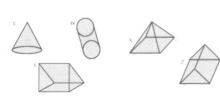

Q4

5 What name is given to a regular four-sided polygon?

☐ (a) Quadrilateral
☐ (b) Rectangle
☐ (c) Parallelogram
☐ (d) Rhombus
☐ (e) Square

Q5

6 What are the names of the solids shown below, numbered 1, 2, and 3 respectively?

☐ (a) Cube, tetrahedron, cone
☐ (b) Cube, triangular-based pyramid, cylinder
☐ (c) Cuboid, triangular prism, cylinder
☐ (d) Cuboid , triangular prism, cone
☐ (e) Cube, tetrahedron, cone

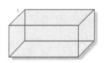

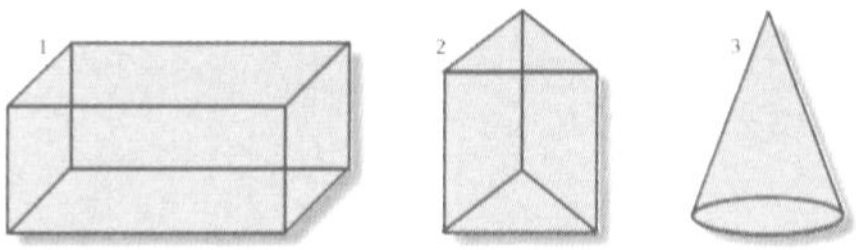

Q6

7 Which of the following nets will fold to make a cube?

☐ (a) V
☐ (b) W
☐ (c) X
☐ (d) Y
☐ (e) Z

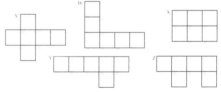

Q7

8 Which of following nets will fold to make a tetrahedron (triangular-based pyramid)?

☐ (a) V and X
☐ (b) V and W
☐ (c) W and X
☐ (d) W and Y

☐ (e) X and Y

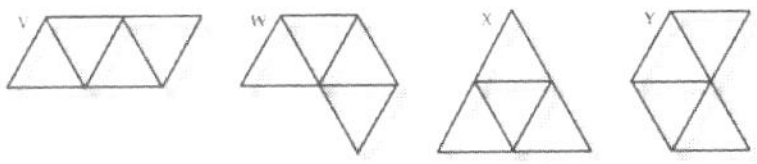

Q8

9 Which of the nets below will fold together to make a pyramid?

☐ (a) W and X
☐ (b) Y and Z
☐ (c) V and U
☐ (d) V, Y, and Z
☐ (e) W, X, and Z

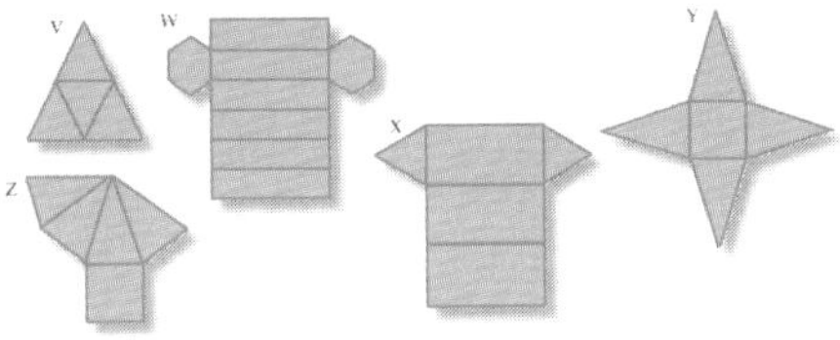

Q9

10 In the following diagram, which solids can be made from the nets numbered 1, 2, and 3 respectively?

☐ (a) Cube, triangular prism, tetrahedron
☐ (b) Cube, triangular prism, square-based pyramid

☐ (c) Cuboid, triangular-based pyramid, tetrahedron
☐ (d) Cube, triangular-based pyramid, square-based pyramid
☐ (e) Cuboid, triangular prism, square-based pyramid

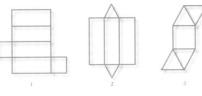

Q10

11 The following diagram shows the net of a cube that has one yellow face, one green face, and one blue face. If opposite faces of the cube were to be made the same colour, what would be the colour of squares B and E?

☐ (a) B yellow, E green
☐ (b) B green, E green
☐ (c) B blue, E blue
☐ (d) B yellow, E blue
☐ (e) B green, E blue

Q11

12 The following diagram shows the net of a solid. When it is folded together, what is the name of the solid formed?

☐ (a) Cuboid
☐ (b) Triangular pyramid
☐ (c) Square-based pyramid
☐ (d) Triangular prism
☐ (e) Pentagonal prism

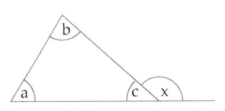

Q12

Classification of polygons

🔵 KEY FACTS

• Polygons are closed 2D shapes with straight sides.

• The sum of the angles in any triangle is 180°. Triangles can be equilateral (all three sides equal), isosceles (two sides equal), or scalene (all sides different).

• The sum of the angles in any quadrilateral is 360°. Some quadrilaterals (four-sided polygons) have special names.

• A square has all four sides equal and all four angles are 90° (right angles).

• A rectangle has four right angles and two pairs of equal sides.

• A rhombus has four equal sides and two pairs of equal angles opposite each other.

• A parallelogram has two pairs of parallel sides and two pairs of equal angles opposite each other.

• A trapezium has one pair of parallel sides.

• A kite has two pairs of equal, adjacent sides.

• Regular polygons have all sides and angles equal. A pentagon has five sides, a hexagon has six sides, and an octagon has eight sides.

🔵 QUESTIONS

1 "In the following diagram, $x = b + c$." Is this statement true or false?

☐ (a) True
☐ (b) False

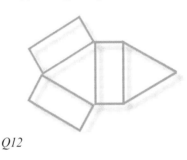

Q1

2 "A polygon of n sides has $(n - 1)$ interior angles." Is this statement true or false?

☐ (a) True
☐ (b) False

3 "A polygon of six sides (a hexagon) can have five interior angles that are right angles." Is this statement true or false?

☐ (a) True
☐ (b) False

4 "In the quadrilateral shown in the following diagram, angles a and c

57

add up to 180°. Therefore, angles b and d also add up to 180°." Is this statement true or false?

- ☐ (a) True
- ☐ (b) False

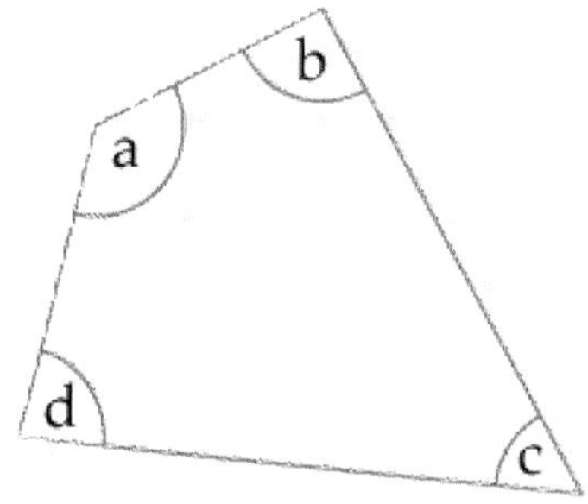

Q4

5 "A quadrilateral has equal opposite sides. It is therefore a rectangle." Is this statement true or false?

- ☐ (a) True
- ☐ (b) False

6 "A quadrilateral has all four sides equal. It is therefore a rhombus." Is this statement true or false?

- ☐ (a) True
- ☐ (b) False

7 "A quadrilateral has two pairs of equal sides. It is therefore a parallelogram." Is this statement true or false?

- ☐ (a) True
- ☐ (b) False

8 "Two opposite angles of a quadrilateral are both 90°. The quadrilateral is therefore a rectangle." Is this statement true or false?

- ☐ (a) True
- ☐ (b) False

9 "In the following diagram ABCD is a square and triangle ABX is equilateral. Angle DXC is 120°." Is this statement true or false?

- ☐ (a) True
- ☐ (b) False

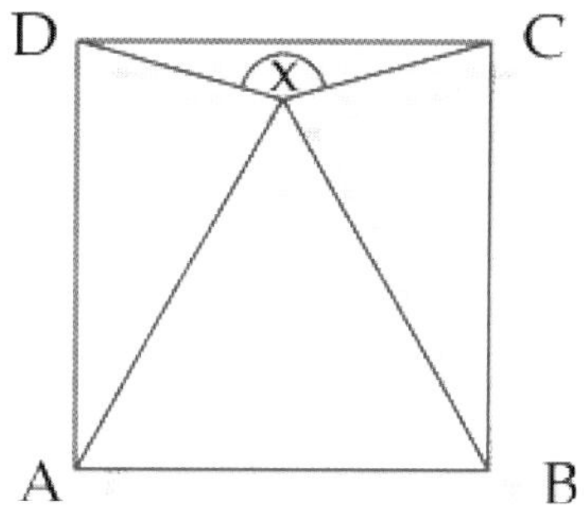

Q9

10 "A rhombus is cut along its diagonals into four triangular pieces. The four triangles are congruent." Is this statement true or false?

- ☐ (a) True
- ☐ (b) False

11 Calculate the size of angle a in the following diagram.

- ☐ (a) 20°
- ☐ (b) 30°
- ☐ (c) 40°
- ☐ (d) 45°
- ☐ (e) 50°

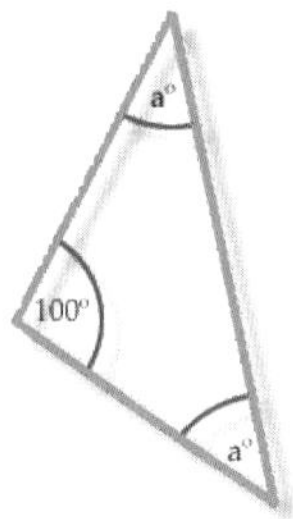

Q11

12 In the following diagram ABCD is a parallelogram. Calculate the size of angle c.

- ☐ (a) 30°
- ☐ (b) 35°
- ☐ (c) 65°
- ☐ (d) 110°
- ☐ (e) 115°

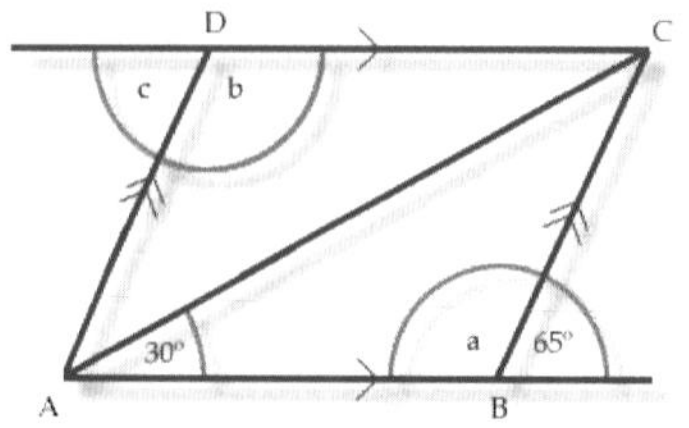

Q12

13 In the following diagram ABCD is a rhombus. Angle CAB is 70°. Calculate the size of angle BDC.

- ☐ (a) 20°
- ☐ (b) 35°

- ☐ (c) 40°
- ☐ (d) 50°
- ☐ (e) 70°

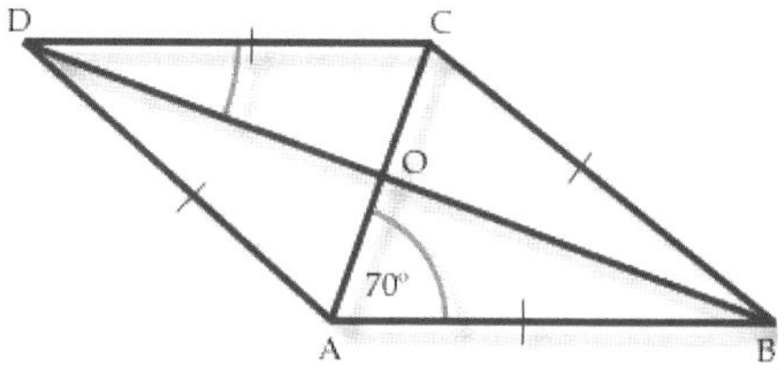

Q13

14 In the following diagram the dots form a grid of equilateral triangles. What names are given to each of the shapes ABCDEF, BCIH, and AGID respectively.

- ☐ (a) Pentagon, parallelogram, trapezium
- ☐ (b) Hexagon, rhombus, kite
- ☐ (c) Hexagon, parallelogram, trapezium
- ☐ (d) Octagon, rhombus, parallelogram
- ☐ (e) Pentagon, parallelogram, kite

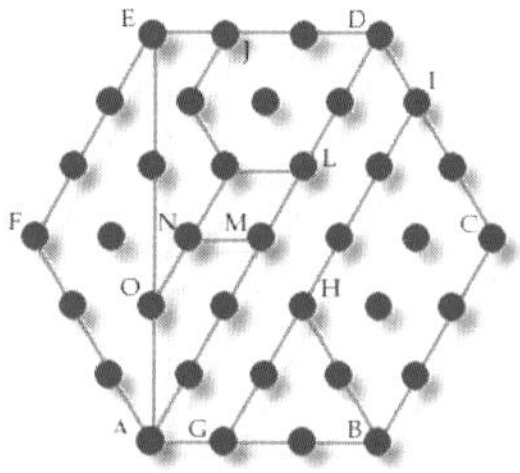

Q14

15 The following diagram shows a circle with centre O. What are the correct names for the lines AB, CD, and EF respectively?

- ☐ (a) Diameter, arc, tangent
- ☐ (b) Diameter, chord, tangent
- ☐ (c) Diameter, circumference, chord
- ☐ (d) Radius, arc, chord
- ☐ (e) Radius, chord, circumference

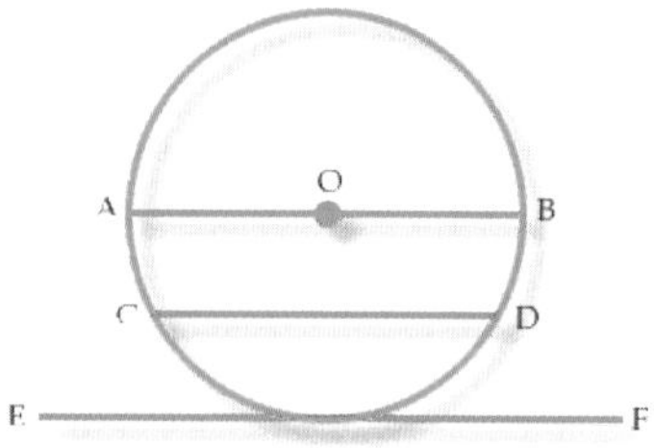

Q15

16 Which of the following properties is true of a kite?

- ☐ (a) Two sets of equal sides, which are adjacent (next to each other)
- ☐ (b) Two sets of equal sides, which are parallel

☐ (c) Opposite angles are equal
☐ (d) Four equal sides
☐ (e) Opposite angles add up to 180°

17 Which of the following properties is true of a rhombus?

☐ (a) Two sets of parallel sides and one line of symmetry
☐ (b) One set of parallel sides and one line of symmetry
☐ (c) Two sets of parallel sides and four lines of symmetry
☐ (d) Four equal sides and two lines of symmetry
☐ (e) Four equal sides and four lines of symmetry

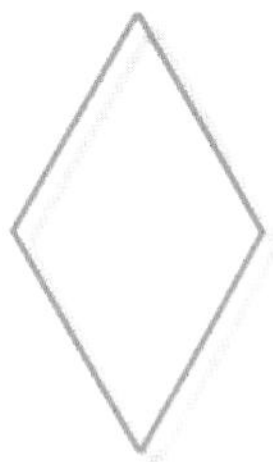

Q17

18 What is a quadrilateral called that has only two parallel sides?

☐ (a) Kite
☐ (b) Parallelogram
☐ (c) Rectangle
☐ (d) Rhombus
☐ (e) Trapezium

19 The diagram below shows a quadrilateral. Calculate the size of the missing angle.

☐ (a) 74°
☐ (b) 77°
☐ (c) 78°
☐ (d) 102°
☐ (e) 103°

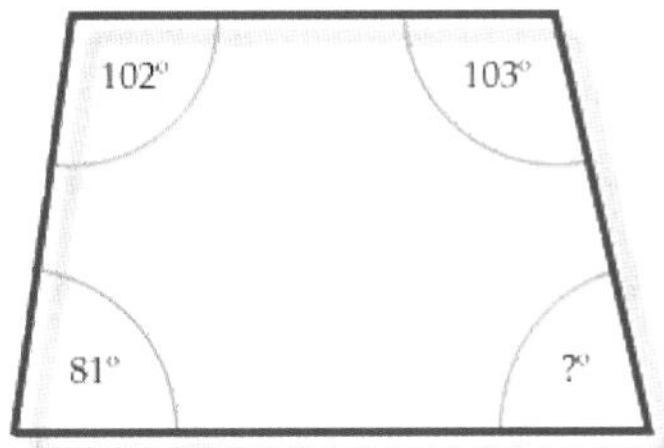

Q19

20 The following diagram shows four quadrilaterals. In which two are the diagonals perpendicular?

☐ (a) Rectangle and square
☐ (b) Rectangle and rhombus
☐ (c) Square and parallelogram
☐ (d) Square and rhombus
☐ (e) Rectangle and parallelogram

Rectangle   Square   Parallelogram   Rhombus

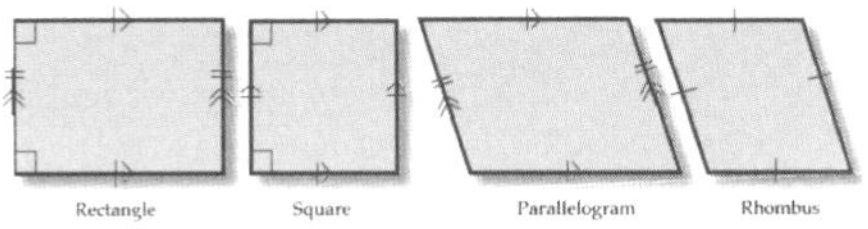

Q20, Q21

21 The diagram above shows four quadrilaterals. In which quadrilaterals are the diagonals equal in length?

☐ (a) Rectangle and parallelogram
☐ (b) Rectangle and square
☐ (c) Rectangle and rhombus
☐ (d) Square and parallelogram
☐ (e) Square and rhombus

22 The following diagram shows a quadrilateral. Calculate the size of angle a.

☐ (a) 100°
☐ (b) 108°
☐ (c) 106°
☐ (d) 114°
☐ (e) 146°

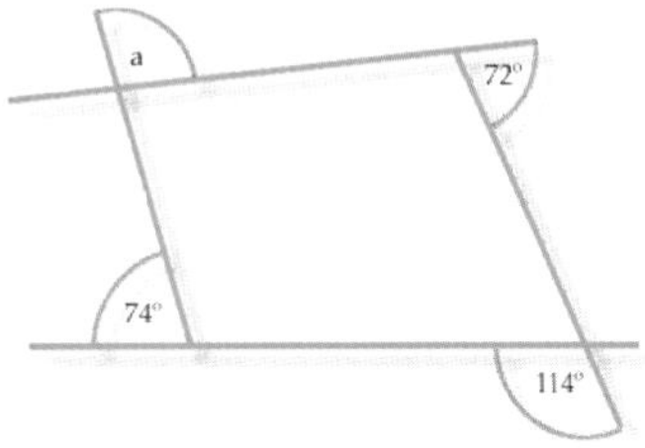

Q22

23 In the following diagram ABCD is a square and triangle ABE is equilateral. Calculate the size of angle ADE.

☐ (a) 30°
☐ (b) 45°
☐ (c) 60°
☐ (d) 70°
☐ (e) 75°

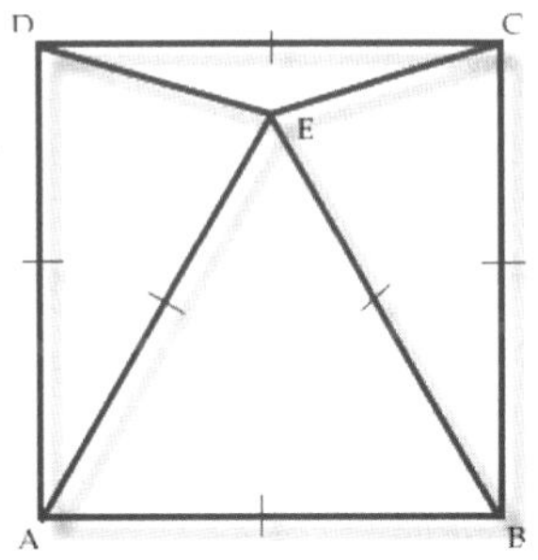

Q23

24 The following diagram shows a quadrilateral. Calculate the size of angles s and t.

☐ (a) s = 34°, t = 57°

☐ (b) s = 34°, t = 79°
☐ (c) s = 44°, t = 38°
☐ (d) s = 38°, t = 44°
☐ (e) s = 38°, t = 57°

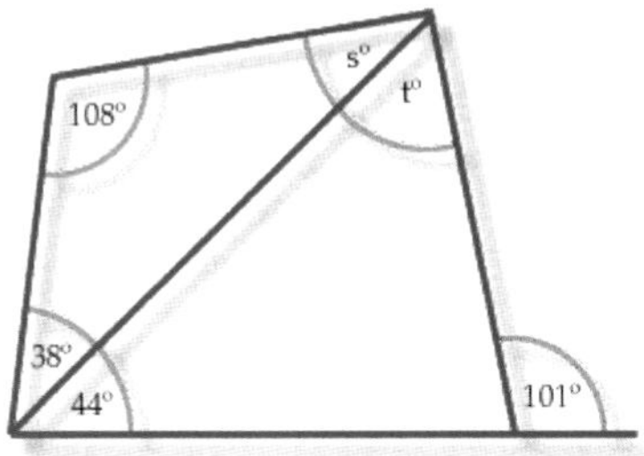

Q24

25 A nonagon is a polygon that has nine sides. Use the following diagram to calculate the size of the interior angle of a regular nonagon.

☐ (a) 40°
☐ (b) 60°
☐ (c) 120°
☐ (d) 140°
☐ (e) 160°

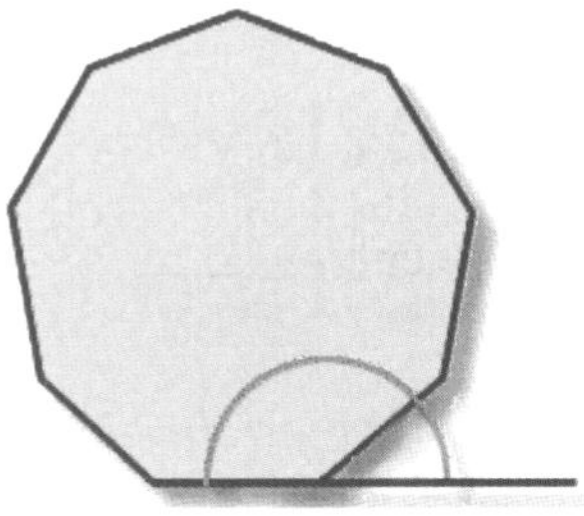

Q25

26 Calculate the size of angle e in the following diagram.

☐ (a) 42°
☐ (b) 56°
☐ (c) 69°
☐ (d) 111°
☐ (e) 138°

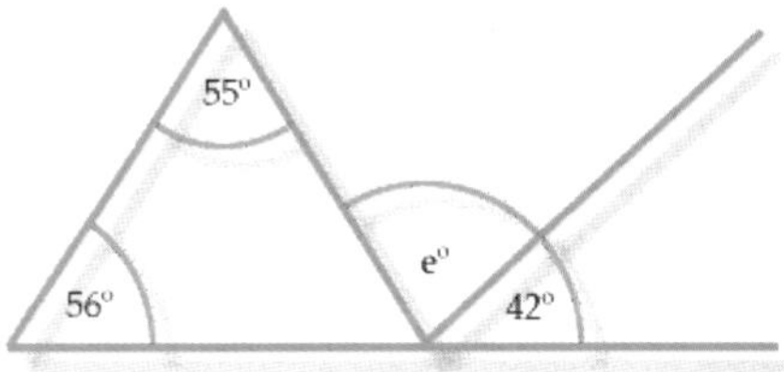

Q26

27 Which of the triangles shown in the following diagram are similar?

☐ (a) V and Y
☐ (b) V and W
☐ (c) X and Y

59

☐ (d) W and Z
☐ (e) V, X, and Y

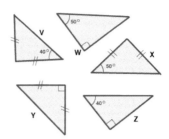

Q27

28 The two triangles shown in the following diagram are similar. Calculate the value of X.

☐ (a) 16 cm
☐ (b) 4 cm
☐ (c) 4.8 cm
☐ (d) 13 cm
☐ (e) 6 cm

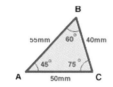

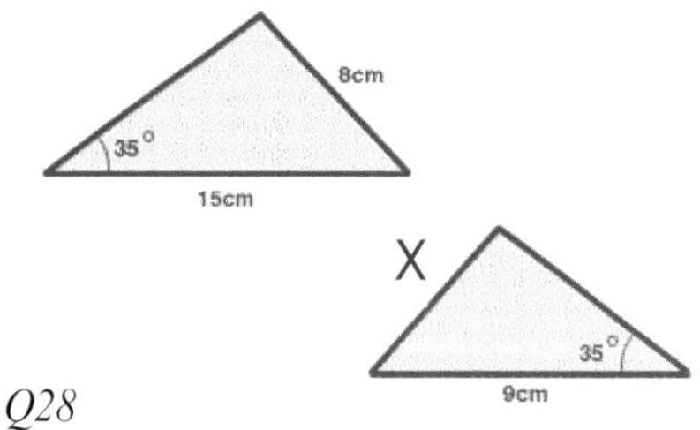

Q28

29 Triangles ABC and LMN shown in the diagram below are similar. Find the lengths of LM and MN.

☐ (a) LM = 92 mm, MN = 66mm
☐ (b) LM = 41 mm, MN = 30 mm
☐ (c) LM = 33 mm, MN = 30 mm
☐ (d) LM = 24 mm, MN = 33 mm
☐ (e) LM = 33 mm, MN = 24 mm

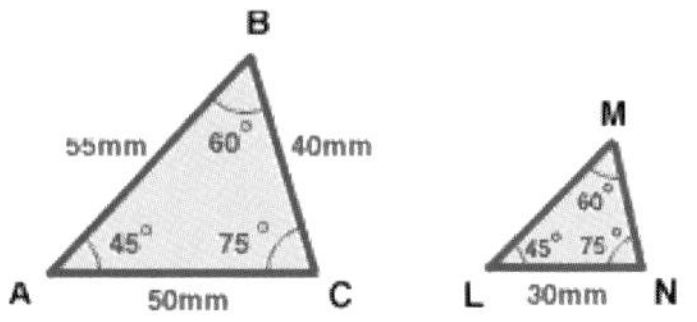

Q29

30 Triangles FDE and LMN shown in the diagram below are similar. Calculate the lengths of DF and LN.

☐ (a) DF = 16 mm, LN = 22.5 mm
☐ (b) DF = 14.4 mm, LN = 25 mm
☐ (c) DF = 16 mm, LN = 25 mm
☐ (d) DF = 22.5 mm, LN = 16 mm
☐ (e) DF = 25 mm, LN = 14.4 mm

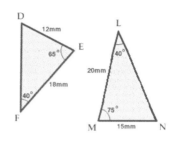

Q30

Symmetry

 KEY FACTS

• A 2D shape has reflection (mirror) symmetry if one half can be reflected in a line (mirror line) exactly on to the other half.

• A 2D shape has rotational symmetry if it can fit into its own shape more than once in one revolution about a point, called the centre of rotation.

• A 3D shape has reflection (mirror) symmetry if one half can be reflected in a plane (mirror) exactly on to the other half.

• A 3D shape has rotational symmetry if it can fit into its own shape more than once in one revolution about a line, called the axis of rotation.

 QUESTIONS

1 "Any 2D shape which has rotational symmetry must also have reflectional symmetry." Is this statement true or false?

☐ (a) True

☐ (b) False

Q1

2 "The only triangles with symmetry are equilateral triangles." Is this statement true or false?

☐ (a) True
☐ (b) False

3 What are the characteristics of an isosceles triangle?

☐ (a) No equal sides and no lines of symmetry
☐ (b) Two equal sides and one line of symmetry
☐ (c) Three equal sides and three lines of symmetry
☐ (d) Three equal angles and three lines of symmetry
☐ (e) Two equal angles and two lines of symmetry

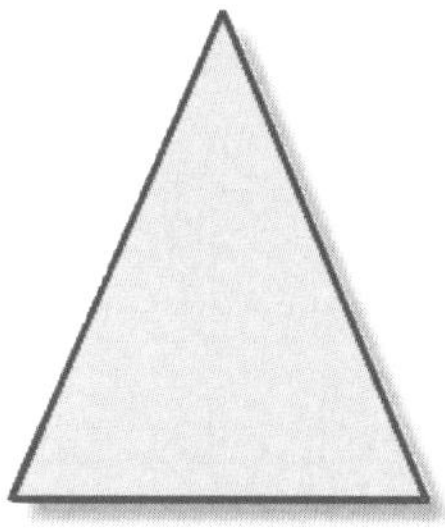

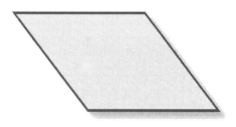

Q3

4 Which of the following statements are true of a parallelogram?

☐ (a) Rotational symmetry of order 2 and no lines of symmetry
☐ (b) Rotational symmetry of order 2 and two lines of symmetry
☐ (c) Rotational symmetry of order 2 and four lines of symmetry
☐ (d) Rotational symmetry of order 4 and no lines of symmetry
☐ (e) Rotational symmetry of order 4 and two lines of symmetry

Q4

5 The Egyptians built the pyramids nearly 5000 years ago. How many planes of symmetry does a square-based pyramid have?

- ☐ (a) 8
- ☐ (b) 4
- ☐ (c) 2
- ☐ (d) 1
- ☐ (e) 0

6 The diagram below shows a cuboid. How many planes of symmetry does this solid have?

- ☐ (a) 3
- ☐ (b) 4
- ☐ (c) 6
- ☐ (d) 9
- ☐ (e) 12

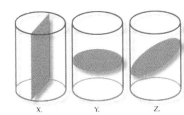

Q6

7 The diagram below shows plane sections of a cylinder. Which of these sections are planes of symmetry of the cylinder?

- ☐ (a) X only
- ☐ (b) Y only
- ☐ (c) X and Y
- ☐ (d) Y and Z
- ☐ (e) All of them

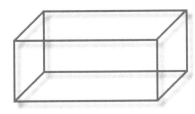

X.   Y.   Z.

Q7

8 A die is a cube. How many planes of symmetry does a cube have?

- ☐ (a) 3
- ☐ (b) 4
- ☐ (c) 6
- ☐ (d) 9
- ☐ (e) 12

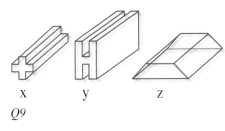

Q8

9 The following diagram shows three prisms. How many planes of symmetry does each solid have?

- ☐ (a) X = 3, Y = 2, Z = 1
- ☐ (b) X = 3, Y = 3, Z = 1
- ☐ (c) X = 5, Y = 3, Z = 1
- ☐ (d) X = 5, Y = 2, Z = 2
- ☐ (e) X = 5, Y = 3, Z = 2

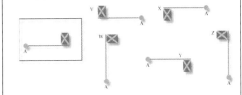

X   y   z

Q9

10 Which of the following flags, when added to the original diagram in the box, will make a diagram that has rotational symmetry of order 2?

- ☐ (a) V
- ☐ (b) W
- ☐ (c) X
- ☐ (d) Y
- ☐ (e) Z

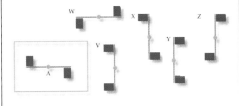

Q10

11 Which of the following, when added to diagram A in the box, will make a diagram that has rotational symmetry of order 4?

- ☐ (a) V
- ☐ (b) W
- ☐ (c) X
- ☐ (d) Y
- ☐ (e) Z

Q11

12 Which of the following, when added to diagram A in the box, will make a diagram which has rotational symmetry of order 3?

- ☐ (a) V
- ☐ (b) W
- ☐ (c) X

- ☐ (d) Y
- ☐ (e) Z

Q12

13 What is the order of rotational symmetry of a regular hexagon?

- ☐ (a) 2
- ☐ (b) 3
- ☐ (c) 4
- ☐ (d) 6
- ☐ (e) 12

Q13

14 How many lines of symmetry does a regular hexagon have?

- ☐ (a) 2
- ☐ (b) 3
- ☐ (c) 4
- ☐ (d) 6
- ☐ (e) 12

Q14

15 The Pentagon in the United States of America houses the Defence Department. It is a regular pentagonal building. How many lines of symmetry does a regular pentagon have?

- ☐ (a) 1
- ☐ (b) 2
- ☐ (c) 3
- ☐ (d) 5
- ☐ (e) 10

16 The following diagram shows the logos of five different companies. Which one has rotational symmetry of order 3?

- ☐ (a) V
- ☐ (b) W
- ☐ (c) X
- ☐ (d) Y
- ☐ (e) Z

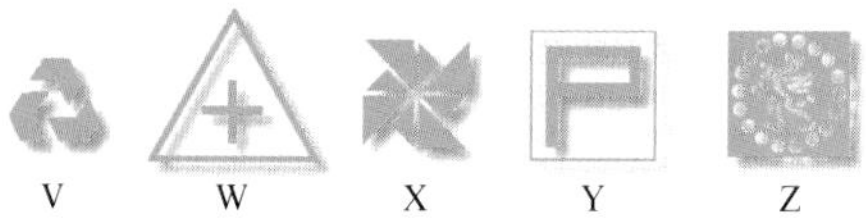

   V   W   X   Y   Z

Q16

17 The children in a class were asked to design a badge. The following diagram shows the winning badge. What is the order of rotational symmetry of the badge?

- ☐ (a) 1
- ☐ (b) 2
- ☐ (c) 4
- ☐ (d) 6
- ☐ (e) 8

Q17

18 Which of the shapes in the following diagram has no rotational symmetry?

- ☐ (a) W
- ☐ (b) Y
- ☐ (c) Z
- ☐ (d) V and Y
- ☐ (e) X and V

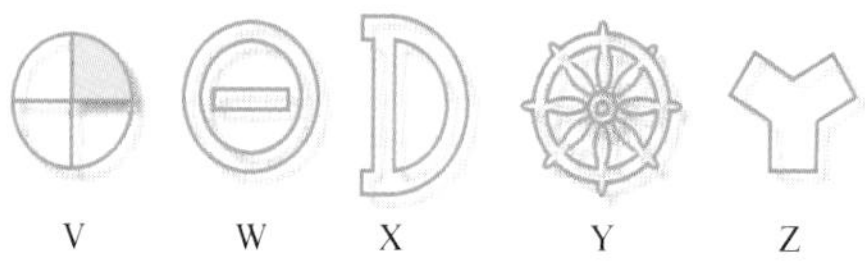

   V   W   X   Y   Z

Q18

19 The 50p and 20p coins are curved regular heptagons. What is the order of rotational symmetry of a regular heptagon?

- ☐ (a) 7
- ☐ (b) 5
- ☐ (c) 3
- ☐ (d) 2
- ☐ (e) 1

20 The following diagram shows a tile pattern. How many lines of symmetry does the pattern have?

- ☐ (a) 0
- ☐ (b) 1
- ☐ (c) 2
- ☐ (d) 4
- ☐ (e) 8

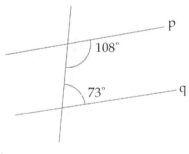

Q20

Angles

🔵 KEY FACTS

- An angle measures the amount of turn.

- One complete turn (revolution) is a turn of 360°. A half-turn is 180°, and a quarter-turn is 90°.

- An acute angle is less than 90°, an obtuse angle is between 90° and 180°, and a reflex angle is greater than 180°.

- Parallel lines do not meet – the angle between them is 0°.

- Perpendicular lines are at 90° (right angles) to each other.

- The sum of the interior angles of a polygon having n sides is $(2n - 4) \times 90°$.

- Angle properties of circles:
i) Angle at the centre is equal to twice the angle at the circumference.
ii) Angle in a semicircle is a right angle.
iii) Angles in the same segment are equal.
iv) Opposite angles in a cyclic quadrilateral add up to 180°.
v) Angle between tangent and radius is a right angle.
vi) Angle between tangent and chord is equal to the angle in the alternate segment.

🔵 QUESTIONS

1 "In the following diagram, the lines marked with arrows are parallel. $x + y + z = 180°$." Is this statement true or false?

- ☐ (a) True
- ☐ (b) False

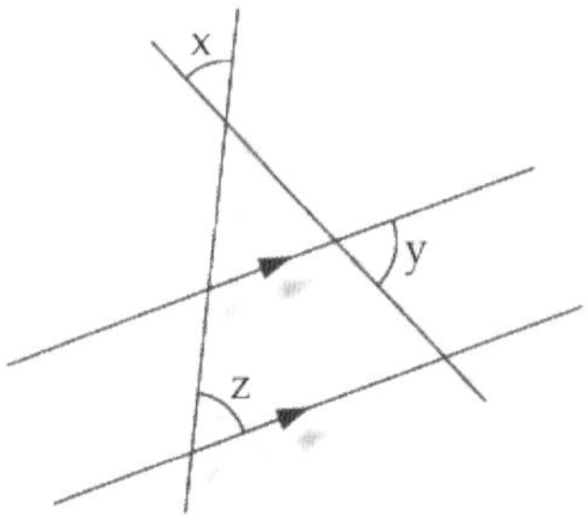

Q1

2 "If extended sufficiently far the lines marked p and q will meet to the right of the following diagram." Is this statement true or false?

- ☐ (a) True
- ☐ (b) False

Q2

3 "The sum of the interior angles of a polygon of n sides is $(n - 2) \times 180°$." Is this statement true or false?

- ☐ (a) True
- ☐ (b) False

4 "A regular polygon has each interior angle equal to 144°. The polygon has 10 sides." Is this statement true or false?

- ☐ (a) True
- ☐ (b) False

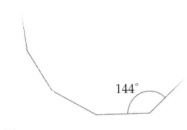

Q4

5 "In the diagram below, the lines marked with arrows are parallel. Angles x and y add up to 180°." Is this statement true or false?

☐ (a) True
☐ (b) False

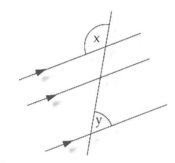

Q5

6 "In the diagram below, the two parallelograms both have longer sides of length 10 cm and shorter sides of length 6 cm. The parallelograms are congruent". Is this statement true or false?

☐ (a) True
☐ (b) False

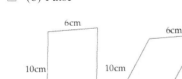

Q6

7 What are the interior and exterior angles of a regular pentagon?

☐ (a) 108° and 72°
☐ (b) 120° and 60°
☐ (c) 135° and 45°
☐ (d) 140° and 40°
☐ (e) 150° and 30°

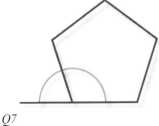

Q7

8 A bee's honeycomb is made up of regular hexagons. What is the size of the interior angle at each vertex of a regular hexagon?

☐ (a) 30°
☐ (b) 60°
☐ (c) 120°
☐ (d) 135°
☐ (e) 150°

9 A regular polygon has exterior angles of 60°. What is the name of the polygon?

☐ (a) Equilateral triangle
☐ (b) Hexagon
☐ (c) Quadrilateral
☐ (d) Pentagon
☐ (e) Octagon

10 Calculate the size of angle x in the following diagram.

☐ (a) 30°
☐ (b) 45°
☐ (c) 55°
☐ (d) 60°
☐ (e) 75°

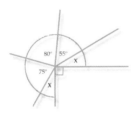

Q10

11 In the following diagram, ABCD is a trapezium. Calculate the size of angle p.

☐ (a) 30°
☐ (b) 40°
☐ (c) 50°
☐ (d) 60°
☐ (e) 70°

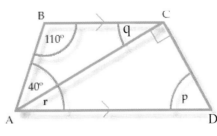

Q11

12 The following diagram shows a pentagon. Calculate the size of the angle marked x.

☐ (a) 45°
☐ (b) 52°
☐ (c) 60°

☐ (d) 67.5°
☐ (e) 75°

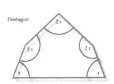

Q12

13 Use the diagram below to calculate the size of the angles marked a, b, and c.

☐ (a) a = 32°, b = 148°, c = 148°
☐ (b) a = 32°, b = 158°, c = 158°
☐ (c) a = 58°, b = 122°, c = 122°
☐ (d) a = 58°, b = 112°, c = 112°
☐ (e) a = 58°, b = 116°, c = 116°

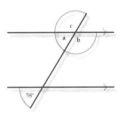

Q13

14 In the diagram below, triangle ABD is isosceles. AD is parallel to BC. Calculate the size of angle ABC.

☐ (a) 54°
☐ (b) 63°
☐ (c) 108°
☐ (d) 117°
☐ (e) 126°

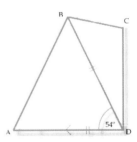

Q14

15 In the following diagram, triangle ABC is equilateral. Triangle BCD is isosceles, with BC = CD. Angle BCD equals 140°. Find the size of angle ABD.

☐ (a) 20°
☐ (b) 30°
☐ (c) 40°
☐ (d) 50°
☐ (e) 60°

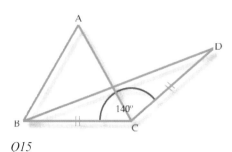

Q15

16 In the diagram below, triangle ABC is isosceles and triangle BCD is equilateral. What is the size of angle ABD?

☐ (a) 45°
☐ (b) 60°
☐ (c) 105°
☐ (d) 120°
☐ (e) 135°

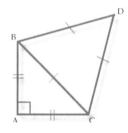

Q16

17 In the diagram below, triangles ABD and BCD are isosceles. Calculate the size of angle p.

☐ (a) 50°
☐ (b) 55°
☐ (c) 60°
☐ (d) 65°
☐ (e) 70°

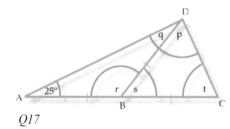

Q17

18 The diagram below shows a parallelogram and an isosceles triangle. Calculate the size of angles a, b, and c.

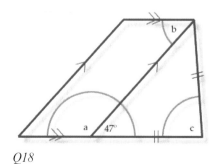

Q18

☐ (a) a = 123°, b = 43°, c = 86°
☐ (b) a = 133°, b = 43°, c = 94°
☐ (c) a = 123°, b = 47°, c = 86°
☐ (d) a = 133°, b = 47°, c = 86°
☐ (e) a = 133°, b = 47°, c = 94°

19 A regular polygon has an exterior angle of 72°. What is the name of this polygon?

☐ (a) Decagon
☐ (b) Hexagon
☐ (c) Nonagon
☐ (d) Octagon
☐ (e) Pentagon

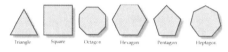

Q19

20 A regular polygon has an angle of 170° at each vertex. How many sides does the polygon have?

☐ (a) 12
☐ (b) 18
☐ (c) 30
☐ (d) 32
☐ (e) 36

Q20

21 In the diagram below, ABCDEF is a regular hexagon. Calculate the size of angle a.

☐ (a) 15°
☐ (b) 30°
☐ (c) 45°
☐ (d) 60°
☐ (e) 75°

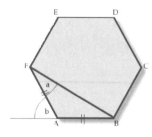

Q21

22 In the following diagram, triangle ABC is isosceles. Calculate the size of the angles a and b.

☐ (a) a = 30°, b = 30°

☐ (b) a = 30°, b = 55°
☐ (c) a = 75°, b = 30°
☐ (d) a = 75°, b = 75°
☐ (e) a = 110°, b = 110°

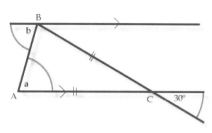

Q22

23 The diagram below shows a pentagon. Calculate the size of the angle marked x.

☐ (a) 90°
☐ (b) 100°
☐ (c) 105°
☐ (d) 108°
☐ (e) 110°

Q23

24 The diagram below shows a hexagon. Calculate the size of the angle marked a.

☐ (a) 90°
☐ (b) 95°
☐ (c) 100°
☐ (d) 105°
☐ (e) 110°

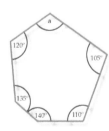

Q24

25 The diagram below shows a plan of a school playing field. Calculate the size of angle d.

Q25

☐ (a) 55°
☐ (b) 65°
☐ (c) 80°
☐ (d) 90°
☐ (e) 100°

26 In the diagram below, a symmetrical stepladder is opened so that the angle between the two legs is 40°. What is the angle between each leg of the stepladder and the ground?

☐ (a) 50°
☐ (b) 60°
☐ (c) 70°
☐ (d) 100°
☐ (e) 140°

Q26

27 Which of the following triangles contain an obtuse angle?

☐ (a) V and W
☐ (b) X and Z
☐ (c) W and Y
☐ (d) V, X, and Z
☐ (e) V, W, and Y

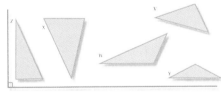

Q27

28 What is the correct name for each of the angles shown in the following diagram, numbered 1, 2, 3, and 4 respectively?

☐ (a) Acute, obtuse, right, obtuse
☐ (b) Acute, obtuse, acute, obtuse
☐ (c) Acute, obtuse, obtuse, obtuse
☐ (d) Obtuse, acute, right, acute
☐ (e) Obtuse, acute, acute, acute

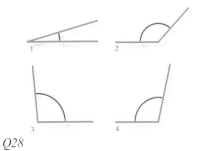

Q28

29 How many degrees does the hour hand of a clock turn through between 4 pm and 7 pm?

☐ (a) 30°
☐ (b) 45°
☐ (c) 60°
☐ (d) 90°
☐ (e) 120°

30 A ladder is leaning against a wall. The angle between the ladder and the ground is 63°, as shown in the following diagram. What is the size of the angle between the ladder and the wall?

☐ (a) 17°
☐ (b) 27°
☐ (c) 33°
☐ (d) 90°
☐ (e) 117°

Q30

31 Calculate the size of angle e in the diagram below.

☐ (a) 22.5°
☐ (b) 30°
☐ (c) 40°
☐ (d) 45°
☐ (e) 60°

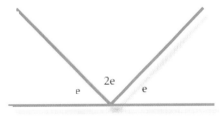

Q31

 QUESTIONS

Higher Level only

32 "In the following diagram, AT is a tangent and CT is a diameter of the circle. Angle x = angle y". Is this statement true or false?

☐ (a) True
☐ (b) False

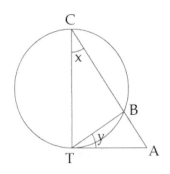

Q32

33 Find the size of angles a and b in the diagram below.

☐ (a) a = 42°, b = 53°
☐ (b) a = 53°, b = 42°
☐ (c) a = 53°, b = 85°
☐ (d) a = 85°, b = 53°
☐ (e) a = 85°, b = 42°

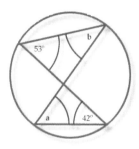

Q33

34 In the diagram below, O is the centre of the circle. Find the size of angle a.

☐ (a) 35°
☐ (b) 55°
☐ (c) 70°
☐ (d) 72½°
☐ (e) 110°

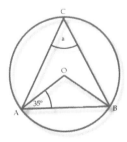

Q34

35 In the following diagram, O is the centre of the circle. Calculate the size of angles p and q.

☐ (a) p = 21°, q = 42°
☐ (b) p = 21°, q = 79½°
☐ (c) p = 84°, q = 42°
☐ (d) p = 84°, q = 46°
☐ (e) p = 84°, q = 48°

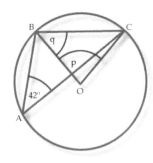

Q35

36 In the diagram below, O is the centre of the circle. Calculate the size of angles s and t.

- ☐ (a) s = 38°, t = 52°
- ☐ (b) s = 52°, t = 26°
- ☐ (c) s = 52°, t = 38°
- ☐ (d) s = 76°, t = 14°
- ☐ (e) s = 76°, t = 38°

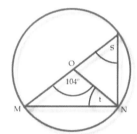

Q36

37 In the diagram below, O is the centre of the circle. Calculate the size of angle x.

- ☐ (a) 15°
- ☐ (b) 16°
- ☐ (c) 30°
- ☐ (d) 45°
- ☐ (e) 75°

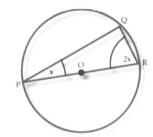

Q37

38 In the following diagram, O is the centre of the circle. Calculate the size of angles p and q.

- ☐ (a) p = 25°, q = 105°
- ☐ (b) p = 40°, q = 80°
- ☐ (c) p = 40°, q = 90°
- ☐ (d) p = 50°, q = 80°
- ☐ (e) p = 50°, q = 90°

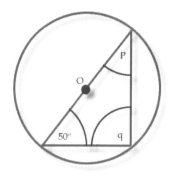

Q38

39 In the diagram below, O is the centre of the circle. Calculate the size of angle x.

- ☐ (a) 30°
- ☐ (b) 60°
- ☐ (c) 75°
- ☐ (d) 105°
- ☐ (e) 150°

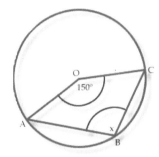

Q39

40 Find angles a and b in the diagram below.

- ☐ (a) a = 50°, b = 80°
- ☐ (b) a = 64°, b = 50°
- ☐ (c) a = 64°, b = 66°
- ☐ (d) a = 65°, b = 65°
- ☐ (e) a = 66°, b = 64°

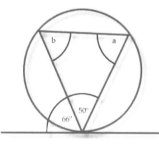

Q40

41 Calculate the size of angle p in the following diagram.

- ☐ (a) 15°
- ☐ (b) 25°
- ☐ (c) 30°
- ☐ (d) 35°
- ☐ (e) 37°

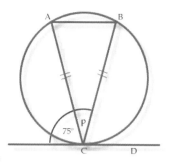

Q41

42 In the diagram below, QP and QR are tangents to the circle, and O is the centre. Find the size of angles m and n.

- ☐ (a) m = 38°, n = 52°
- ☐ (b) m = 52°, n = 14°
- ☐ (c) m = 52°, n = 38°
- ☐ (d) m = 76°, n = 14°
- ☐ (e) m = 76°, n = 38°

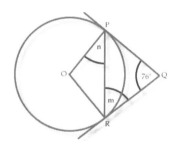

Q42

43 In the diagram below, RP and RQ are tangents to the circle. Calculate the size of the angles q and r.

- ☐ (a) q = 48°, r = 84°
- ☐ (b) q = 66°, r = 24°
- ☐ (c) q = 66°, r = 48°
- ☐ (d) q = 66°, r = 57°
- ☐ (e) q = 69°, r = 42°

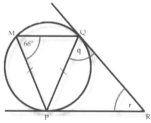

Q43

44 In the following diagram the tangent at A is parallel to the chord at BC. Find the size of the angles a and b.

- ☐ (a) a = 37°, b = 90°
- ☐ (b) a = 53°, b = 74°
- ☐ (c) a = 71½°, b = 37°
- ☐ (d) a = 74°, b = 53°
- ☐ (e) a = 90°, b = 37°

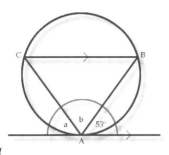

Q44

45 In the diagram below, O is the centre of the circle. Calculate the size of the angle t.

☐ (a) 35°
☐ (b) 49°
☐ (c) 54°
☐ (d) 70°
☐ (e) 98°

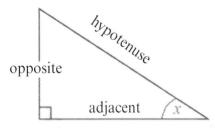

Q45

46 In the diagram below, ABCD is a cyclic quadrilateral. Calculate the size of angles a, b, and c.

☐ (a) a = 29°, b = 29°, c = 41°
☐ (b) a = 29°, b = 41°, c = 41°
☐ (c) a = 35°, b = 35°, c = 29°
☐ (d) a = 35°, b = 29°, c = 35°
☐ (e) a = 35°, b = 32°, c = 35°

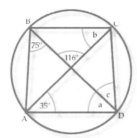

Q46

47 Which of the following angles cannot be the interior angle of a regular polygon?

☐ (a) 108°
☐ (b) 120°
☐ (c) 130°
☐ (d) 140°
☐ (e) 150°

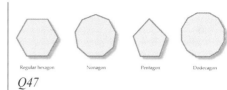

Q47

48 The diagram below shows a regular octagon. Calculate the size of angle a.

☐ (a) 15°
☐ (b) 22.5°
☐ (c) 27.5°
☐ (d) 30°
☐ (e) 45°

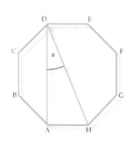

Q48

Trigonometry and Pythagoras

⬤ KEY FACTS

• In a right-angled triangle, the hypotenuse (opposite the right angle) is the longest side. If angle x is chosen, then $^{opposite}/_{hypotenuse}$ is the sine of x, $^{adjacent}/_{hypotenuse}$ is the cosine of x, and $^{opposite}/_{adjacent}$ is the tangent of x. These are normally written as: $\sin x = {^{opp}/_{hyp}}$, $\cos x = {^{adj}/_{hyp}}$, and $\tan x = {^{opp}/_{adj}}$.

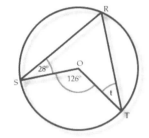

Right-angled triangle

• Using these ratios, it is possible to find the sides and angles in a right-angled triangle.

• A bearing is an angle, measured from the north, in a clockwise direction. To find the bearing of a point P from point Q, firstly draw a north line at Q, and then measure the angle, clockwise, that you need to turn until you are in a line with P.

• Pythagoras' theorem states that $(hyp)^2 = (opp)^2 + (adj)^2$. Given any two sides in a right-angled triangle, Pythagoras' theorem can be used to calculate the third side.

• In any triangle, we can use the sine rule and cosine rule to calculate sides and angles.

Sine rule: $^a/_{\sin A} = {^b/_{\sin B}} = {^c/_{\sin C}}$.
Cosine rule: $a^2 = b^2 + c^2 - 2bc \cos A$
or $\cos A = {^{(b^2 + c^2 - a^2)}/_{2bc}}$.

• By defining sine and cosine as projections on the axes, we can find the sine and cosine (and tangent) of angles of any size.

⬤ QUESTIONS

1 "In the following diagram, $a^2 + b^2 = c^2$." Is this statement true or false?

☐ (a) True
☐ (b) False

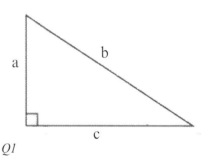

Q1

2 "The triangle in the following diagram is right-angled." Is this statement true or false?

☐ (a) True
☐ (b) False

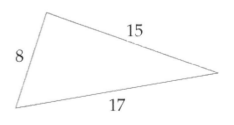

Q2

67

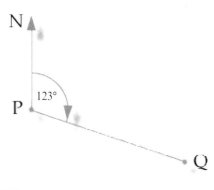

Q3

3 "The bearing of Q from P is 123°, as shown on the diagram above." Is this statement true or false?

- ☐ (a) True
- ☐ (b) False

4 A cube has sides of 5 cm. Find the length of the diagonal BE. Give the answer correct to 1 d.p.

- ☐ (a) 5.9 cm
- ☐ (b) 7.1 cm
- ☐ (c) 7.4 cm
- ☐ (d) 8.7 cm
- ☐ (e) 11.2 cm

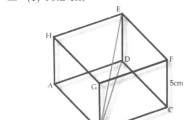

Q4

5 In the diagram below, triangle PQR is right-angled at Q. Calculate the length of the line PR.

- ☐ (a) 8 cm
- ☐ (b) 15 cm
- ☐ (c) 21 cm
- ☐ (d) 112.5 cm
- ☐ (e) 225 cm

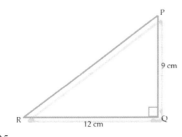

Q5

6 Calculate the length of the line *a* in the following diagram.

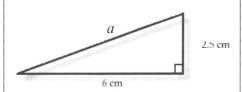

Q6

- ☐ (a) 5.45 cm
- ☐ (b) 6.5 cm
- ☐ (c) 8.5 cm
- ☐ (d) 21.125 cm
- ☐ (e) 42.25 cm

7 Calculate the length of the line X in the following diagram. Give the answer correct to 1 d.p.

- ☐ (a) 2.9 cm
- ☐ (b) 3.1 cm
- ☐ (c) 6.7 cm
- ☐ (d) 8.6 cm
- ☐ (e) 9.5 cm

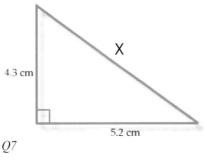

Q7

8 In the diagram below, the triangle STR is right-angled at S. Calculate the length of the line ST.

- ☐ (a) 1 cm
- ☐ (b) 5 cm
- ☐ (c) 12.5 cm
- ☐ (d) 17.7 cm
- ☐ (e) 25 cm

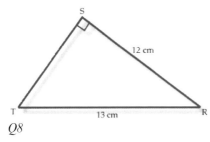

Q8

9 Calculate the length of the line z in the following diagram.

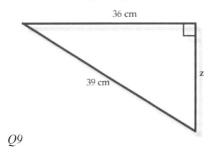

Q9

- ☐ (a) 15 cm
- ☐ (b) 37.5 cm
- ☐ (c) 53.1 cm
- ☐ (d) 75 cm
- ☐ (e) 225 cm

10 Calculate the length of the diagonal of a rectangle that has sides of 7 cm and 12 cm. Give the answer correct to 1 d.p.

- ☐ (a) 9.5 cm
- ☐ (b) 11.7 cm
- ☐ (c) 12.3 cm
- ☐ (d) 13.9 cm
- ☐ (e) 19 cm

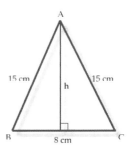

Q10

11 In the diagram below, an isosceles triangle has two sides of 15 cm and one side that is 8 cm long. Calculate the height of the triangle. Give the answer correct to 1 d.p.

- ☐ (a) 4.7 cm
- ☐ (b) 9.5 cm
- ☐ (c) 11.5 cm
- ☐ (d) 12.7 cm
- ☐ (e) 14.5 cm

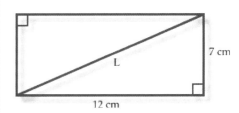

Q11

12 In the following diagram the diagonal of a square is 11.5 cm long. Calculate the length of one side of the square. Give the answer correct to 1 d.p.

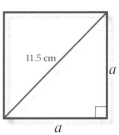

Q12

- ☐ (a) 5.4 cm

☐ (b) 5.75 cm
☐ (c) 6.1 cm
☐ (d) 8.1 cm
☐ (e) 12.2 cm

13 Use the diagram below to calculate the height of an equilateral triangle with each side 12 cm long. Give the answer correct to 1 d.p.

☐ (a) 6 cm
☐ (b) 6.7 cm
☐ (c) 8.5 cm
☐ (d) 10.4 cm
☐ (e) 13.4 cm

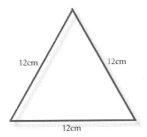

12cm   12cm

12cm

Q13

14 In the diagram below a helicopter flies 18 km due north and then 24 km due west. How far is the helicopter from its starting point?

☐ (a) 6.5 km
☐ (b) 15.9 km
☐ (c) 21 km
☐ (d) 30 km
☐ (e) 42 km

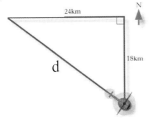

24km   N

d   18km

Q14

15 The diagram below shows the back of a picture, which will be held up by the triangular piece of wire attached to it. How long is the piece of wire?

☐ (a) 26.6 cm
☐ (b) 28 cm
☐ (c) 32 cm
☐ (d) 36 cm
☐ (e) 50.2 cm

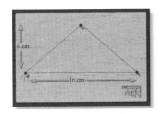

6 cm

16 cm

Q15

16 In the diagram below, a ladder, 3 m long, leans against a wall. The foot of the ladder is 1.4 m away from the wall. How high does the ladder reach up the wall? Give the answer correct to 1 d.p.

☐ (a) 3.3 m
☐ (b) 2.7 m
☐ (c) 2.1 m
☐ (d) 1.6 m
☐ (e) 1.3 m

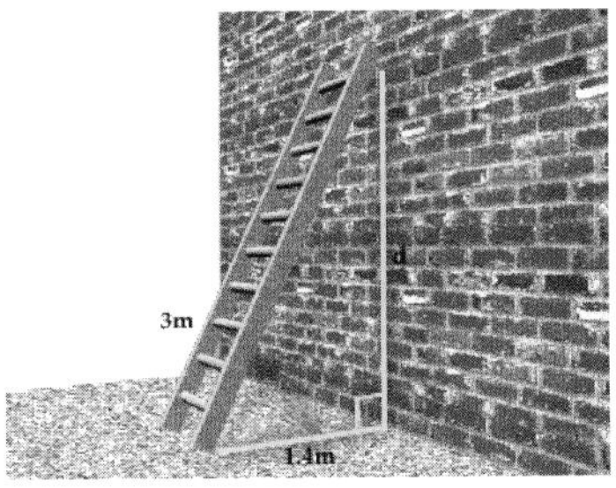

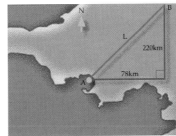

3m   d

1.4m

Q16

17 In the diagram below, a pipeline runs into the North Sea, from A to B. B is 220 km north of A, and 78 km east of A. How long is the pipeline? Give the answer correct to the nearest km.

☐ (a) 298 km
☐ (b) 233 km
☐ (c) 220 km
☐ (d) 210 km
☐ (e) 208 km

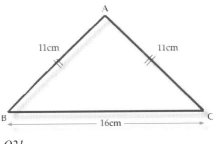

N   B

L   220km

A   78km

Q17

18 Calculate the angle x in the diagram below. Give the answer correct to the nearest degree.

☐ (a) 70°
☐ (b) 55°
☐ (c) 46°
☐ (d) 44°
☐ (e) 35°

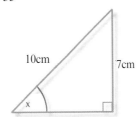

10cm   7cm

x

Q18

19 Calculate the angle x in the diagram below. Give the answer correct to 1 d.p.

☐ (a) 27.8°
☐ (b) 31.8°
☐ (c) 58.2°
☐ (d) 62.2°
☐ (e) 10.8°

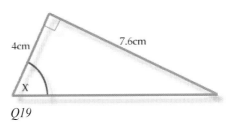

4cm   7.6cm

x

Q19

20 Calculate the angle x in the diagram below. Give the answer correct to 1 d.p.

☐ (a) 36.9°
☐ (b) 38.7°
☐ (c) 51.3°
☐ (d) 53.1°
☐ (e) 85.4°

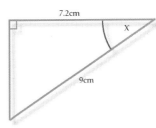

7.2cm   x

9cm

Q20

21 The diagram below shows an isosceles triangle, in which AB = AC = 11 cm and BC = 16 cm. Find angle ABC. Give the answer correct to 1 d.p.

☐ (a) 7.8°
☐ (b) 36.0°
☐ (c) 43.3°
☐ (d) 46.7°
☐ (e) 54.0°

A

11cm   11cm

B   16cm   C

Q21

22 In the isosceles triangle in the following diagram, AB = AC, BC = 18 cm, and angle BAC = 130°. Calculate the length of AB. Give the answer correct to 1 d.p.

☐ (a) 6.9 cm
☐ (b) 8.2 cm
☐ (c) 9.9 cm
☐ (d) 19.3 cm
☐ (e) 21.3 cm

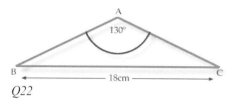

Q22

23 In the diagram below, a ladder, 4 m long, leans against a wall. The foot of the ladder is 1.2 m away from the base of the wall. Calculate the angle between the ladder and the ground. Give the answer correct to 1 d.p.

☐ (a) 73°
☐ (b) 72°
☐ (c) 71°
☐ (d) 17°
☐ (e) 16°

Q23

24 In the diagram below, the diagonal of a rectangle makes an angle of 60° with the shorter side of the rectangle. The diagonal is 1.8 m long. How long is the shorter side? Give the answer correct to 2 d.p.

☐ (a) 1.56 m
☐ (b) 1.04 m
☐ (c) 0.96 m
☐ (d) 0.90 m
☐ (e) 0.19 m

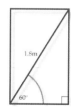

Q24

25 In the following diagram a boy cycles 25 km due north from P to Q. He then cycles 17 km east to R. What is the bearing of R from P, to the nearest degree?

☐ (a) 034°
☐ (b) 042°
☐ (c) 047°
☐ (d) 055°
☐ (e) 086°

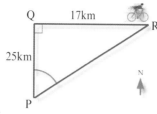

Q25

26 In the diagram below, C is 63 miles due north of B and A is 115 miles due west of C. What is the bearing of A from B? Give the answer correct to 1 d.p.

☐ (a) 028.7°
☐ (b) 061.3°
☐ (c) 298.7°
☐ (d) 326.8°
☐ (e) 331.3°

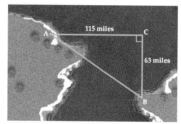

Q26

27 In the diagram below, Q is on a bearing of 055° from P. What is the bearing of P from Q?

☐ (a) 055°
☐ (b) 125°
☐ (c) 215°
☐ (d) 235°
☐ (e) 305°

Q27

28 In the following diagram the bearing of B from A is 310°. What is the bearing of A from B?

☐ (a) 040°
☐ (b) 050°
☐ (c) 130°
☐ (d) 140°
☐ (e) 230°

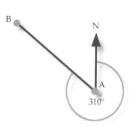

Q28

29 Calculate the size of the smallest angle in triangle LMN shown in the diagram below, giving the answer correct to 1 d. p.

☐ (a) 16.4°
☐ (b) 25.7°
☐ (c) 42.1°
☐ (d) 47.9°
☐ (e) 55.6°

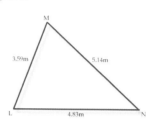

Q29

30 In the following diagram, A and B are two points 250 m apart, on the opposite side bank of a river to the point X. A is 65 m from X and angle AXB is 97°. Calculate angle XAB, giving the answer correct to 1 d.p.

☐ (a) 15.0°
☐ (b) 68.0°
☐ (c) 75.0°
☐ (d) 81.2°
☐ (e) 88.2°

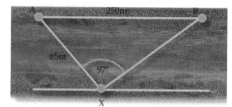

Q30

31 In the diagram below, C is on a bearing of 065° from A, and 040° from B. AB is 9 km long. Find the distance of C from B, giving the answer correct to 1 d.p.

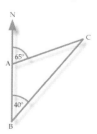

Q31

☐ (a) 10.6 km
☐ (b) 12.7 km
☐ (c) 13.7 km
☐ (d) 19.3 km
☐ (e) 23.5 km

32 The diagram below shows the two villages of Burford and Charlton. What is the bearing of Charlton from Burford?

☐ (a) 150°
☐ (b) 030°
☐ (c) 240°
☐ (d) 210°
☐ (e) 300°

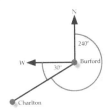

Q32

33 The following diagram shows the two villages of Pensley and Fordham. The bearing of Fordham from Pensley is 150°. What is the bearing of Pensley from Fordham?

☐ (a) 300°
☐ (b) 240°
☐ (c) 030°
☐ (d) 330°
☐ (e) 120°

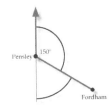

Q33

○ QUESTIONS

Higher Level only

34 TABCD is a square-based pyramid. TA = TB = TC = TD = 12 cm. AB = 8 cm. Calculate the height of the pyramid. Give the answer correct to 1 d.p.

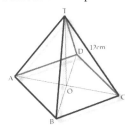

Q34

☐ (a) 8.0 cm
☐ (b) 9.8 cm
☐ (c) 10.6 cm
☐ (d) 11.3 cm
☐ (e) 13.3 cm

35 Marsden is 12 km from Preston, on a bearing of 33°. Norfield is 10 km from Marsden, on a bearing of 123°. By showing that the triangle is right-angled, calculate the distance from Norfield to Preston. Give the answer correct to 3 s.f.

☐ (a) 10.6 km
☐ (b) 11.6 km
☐ (c) 12.4 km
☐ (d) 15.6 km
☐ (e) 22.0 km

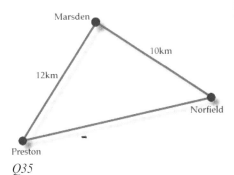

Q35

36 LMNOPQRS is a cuboid. LM = 7.4 cm, MN = 8.6 cm, and NQ = 5.3 cm. Calculate the length of the diagonal SN of the cuboid, giving the answer correct to 3 s.f.

☐ (a) 10.0 cm
☐ (b) 10.7 cm
☐ (c) 11.0 cm
☐ (d) 12.5 cm
☐ (e) 16.6 cm

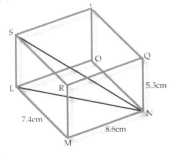

Q36

37 The following diagram shows a flagpole TU at the edge of a parade ground. S is 80 m due west of U and V is 105 m due south of U. The angle of elevation of T from S is 11°. Calculate the angle of elevation of T from V, giving the answer to 1 d.p.

☐ (a) 5.9°
☐ (b) 8.4°

☐ (c) 14.4°
☐ (d) 30.7°
☐ (e) 36.8°

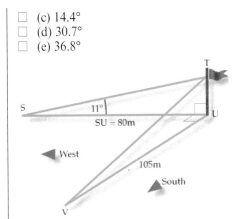

Q37

38 In the diagram below, B is 20 km from A on a bearing of 052°. C is 35 km from B on a bearing of 160°. How far south of A is C? Give the answer correct to 3 s.f.

☐ (a) 3.8 km
☐ (b) 20.6 km
☐ (c) 24.3 km
☐ (d) 27.7 km
☐ (e) 28.4 km

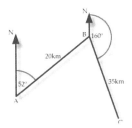

Q38

39 In the diagram below, B is 15 km from A, on a bearing of 285°. C is 18 km from B, on a bearing of 312° (diagram is not to scale). How far due west of A is C? Give the answer correct to 1 d.p.

☐ (a) 15.9 km
☐ (b) 17.3 km
☐ (c) 26.5 km
☐ (d) 27.9 km
☐ (e) 30.7 km

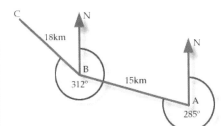

Q39

40 Find the length of QR in the following diagram using the cosine formula, giving the answer correct to 1 d.p.

(a) 7.9 cm
(b) 8.1 cm
(c) 9.3 cm
(d) 10.6 cm
(e) 12.4 cm

(a) 77.0°
(b) 94.7°
(c) 103.0°
(d) 127.1°
(e) 145.9°

(a) 53.7°
(b) 57.0°
(c) 65.8°
(d) 69.7°
(e) 80.2°

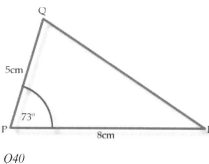

Q40

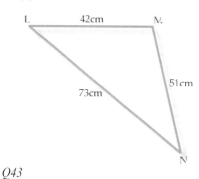

Q43

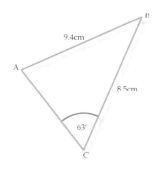

Q46

41 Find the length of AC in the diagram below using the cosine formula, giving the answer correct to 1 d.p.

(a) 10.7 mm
(b) 10.8 mm
(c) 12.1 mm
(d) 16.1 mm
(e) 18.9 mm

44 Find the length of DE in the diagram below using the sine formula, giving the answer correct to 1 d.p.

(a) 6.1 cm
(b) 7.7 cm
(c) 7.9 cm
(d) 8.5 cm
(e) 16.5 cm

47 Calculate the size of the largest angle in triangle PQR shown in the diagram below, giving the answer correct to 1 d.p.

(a) 63.0°
(b) 82.4°
(c) 97.6°
(d) 130.1°
(e) 147.4°

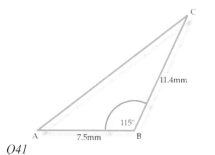

Q41

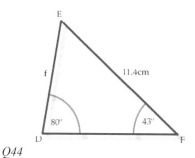

Q44

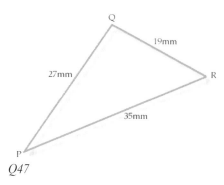

Q47

42 Calculate angle A in the diagram below using the cosine formula, giving the answer correct to 1 d.p.

(a) 35.2°
(b) 49.4°
(c) 51.1°
(d) 60.4°
(e) 95.4°

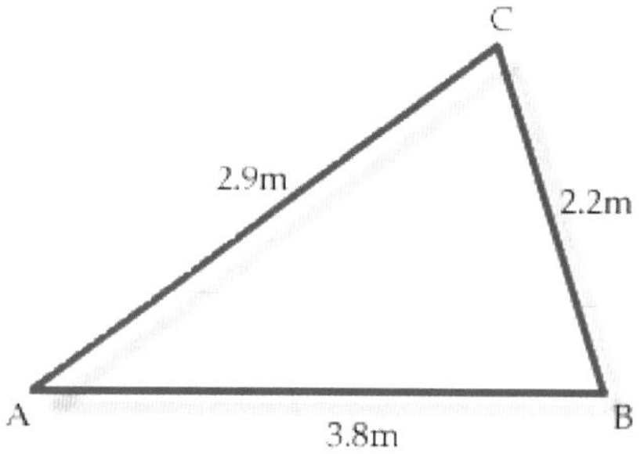

45 Find the length of QR in the diagram below using the sine formula, giving the answer correct to 1 d.p.

(a) 6.9 mm
(b) 10.1 mm
(c) 14.9 mm
(d) 15.5 mm
(e) 23.3 mm

48 In the diagram below, students of a class are surveying the school field. They measure the distance between two points X and Y as 100 m. A tree is some distance away. They measure angle TXY as 102°, and angle TYX as 47°. How far is T from X? Give the answer correct to 1 d.p.

(a) 70.4 m
(b) 74.8 m
(c) 125.7 m
(d) 133.7 m
(e) 142.0 m

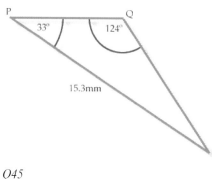

Q42

43 Calculate angle M in the following diagram using the cosine formula, giving the answer correct to 1 d.p.

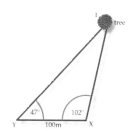

Q45

46 Calculate angle A in the following diagram using the sine formula, giving the answer correct to 1 d.p.

Q48

72

49 In the diagram below, a golfer is at a hole which measures 215 m from the tee, T, to the hole, H, on the green. He hits the ball at an angle of 10° away from the direct line between T and H. The ball stops at B, 170 m from T. How far is B from H? Give the answer correct to 1 d.p.

- ☐ (a) 30.9 m
- ☐ (b) 56.0 m
- ☐ (c) 97.8 m
- ☐ (d) 136.6 m
- ☐ (e) 233.8 m

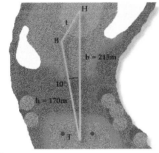

Q49

50 In the following diagram, two boats D and E are 400 m apart. The base, A, of a lighthouse is in line with D and E. From the top, B, of the lighthouse, the angles of depression of D and E are 18° and 31° respectively. Calculate the height of the lighthouse, giving the

answer correct to the nearest metre.

- ☐ (a) 150 m
- ☐ (b) 175 m
- ☐ (c) 250 m
- ☐ (d) 283 m
- ☐ (e) 330 m

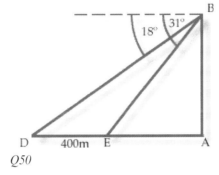

Q50

51 Pete estimates the height of a tree. He measures the angle of elevation of the top of the tree T from A, as 18°. He moves to a point B, 20 m closer to the tree, and measures the angle of elevation of T as 25°. What estimate of the height of the tree will he get from this information, shown in the following diagram? Give the answer to the nearest metre.

- ☐ (a) 3 m
- ☐ (b) 6 m
- ☐ (c) 21 m

- ☐ (d) 24 m
- ☐ (e) 46 m

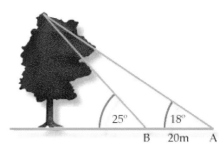

Q51

52 In the following diagram, OC is perpendicular to the base AOB. Calculate the size of angle ACB, giving the answer correct to the nearest degree.

- ☐ (a) 52°
- ☐ (b) 65°
- ☐ (c) 89°
- ☐ (d) 90°
- ☐ (e) 115°

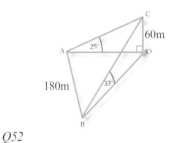

Q52

Co-ordinates and transformations

 KEY FACTS

- Co-ordinates can be used to define the position of a point relative to two fixed perpendicular lines, the x- and y-axes.

- The point where the axes intersect is called the origin.

- Starting from the origin and moving *a* units parallel to the x direction and then *b* units parallel to the y direction, we arrive at the point (a, b), where *a* is the x co-ordinate and *b* the y co-ordinate. Since the axes are at right angles, the distances between points can be found using Pythagoras' theorem.

- By convention, the x-axis is drawn horizontally and the y-axis vertically, and the x co-ordinate always comes first in the bracket.

- A translation is a sliding, without any rotation. It can be described by a vector.

- A rotation is a turning. It can be described by a centre, and angle, and a direction (clockwise or anticlockwise).

- A reflection is a mirror image. It can be described by stating the mirror line.

- Translations, rotations, and reflections do not alter the size or shape of an object. The transformed shape is congruent (alike in all respects) to the original shape.

- An enlargement makes a shape larger (or smaller), but remains similar to the original. It can be described by a centre of enlargement and a scale factor. Corresponding sides in the enlargement and in the original shape are parallel, but

corresponding angles remain the same size.

- A scale factor greater than 1 makes a larger shape. A scale factor less than 1 makes a smaller shape.

- If a shape is moved by one translation followed by another, the total translation can be found by adding the vector of each translation.

 QUESTIONS

1 "The two shapes A and B shown in the following diagram are similar. B is an enlargement of A." Is this statement true or false?

- ☐ (a) True
- ☐ (b) False

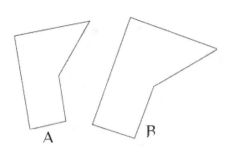

Q1

2 "In right-angled triangle ABC the perpendicular from B to D is drawn. The triangles ADB and BDC are both similar to triangle ABC." Is this statement true or false?

☐ (a) True
☐ (b) False

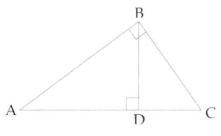

Q2

3 "After rotation through a quarter turn anticlockwise about the origin, the co-ordinates of P become (–4, 7)." Is this statement true or false?

☐ (a) True
☐ (b) False

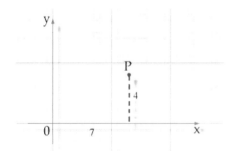

Q3

4 "The following diagram shows the rotation of a flag from position A to position B, which can be achieved by two reflections." Is this statement true or false?

☐ (a) True
☐ (b) False

Q4

5 "Reflection in the x-axis followed by rotation through 90° anticlockwise about the origin is equivalent to reflection in the line y = x." Is this statement true or false?

☐ (a) True
☐ (b) False

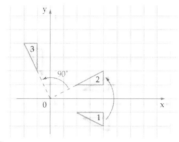

Q5

6 "Reflection in the y-axis followed by a rotation clockwise through 90° about the origin is the same as rotation clockwise through 90° about the origin followed by reflection in the y-axis." Is this statement true or false?

☐ (a) True
☐ (b) False

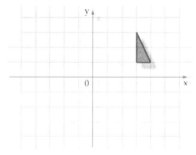

Q6

7 "A translation can be achieved by two reflections." Is this statement true or false?

☐ (a) True
☐ (b) False

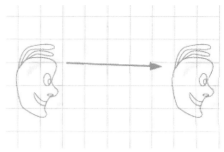

Q7

8 "If two plane figures, such as the ones shown in the diagram below, are similar, then all pairs of corresponding lengths in the two figures are in equal ratio." Is this statement true or false?

☐ (a) True
☐ (b) False

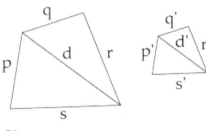

Q8

9 "Triangle S, shown on the diagram below, can be mapped onto triangle T by a single rotation." Is this statement true or false?

☐ (a) True
☐ (b) False

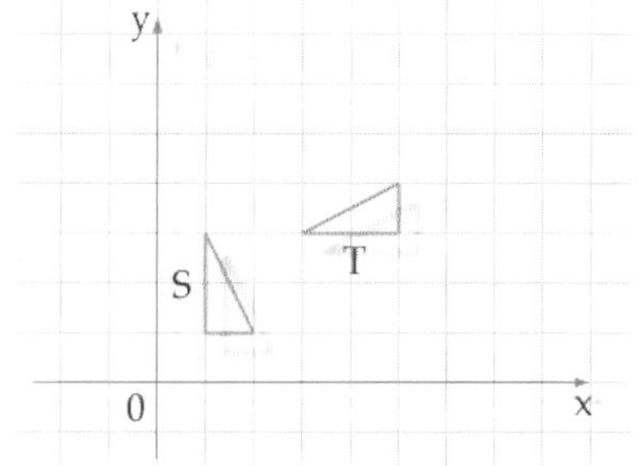

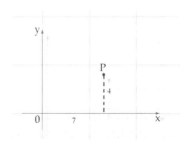

Q9

10 "After reflection in the line y = –x, the co-ordinates of P become (–7, –4)." Is this statement true or false?

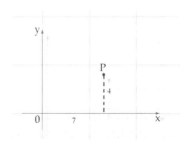

Q10

☐ (a) True
☐ (b) False

11 "In the following diagram, shape B is an enlargement of shape A. The centre of enlargement is the origin." Is this statement true or false?

☐ (a) True
☐ (b) False

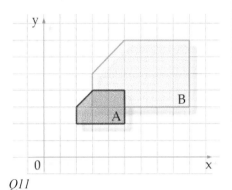

Q11

12 "In the following diagram, AB is parallel to XY. Triangle OXY is an enlargement of triangle OAB by scale factor 2." Is this statement true or false?

☐ (a) True
☐ (b) False

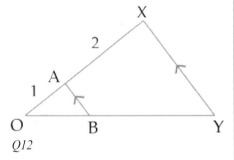

Q12

13 "In the following diagram, Sector Q is an enlargement of sector P." Is this statement true or false?

☐ (a) True
☐ (b) False

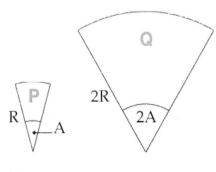

Q13

14 "After reflection in the y-axis, the co-ordinates of the point P become

(7, –4)." Is this statement true or false?

☐ (a) True
☐ (b) False

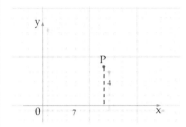

Q14

15 "A parallelogram is divided into two pieces by a straight line through its centre (where the diagonals meet). The two pieces are congruent." Is this statement true or false?

☐ (a) True
☐ (b) False

16 The diagram below shows two sides of a parallelogram ABDC. What are the co-ordinates of the point D?

☐ (a) (6, 0
☐ (b) (6, 5)
☐ (c) (4, 0)
☐ (d) (0, 4)
☐ (e) (7, 7)

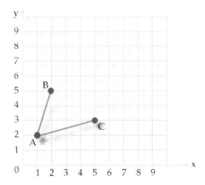

Q16

17 The following diagram shows two sides of a square ABCD. What are the co-ordinates of the point D?

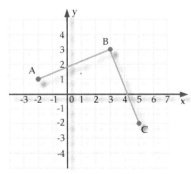

Q17

☐ (a) (–1, 3)
☐ (b) (0, –4)
☐ (c) (0, –3)
☐ (d) (–4, 0)
☐ (e) (–1, 4)

18 In the following diagram, which of the shapes are congruent?

☐ (a) A and F only
☐ (b) B and D only
☐ (c) C, E, and G
☐ (d) A, F and E, G
☐ (e) A, C, E, F, and G

Q18

19 Which of the following shapes has rotational symmetry of order 2?

☐ (a) Kite
☐ (b) Rhombus
☐ (c) Square
☐ (d) Equilateral triangle
☐ (e) Isosceles triangle

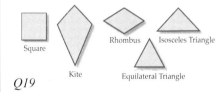

Q19

20 On the diagram below, Shape G can be moved to shape H by a translation. Describe the translation.

☐ (a) $\begin{pmatrix} 1 \\ 4 \end{pmatrix}$

☐ (b) $\begin{pmatrix} 3 \\ 1 \end{pmatrix}$

☐ (c) $\begin{pmatrix} -1 \\ -4 \end{pmatrix}$

☐ (d) $\begin{pmatrix} -1 \\ 4 \end{pmatrix}$

☐ (e) $\begin{pmatrix} 1 \\ -3 \end{pmatrix}$

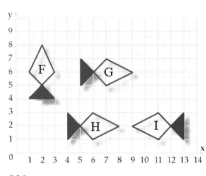

Q20

21 On the diagram below, what types of transformation will change A to A', B to B', and C to C'?

☐ (a) Translation, rotation, and translation
☐ (b) Rotation, rotation, and translation
☐ (c) Translation, reflection, and rotation
☐ (d) Enlargement, reflection, and reflection
☐ (e) Enlargement, reflection, and translation

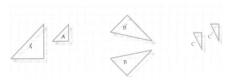

Q21

22 On the diagram below, which of the following describe the translations that move S to T and T to R?

☐ (a) $\begin{pmatrix} 2 \\ 5 \end{pmatrix} \begin{pmatrix} -3 \\ 3 \end{pmatrix}$

☐ (b) $\begin{pmatrix} 2 \\ 5 \end{pmatrix} \begin{pmatrix} 3 \\ -3 \end{pmatrix}$

☐ (c) $\begin{pmatrix} 5 \\ 2 \end{pmatrix} \begin{pmatrix} 3 \\ 3 \end{pmatrix}$

☐ (d) $\begin{pmatrix} 2 \\ -5 \end{pmatrix} \begin{pmatrix} 3 \\ 3 \end{pmatrix}$

☐ (e) $\begin{pmatrix} 5 \\ -2 \end{pmatrix} \begin{pmatrix} 3 \\ -3 \end{pmatrix}$

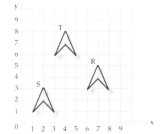

Q22

23 On the following diagram, what type of transformations will transform T to T1, T to T2, and T to T3 respectively?

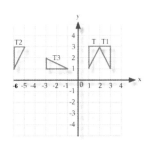

Q23

☐ (a) Translation, reflection, and reflection

☐ (b) Rotation, translation, and rotation
☐ (c) Rotation, reflection, and rotation
☐ (d) Reflection, translation, and rotation
☐ (e) Reflection, translation, and reflection

24 Which of the triangles shown below is a reflection of A in the line y = x?

☐ (a) G
☐ (b) H
☐ (c) B
☐ (d) C
☐ (e) E

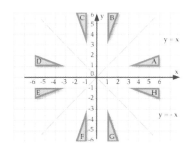

Q24

25 On the diagram below, which triangle is obtained by reflecting E in the line y = –x?

☐ (a) B
☐ (b) F
☐ (c) C
☐ (d) H
☐ (e) G

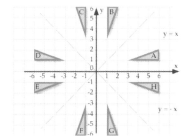

Q25

26 On the following diagram, what transformation will change triangle C to G?

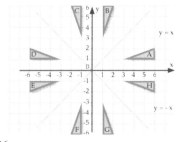

Q26

☐ (a) A reflection in the y-axis

☐ (b) A rotation of 180° about the point (0,0)
☐ (c) A rotation of 90° about the point (0,0)
☐ (d) A reflection in the x-axis
☐ (e) A reflection in the line y = –x

27 If the parallelogram ABCD, as shown below, is reflected in the x-axis, what will be the new co-ordinates of D?

☐ (a) (2,–3)
☐ (b) (–2,3)
☐ (c) (3,–2)
☐ (d) (3,2)
☐ (e) (–2,–3)

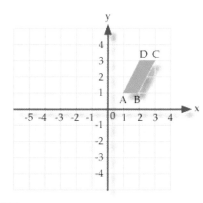

Q27

28 The diagram below shows eight flags. Which flags can be transformed into each other by a reflection in the y-axis?

☐ (a) B and G, A and D
☐ (b) B and C only
☐ (c) A and D only
☐ (d) B and G only
☐ (e) B and C, A and D

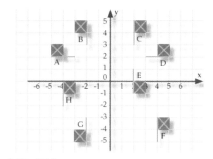

Q28, Q29

29 The diagram above shows eight flags. Flag H can be obtained from flag G by a rotation of 180°. What are the co-ordinates of the centre of rotation?

☐ (a) (–3,–2)
☐ (b) (–3,–2.5)
☐ (c) (–2,–3)
☐ (d) (–2,–2.5)
☐ (e) (–3,–3)

30 In the following diagram, triangle PQR has been enlarged to make P'Q'R'. What is the scale factor of the enlargement?

☐ (a) 3
☐ (b) 2
☐ (c) 1.5
☐ (d) 1
☐ (e) 2.5

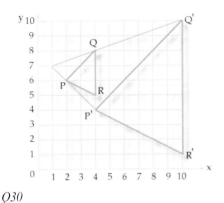

Q30

31 Which of the following enlargements of shape P to Q does not show an enlargement with scale factor 2?

☐ (a) V
☐ (b) W
☐ (c) X
☐ (d) Y
☐ (e) Z

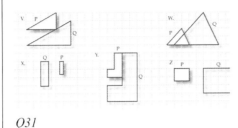

Q31

32 The following diagram shows the start of an enlargement of an octagon, by a scale factor 2. If the enlargement is completed, what will be the co-ordinates of the new positions of P and Q?

☐ (a) P (1, 6) and Q (0, 4)
☐ (b) P (2, 5) and Q (0, 4)
☐ (c) P (2, 6) and Q (0, 4)
☐ (d) P (2, 6) and Q (1, 4)
☐ (e) P (1, 5) and Q (1, 4)

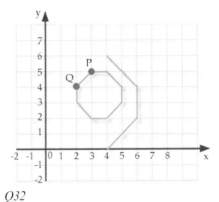

Q32

Scale

⬤ KEY FACTS

• A scale enables a drawing, similar to the original, to be made.

• When drawing a graph, a suitable scale needs to be chosen on each axis.

• A map scale could be 1:25 000, where 1 cm on the map represents 25 000 cm (0.25 km) on the ground.

• In an enlargement, each length in the original is multiplied by the scale factor in order to find the corresponding length in the enlargement.

• If you have two similar shapes, the scale factor from the smaller to the larger can be found by dividing the length on one side in the larger shape by the length of the corresponding side in the smaller shape.

⬤ QUESTIONS

1 The scale of the following map is 1:40 000. What distance is represented by 5 cm on the map?

☐ (a) 20 000 cm
☐ (b) 200 m
☐ (c) 20 m
☐ (d) 2 km
☐ (e) 2000 cm

Q1

2 The scale of the following map is 1:15 000. On the map, the length of the lake in Regent's Park is 6 cm. How long is the lake?

☐ (a) 9 km
☐ (b) 9000 cm
☐ (c) 0.09 km
☐ (d) 9000 m
☐ (e) 900 m

Scale 1 : 15,000

Q2, Q3

3 The scale of the above map is 1:15 000. The distance between two places is 3 km. What distance is this on the map?

☐ (a) 20 cm
☐ (b) 2 cm
☐ (c) 2 mm
☐ (d) 200 cm
☐ (e) 20 mm

4 The town map shown below has a scale of 1:6000. The distance on the map of the lifeboat hut to the pier is 17 cm. What is the real distance between them?

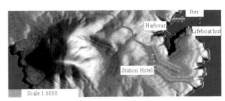

Scale 1:6000

Q4

77

☐ (a) 1 km 200 m
☐ (b) 1 km 20 m
☐ (c) 120 m
☐ (d) 102 m
☐ (e) 1200 m

5 A pole of height 5 m casts a shadow of length 7.5 m on horizontal ground, as shown on the diagram below. At the same time, a building casts a shadow of length 36 m. How tall is the building?

☐ (a) 18 m
☐ (b) 24 m
☐ (c) 54 m
☐ (d) 27 m
☐ (e) 48 m

5m
7.5m

Q5

6 An estate agent took a photo of a house. In the photo, the width of the house was 10.5 cm and the height was 13.5 cm. If the true width of the house was 7 m, what was the height?

☐ (a) 20.25 m
☐ (b) 10 m
☐ (c) 5.4 m
☐ (d) 9 m
☐ (e) 15.75 m

7 A photograph is 16 cm wide and 10.5 cm high. It is enlarged to make a photograph that is 14.7 cm high. What is the new width of the photo?

☐ (a) 11.4 cm
☐ (b) 23.5 cm
☐ (c) 22.4 cm
☐ (d) 20.2 cm
☐ (e) 25.6 cm

Loci

 KEY FACTS

• A locus (plural loci) is the set of all points that obey a given rule.

• The locus of a point that moves so that it is always the same distance, r, from a fixed point, O, is a **circle**, centre O and radius r.

• The locus of a point that moves so that it is always the same distance from two fixed points, P and Q, is the **perpendicular bisector** of the line PQ.

• The locus of a point that moves so that it is always the same distance, x, from a fixed line, is **two lines**, one either side of the given line, each parallel to the given line, and at a distance x from it.

• The locus of a point that moves so that it is always the same distance from two fixed lines is two lines, each being the **bisector of the angles** between the two given lines. The two lines forming the locus are always perpendicular to each other.

 QUESTIONS

1 "The following diagram is a map of an area of desert; Q is the centre of a quicksand, UXB is an unexploded bomb. A soldier in a jeep drives carefully across the desert between them, keeping his distance from Q always the same as his distance from UXB. The soldier drives the jeep in a straight line." Is this statement true or false?

☐ (a) True
☐ (b) False

J

Q   UXB

Q1

2 "Odysseus sails his ship so that it remains equidistant from the rock Scylla (S) and the whirlpool Charybdis (C), as shown in the following diagram. The course of the ship is the perpendicular bisector of the line CS." Is this statement true or false?

☐ (a) True
☐ (b) False

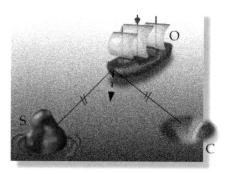

O

S

C

Q2

3 Describe the locus of a point that moves so that it is always 5 cm from a fixed point A.

☐ (a) A circle centre A, radius 5 cm
☐ (b) Two parallel lines, 5 cm on either side of A
☐ (c) A circle, radius 5 cm, passing through A
☐ (d) A line segment 10 cm long, with A as the midpoint

☐ (e) An equilateral triangle of side
5 cm, with A at the centre

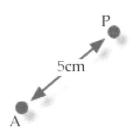

Q3

4 Describe the locus of a point P
which is equidistant from two fixed
points A and B.

☐ (a) Two parallel lines either side
of the line joining A to B
☐ (b) The perpendicular bisector of
the line joining A to B
☐ (c) One point, midway between A
and B
☐ (d) A circle, with AB as diameter
☐ (e) Two circles, one with centre A
and one with centre B, both
having a radius equal to AB

Q4

5 Describe the locus of a point that
moves so that it is always equidistant
from two intersecting lines AB and
CD.

☐ (a) The perimeter of a rectangle
through A, B, C, and D
☐ (b) A circle passing through A, B,
C, and D
☐ (c) The point of intersection of
the two lines
☐ (d) The two lines that bisect the
angles between AB and CD
☐ (e) Two lines – one perpendicular
to AB and one perpendicular to
CD, both passing through the
point of intersection of AB and CD

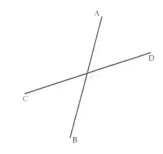

Q5

6 Describe the locus of a point P
which is always 5 cm from the line
segment AB.

☐ (a) Z
☐ (b) V
☐ (c) X
☐ (d) Y
☐ (e) W

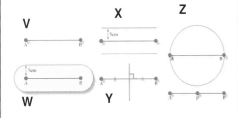

Q6

7 AB is a hedge 15 m long. Grass
does not grow well within a region
which is 1.5 m of the hedge. Which
of the diagrams below shows this
region?

☐ (a) Y
☐ (b) W
☐ (c) V
☐ (d) X
☐ (e) Z

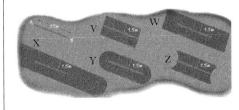

Q7

8 ABCD is a field, 60 m wide and
40 m long. Cows are allowed to
graze in a region of the field that is
closer to CD than AB, and that is
less than 40 m from D. Which of the
following diagrams shows the region
in which the cows can graze?

☐ (a) W
☐ (b) V
☐ (c) X
☐ (d) Y
☐ (e) Z

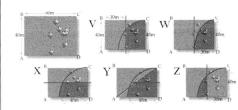

Q8

9 A and B are two radio stations.
A can be received for a 30 km radius
and B can be received for a 20 km
radius. The two stations are 40 km
apart. Which of the following
diagrams represents the region in
which both stations can be received?

☐ (a) X
☐ (b) W
☐ (c) V
☐ (d) Y
☐ (e) Z

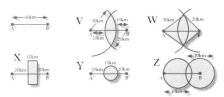

Q9

79

Standard units of measure

KEY FACTS

• Lengths are usually measured in kilometres (km), metres (m), centimetres (cm), or millimetres (mm). 1000 m = 1 km, 100 cm = 1 m, 10 mm = 1 cm.

• Areas are usually measured in square kilometres (km²), square metres (m²), or square centimetres (cm²). 1 000 000 m² = 1 km², 10 000 cm² = 1 m², 100 mm² = 1 cm².

• Volumes are usually in cubic metres (m³) or cubic centimetres (cm³). 100 000 cm³ = 1 m³.

• Capacities (amount that a shape can hold) are usually measured in litres (l) or millilitres (ml). 1000 ml = 1 l. Also, 1 litre = 1000 cm³.

• Masses are usually measured in tonnes (t), kilograms (kg), or grams (g). 1000 kg = 1 tonne, 1000 g = 1kg.

• Time is usually measured in hours, minutes, or seconds.

• Approximate imperial equivalents are: 1 inch = 2.5 cm, 1 foot = 30 cm, 1 yard (3 feet) = 90 cm, 1 mile = 1.6 km, 1 pint = 0.5 litre, 1 gallon (8 pints) = 4.5 litres, 1 lb (pound weight) = 0.5 kg.

QUESTIONS

1 "The graph below will correctly convert weights from kilograms (kg) to pounds (lb)." Is this statement true or false?

☐ (a) True
☐ (b) False

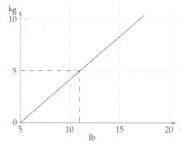

Q1

2 "A bridge over a river is 270 m long. If one foot is approximately 30 cm, then the bridge is approximately 90 feet long." Is this statement true or false?

☐ (a) True
☐ (b) False

3 "The beak of an albatross is 2.8 inches long. If one inch is approximately 2.5 cm, the beak is approximately 7 cm long." Is this statement true or false?

☐ (a) True
☐ (b) False

4 The record for speed in water stands at 319 mph. If there are 1.6 km in a mile, change this to km/h.

☐ (a) 510.4 km/h
☐ (b) 406 km/h
☐ (c) 306.24 km/h
☐ (d) 199.4 km/h
☐ (e) 5.3 km/h

5 A candle is 9 cm high. As it burns it shrinks 32 mm. How tall is it now?

☐ (a) 68 mm
☐ (b) 58 mm
☐ (c) 48 mm
☐ (d) 41 mm
☐ (e) 6.2 cm

6 The length of a grasshopper's jump is 25.87 cm. Convert this measurement to millimetres.

☐ (a) 259 mm
☐ (b) 258.7 mm
☐ (c) 257.8 mm
☐ (d) 256 mm
☐ (e) 25.87 mm

7 The distance travelled by a fox chasing a hen is 1267 cm. Convert this measurement to metres.

☐ (a) 12.67 m
☐ (b) 12.7 m
☐ (c) 12.76 m
☐ (d) 1.267 m
☐ (e) 126.7 m

8 A hippopotamus weighs 4560 kg. Convert this measurement to tonnes.

☐ (a) 0.456 tonnes
☐ (b) 4.56 tonnes
☐ (c) 4.65 tonnes
☐ (d) 45.6 tonnes
☐ (e) 456 tonnes

9 A naval ship is 60 500 cm long. Convert this measurement to kilometres.

☐ (a) 6050 km
☐ (b) 605 km
☐ (c) 60.5 km
☐ (d) 6.05 km
☐ (e) 0.605 km

10 A frog jumps 34 cm. If it repeats this five times, how many metres has the frog travelled?

☐ (a) 0.017 m
☐ (b) 0.17 m
☐ (c) 1.7 m
☐ (d) 17 m
☐ (e) 170 m

11 A flea can jump 45 mm. How many jumps does he have to do to reach a total distance of 9 m?

☐ (a) 20
☐ (b) 200
☐ (c) 450
☐ (d) 900
☐ (e) 2000

12 A fish tank holds 45 000 ml of water. How much is this in litres?

☐ (a) 0.45 litres
☐ (b) 4.5 litres
☐ (c) 45 litres
☐ (d) 450 litres
☐ (e) 4500 litres

13 A postman's sack weighs 45 360 g. Convert this measurement to kilograms.

☐ (a) 4.536 kg
☐ (b) 45.36 kg
☐ (c) 46.53 kg
☐ (d) 453.6 kg
☐ (e) 4536 kg

14 A teacher fills his stationery cupboard with four boxes of pencils, each weighing 750 g. How many kilograms is this in total?

☐ (a) 0.3 kg
☐ (b) 0.75 kg
☐ (c) 3 kg
☐ (d) 30 kg
☐ (e) 300 kg

15 A baby crab weighs 650 g, and its mother weighs 1.43 kg. What is their difference in weight?

☐ (a) 780 g
☐ (b) 507 g
☐ (c) 0.88 kg
☐ (d) 1.365 kg
☐ (e) 648.57 kg

16 A firm's television advert lasts 28 seconds. If it is shown 20 times, how many minutes and seconds of advertising time will the firm have to pay for?

☐ (a) 9.3 minutes
☐ (b) 9.2 minutes
☐ (c) 9 minutes 2 seconds
☐ (d) 9 minutes 20 seconds
☐ (e) 560 seconds

17 One turn of a fishing reel extends a fishing line by 10.6 cm. If it takes 100 turns to extend this line fully, how long is the line? Give the answer in metres.

☐ (a) 10.6 m
☐ (b) 106 cm
☐ (c) 106 m
☐ (d) 1060 m
☐ (e) 1060 cm

18 A bridge over a river is 300 m long. If 1 foot is equivalent to 0.30 m, how long is the bridge? Give the answer in feet.

☐ (a) 100 feet
☐ (b) 300 feet
☐ (c) 900 feet
☐ (d) 1000 feet
☐ (e) 3000 feet

19 An iceberg has its tip emerging 6 m above seawater. If 1 m is equivalent to 3.3 feet, how far above seawater is the tip of the iceberg emerged? Give the answer in feet.

☐ (a) 1.8 feet
☐ (b) 3.3 feet
☐ (c) 9.3 feet
☐ (d) 19.8 feet
☐ (e) 33 feet

20 The wingspan of an eagle is 95 cm. If 1 m equals 3.3 feet, convert the wingspan to feet.

☐ (a) 313.5 feet
☐ (b) 31.35 feet
☐ (c) 3.3 feet
☐ (d) 3.135 feet
☐ (e) 3 feet

21 A water mill churns water at a rate of 700 000 cm³ per minute. If 1000 cm³ is equivalent to 1 litre, convert this rate to litres/minutes.

☐ (a) 7 litres/minute
☐ (b) 70 litres/minute
☐ (c) 700 litres/minute
☐ (d) 1000 litres/minute
☐ (e) 6000 litres/minute

22 A cow produces 5 gallons of milk. If 1 gallon equals 8 pints, how many pints are produced?

☐ (a) 10 pints
☐ (b) 40 pints
☐ (c) 13 pints
☐ (d) 8 pints
☐ (e) 5 pints

23 The length of the hour hand on a watch is 0.5 inches. If 1 inch is equivalent to 25.4 mm, how many millimetres is the hour hand?

☐ (a) 1.27 mm
☐ (b) 12.7 mm
☐ (c) 20.4 mm
☐ (d) 24.9 mm
☐ (e) 25.4 mm

24 A goldfish bowl has 3 litres of water in it. If 1 gallon equals to 4.55 litres, how many gallons is this? Give the answer correct to 2 d.p.

☐ (a) 0.22 gallons
☐ (b) 0.66 gallons
☐ (c) 0.67 gallons
☐ (d) 4.55 gallons
☐ (e) 12 gallons

25 Chips fry in a pan with 400 ml of oil. If 1.76 pints equals 1 litre, how much is this in pints?

☐ (a) 0.176 pints
☐ (b) 0.5 pints
☐ (c) 0.704 pints
☐ (d) 0.8 pints
☐ (e) 1 pint

26 A doll weighs 6 oz. If 1 oz equals 28 g approximately, how many grams does the doll weigh?

☐ (a) 4.67 g
☐ (b) 28 g
☐ (c) 168 g
☐ (d) 466 g
☐ (e) 467 g

27 A car travels 160 miles and uses 5 gallons of petrol. On average, how many miles to the gallon does the car do?

☐ (a) 3.2 miles/gallon
☐ (b) 16 miles/gallon
☐ (c) 32 miles/gallon
☐ (d) 155 miles/gallon

☐ (e) 320 miles/gallon

28 A matchstick weighs 1.2 g. How many matchsticks are there in a box weighing 0.6 kg?

☐ (a) 2
☐ (b) 20
☐ (c) 50
☐ (d) 500
☐ (e) 5000

29 A swimming pool is 50 m long. How many lengths would be swum in a 25 km race?

☐ (a) 2
☐ (b) 5
☐ (c) 20
☐ (d) 200
☐ (e) 500

30 A watering can weighs 4560 g with water in it and 1.1 kg when empty. What is the weight of the water in the watering can?

☐ (a) 3.46 g
☐ (b) 346 g
☐ (c) 3460 g
☐ (d) 4558.9 g
☐ (e) 34.6 kg

31 It takes 20 minutes to cook 500 g of chicken. How long will it take to cook 2.75 kg of chicken?

☐ (a) 110 minutes
☐ (b) 100 minutes
☐ (c) 90 minutes
☐ (d) 55 minutes
☐ (e) 27 minutes

32 Approximately how many litres are there in one gallon?

☐ (a) 2.2 litres
☐ (b) 2 litres
☐ (c) 4.5 litres
☐ (d) 8 litres
☐ (e) 2.5 litres

33 A man's stride is about 1 m long. 3 feet = 1 yard. A metre is approximately how many feet?

☐ (a) 1.5
☐ (b) 2
☐ (c) 4
☐ (d) 3
☐ (e) 2.5

34 The length of a ruler is 12 inches or 1 foot. Approximately how many centimetres is this?

☐ (a) 40

☐ (b) 20
☐ (c) 25
☐ (d) 35
☐ (e) 30

35 Sally has an average pace length of 75 cm. How many paces has she taken when she has walked a distance of 1.5 km?

☐ (a) 2000
☐ (b) 20 000
☐ (c) 200
☐ (d) 20
☐ (e) 200 000

36 The Jones family went to Scotland for their holidays. They travelled a distance of about 560 km from their home. What distance is this in miles (8 km is approximately equal to 5 miles)?

☐ (a) 450 miles
☐ (b) 900 miles
☐ (c) 200 miles
☐ (d) 350 miles
☐ (e) 1100 miles

37 In the fridge is a litre bottle of cola. Navin pours out five cups of cola from the bottle. Each cup holds 175 ml. How much is left in the bottle?

☐ (a) 9125 ml
☐ (b) 125 ml
☐ (c) 25 ml
☐ (d) 1025 ml
☐ (e) 875 ml

38 Paul is flying to Hong Kong for his holidays. His luggage allowance is 30 kg. How much is this approximately, in pounds?

☐ (a) 90 lbs
☐ (b) 45 lbs
☐ (c) 15 lbs
☐ (d) 60 lbs
☐ (e) 66 lbs

39 Sian travelled from London to Birmingham by bus. The journey took 1 hour 48 minutes. The bus left at 10:38. What was the time of arrival?

☐ (a) 08:50
☐ (b) 11:86
☐ (c) 12:26
☐ (d) 11:26
☐ (e) 09:50

40 39 inches is approximately equal to 1 metre. 12 inches is 1 foot. How tall, in metres, is a man who is 6 feet 4 inches?

☐ (a) 2 m
☐ (b) 1.64 m
☐ (c) 1.85 m
☐ (d) 1.95 m
☐ (e) 2.05 m

41 The diagram below shows the reading on three scales. What are the readings of A, B, and C respectively?

☐ (a) 8.75, 165, 7.75
☐ (b) 8.65, 162.5, 7.75
☐ (c) 8.75, 162.5, 6.5
☐ (d) 8.65, 162.5, 6.75
☐ (e) 8.65, 170, 6.75

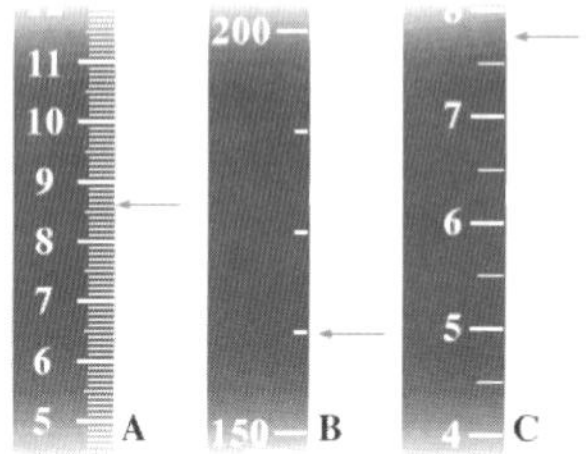

Q41

42 Sally's fastest running speed is 10m/s. What is this speed in km/h?

☐ (a) 60 km/h
☐ (b) 36 km/h
☐ (c) 10 km/h
☐ (d) 27.8 km/h
☐ (e) 16.7 km/h

43 A piece of gold, which has a volume of 12 cm³ weighs 231.6 g. A second piece of gold weighs 328.1 g. What is the volume of the second piece of gold?

☐ (a) 27.3 cm³
☐ (b) 19.3 cm³
☐ (c) 8.5 cm³
☐ (d) 17 cm³
☐ (e) 8 cm³

44 Which of the following could not be used to calculate an area?

☐ (a) $2\pi rl$
☐ (b) $\pi rd/3$
☐ (c) $\pi r^2(l+d)$
☐ (d) $\pi d^2/4$
☐ (e) $4\pi r^2$

QUESTIONS

Higher Level only

45 Which of the following expressions can be used to calculate the perimeter of a shape? The letters r and h represent lengths. π, 2, and 3 are numbers, which have no dimensions.

☐ (a) $r(\pi + 2)$
☐ (b) $r(r + rh)$
☐ (c) $rh/2$
☐ (d) $\frac{2}{3}\pi r^3$
☐ (e) $2\pi r^3$

46 Which of the following expressions can be used to calculate the perimeter of a shape? The letters h, a, b, and c represent lengths. ½, 2, and 4 are numbers, which have no dimensions.

☐ (a) $\frac{1}{2}(a + b)h$
☐ (b) $4(a + b + c)$
☐ (c) $2ab + 2bc + 2ac$
☐ (d) abc
☐ (e) $ab + ch$

47 The following diagram shows a kite. Which of the following could be an expression for the area?

☐ (a) $a^3 + b^3$
☐ (b) $2a + 2b$
☐ (c) $a(a^2 + b^2)$
☐ (d) $b(a^2 + b^2)$
☐ (e) $ab/2$

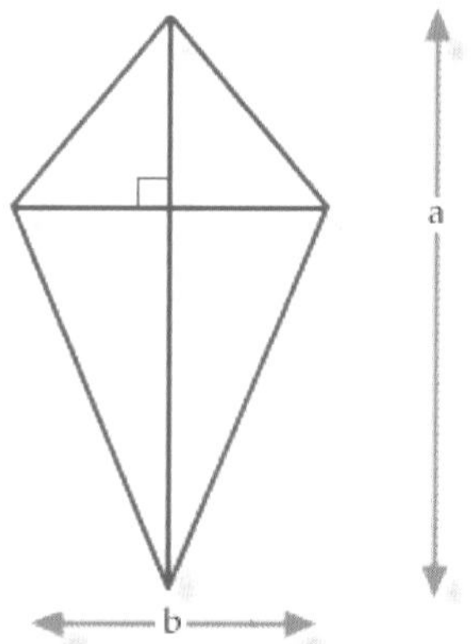

Q47

48 Which of the following expressions could be used to calculate the volume of a pencil?

☐ (a) $2rh + rd$
☐ (b) $\pi r^2 h + \pi r^2 d/3$
☐ (c) $\pi rd/3 + \pi rh$
☐ (d) $2\pi rh + \pi r^2$
☐ (e) $2r + 2h + 2\sqrt{3}d$

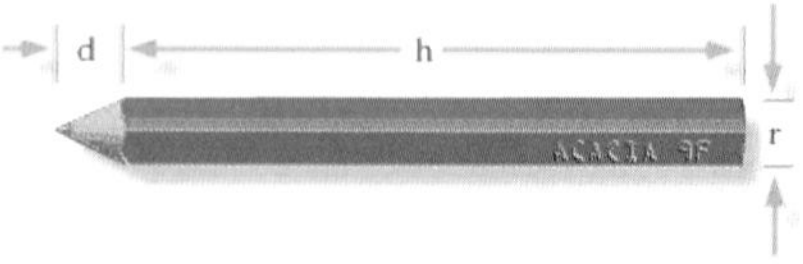

Q48

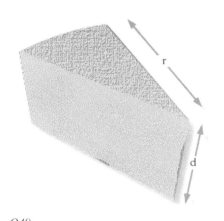

Q49

49 The diagram above shows a piece of cheese. Which of the following could be an expression for the volume?

- ☐ (a) $\frac{\pi r}{6} + 2d$
- ☐ (b) $\frac{\pi r^2 d}{6}$
- ☐ (c) $\frac{\pi r d}{6}$
- ☐ (d) $2rd + \frac{\pi r^2}{3} + \frac{\pi r d}{3}$
- ☐ (e) $3d + 4r + \frac{\pi r}{6}$

50 The following diagram shows a piece of cheese. Which of the following could be an expression for the surface area?

- ☐ (a) $2hr + \frac{\pi r^2}{4} + \frac{\pi r h}{4}$
- ☐ (b) $\frac{\pi r^2 h}{8} + \frac{\pi r h}{4}$

- ☐ (c) $\frac{rh}{4} + rh^2$
- ☐ (d) $3h + 4r + \frac{\pi r}{2}$
- ☐ (e) $\frac{\pi r^2 h}{8}$

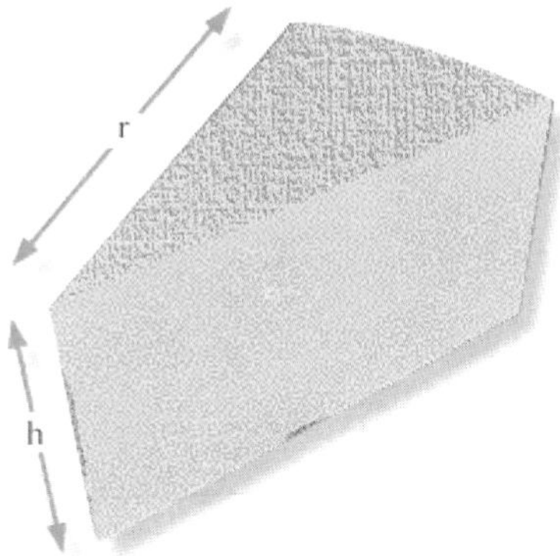

Q50

51 A piece of polystyrene is used for packing around glasses. Which of the following could be used to calculate the volume of polystyrene?

- ☐ (a) $\pi l(R + r)$
- ☐ (b) $\frac{\pi(R + r)(R - r)}{2}$
- ☐ (c) $\pi R l + \pi r l + 2(R - r)$
- ☐ (d) $2(R - r)$
- ☐ (e) $\frac{\pi(R^2 - r^2)l}{2}$

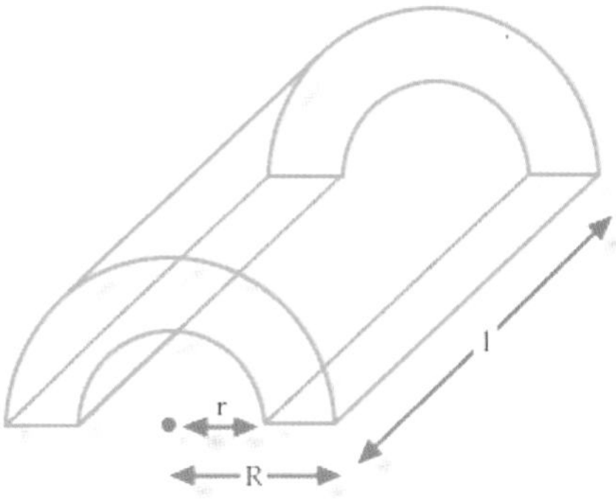

Q51

52 A square quadrangle has sides of 43 m, correct to the nearest metre. Calculate, to the nearest whole number, the lower bound of the area of the quadrangle.

- ☐ (a) 1811 m²
- ☐ (b) 1840 m²
- ☐ (c) 1806 m²
- ☐ (d) 1849 m²
- ☐ (e) 41850 m²

Discrete and continuous measure

 KEY FACTS

- Quantities can be discrete (countable) or continuous (measurable).

- When a continuous quantity is constrained, by the accuracy of the measuring instrument, to the nearest whole number (e.g. time measured as 16 seconds, to the nearest second), the range of possible times is half a second either side of the time stated (i.e. 15.5 to 16.5 seconds).

- In reading scales, care must be taken to identify what each division on the scale stands for.

 QUESTIONS

1 A 100 m running track is guaranteed to be accurate to the nearest half metre. Its length is therefore somewhere between 99.5 m

and 100.5 m. Is this statement true or false?

- ☐ (a) True
- ☐ (b) False

2 "The digital clock at a station gives the time in hours and minutes and is known to be accurate to the nearest second. You can therefore be certain that the time it shows is right to the nearest minute." Is this statement true or false?

- ☐ (a) True
- ☐ (b) False

3 "1 m³ = 1 000 000 cm³." Is this statement true or false?

- ☐ (a) True
- ☐ (b) False

4 "1 m² = 100 cm²." Is this statement true or false?

- ☐ (a) True
- ☐ (b) False

5 A newspaper company estimated that during the previous 10 years it had employed 1200 people. If this figure is correct to the nearest 10, find the least number of people that could have been employed by the company in this time.

- ☐ (a) 1150
- ☐ (b) 1195
- ☐ (c) 1200
- ☐ (d) 1190
- ☐ (e) 1199

6 The length of a pencil is given as 173 mm, correct to the nearest millimetre. The length of the pencil lies between:

- ☐ (a) 172 mm and 174 mm
- ☐ (b) 172.5 mm and 173.5 mm
- ☐ (c) 172.75 mm and 173.25 mm
- ☐ (d) 163 mm and 178 mm
- ☐ (e) 172.5 mm and 173.4 mm

7 The number of schoolboys in a town is 4500, correct to the nearest 100. What is the least number of schoolboys?

☐ (a) 4495
☐ (b) 4490
☐ (c) 4450
☐ (d) 4401
☐ (e) 4499

8 Tom competes in a jet-ski race. His completion time is 13.4 seconds to the nearest 0.1 seconds. What is the shortest possible time in which he completed the race?

☐ (a) 13.345 seconds
☐ (b) 13.39 seconds
☐ (c) 13.349 seconds
☐ (d) 13.35 seconds
☐ (e) 13.395 seconds

9 The length of the straight section of a running track is 122 m, correct to the nearest centimetre. What is the smallest possible length of the track?

☐ (a) 121.995 m
☐ (b) 121.5 m
☐ (c) 121.8 m
☐ (d) 121.95 m
☐ (e) 121.9 m

10 The label on a pack of tomatoes in a supermarket gives the mass as 1.7 kg. This measurement is correct to the nearest tenth of a kilogram. Between what limits does the mass lie?

☐ (a) 1.69 kg and 1.71 kg
☐ (b) 1.65 kg and 1.75 kg
☐ (c) 1.695 kg and 1.745 kg
☐ (d) 1.699 kg and 1.749 kg
☐ (e) 1.645 kg and 1.755 kg

11 The length of a wall is 5.73 m correct to 2 d.p. Between what limits does the length of the wall lie?

☐ (a) 5.7299 m and 5.7349 m
☐ (b) 5.729 m and 5.731 m
☐ (c) 5.7251 m and 5.749 m
☐ (d) 5.7295 m and 5.730 m
☐ (e) 5.725 m and 5.735 m

12 A rectangular room measures 6.2 m by 4.6 m, each length being correct to the nearest tenth of a metre. Find the least possible length of the perimeter of the room.

☐ (a) 21.38 m
☐ (b) 24.56 m
☐ (c) 21.58 m
☐ (d) 21.4 m
☐ (e) 21.398 m

13 Five packages are weighed, each correct to the nearest gram. Their weights are 325 g, 407 g, 494 g, 509 g, and 362 g. Find the upper bound for the total weight of the parcels.

☐ (a) 2097 g
☐ (b) 2097.5 g
☐ (c) 2099.5 g
☐ (d) 2099.25 g
☐ (e) 2099 g

14 The average daily rainfall for a month of 30 days was given as 0.48 cm, to the nearest 0.01 cm. What is the lower bound for the total rainfall for the month?

☐ (a) 14.25 cm
☐ (b) 14.55 cm
☐ (c) 14.4 cm
☐ (d) 14.1 cm
☐ (e) 14.265 cm

15 Tom is on a diet. His weight at the beginning of a three-month period is 101.823 kg, correct to the nearest gram. At the end of that time his weight is recorded as 93.168 kg, correct to the nearest gram. What is the maximum amount of weight that he could have lost?

☐ (a) 8.6548 kg
☐ (b) 8.656 kg
☐ (c) 8.655 kg
☐ (d) 8.6596 kg
☐ (e) 8.654 kg

16 A metal cube of edge 16 cm is melted down and formed into a solid in the shape of a cone of vertical height 21 cm. Calculate the radius of the base of the cone. Give the answer correct to 1 d.p.

☐ (a) 3.4 cm
☐ (b) 27.3 cm
☐ (c) 7.9 cm
☐ (d) 13.6 cm
☐ (e) 15.7 cm

Q16

Higher Level only

17 The two sides of a rectangle measure 7.6 cm and 3.3 cm each correct to the nearest millimetre. Find the upper bound for the area of the rectangle, giving the answer correct to 1 d.p.

☐ (a) 25.6 cm²
☐ (b) 25.3 cm²
☐ (c) 25.5 cm²
☐ (d) 26.1 cm²
☐ (e) 25.4 cm²

18 Sally is trying to find the height of a tower. She is standing 60 m (correct to the nearest metre) away from the base of the tower. Her height is 1.74 m, correct to 2 d.p. and the angle of elevation of the top of the tower is 17°, correct to the nearest degree. Calculate the lower bound for her answer, giving the answer correct to 2 d.p.

☐ (a) 19.36 m
☐ (b) 18.03 m
☐ (c) 20.08 m
☐ (d) 21.82 m
☐ (e) 20.82 m

19 The area of a rectangle is 34 cm² correct to the nearest cm². The length of the rectangle is 7.8 cm (to the nearest millimetre). Find the largest possible value of the width of the rectangle, giving the answer correct to 3 s.f.

☐ (a) 4.27 cm
☐ (b) 4.32 cm
☐ (c) 4.36 cm
☐ (d) 4.45 cm
☐ (e) 4.39 cm

20 The volume of a cylinder is 600 cm³ correct to the nearest cm³. The radius is 7.2 cm correct to the nearest millimetre. Calculate the smallest possible value of the height of the cylinder, giving the answer correct to 1 d.p.

☐ (a) 3.8 cm
☐ (b) 3.5 cm
☐ (c) 4303.7 cm
☐ (d) 3.9 cm
☐ (e) 3.6 cm

21 The radius of a sphere is 5.8 cm correct to the nearest millimetre. Find firstly the upper, and secondly, the lower limits of the volume of the sphere, giving the answers correct to 1 d.p. (In your calculations use the full calculator value for π.)

- [ ] (a) 38.6 cm^3 and 817.3 cm^3
- [ ] (b) 817.3 cm^3 and 796.3 cm^3
- [ ] (c) 834.3 cm^3 and 796.3 cm^3
- [ ] (d) 834.3 cm^3 and 800.5 cm^3
- [ ] (e) 838.6 cm^3 and 796.3 cm^3

22 Mr Jones fills his car with petrol. The capacity of the tank is 42.5 litres, correct to the nearest 0.1 litre. He drives a distance of 890 km (to the nearest 10 km) before the car runs out of petrol. Calculate the greatest possible number of kilometres to litres at which the car uses petrol (1 d.p.).

- [ ] (a) 21.1 km/l
- [ ] (b) 21.0 km/l
- [ ] (c) 4320.8 km/l
- [ ] (d) 21.4 km/l
- [ ] (e) 21.2 km/l

Compound measures

KEY FACTS

- By combining some standard units other (compound) measures can be obtained. For example, speed = $distance/time$, which could be measured in metres per second (m/s), or kilometres per hour (km/h).

- Density = $mass/volume$, which could be measured in kg per m^3 (kg/m^3) or g per cm^3 (g/cm^3).

- Rate of flow of liquid could be measured in litres per second (l/s) or m^3 per hour (m^3/h).

QUESTIONS

1 A speed of 18km/h is equivalent to 5m/s. Is this statement true or false?

- [ ] (a) True
- [ ] (b) False

2 A piece of cheese has a mass of 800 g. It has a volume of 125 cm^3. What is the density, given that the density = $mass/volume$?

- [ ] (a) 6.4 cm/g^3
- [ ] (b) 6.4 g/cm^3
- [ ] (c) 64 g/cm^3
- [ ] (d) 100 g/cm^3
- [ ] (e) 116 g/cm^3

3 The density of the glass in a glass wine decanter is 8.5 g/cm^3. If the volume of glass in the decanter is 120 cm^3, what is its mass?

- [ ] (a) 14.1 g
- [ ] (b) 1020 g
- [ ] (c) 1040 g
- [ ] (d) 14.1 kg
- [ ] (e) 1020 kg

4 A bread cutting board has a mass of 800 g and has a volume of 600 cm^3. What is its density, given

that density = $mass/volume$? Give the answer correct to 1 d.p.

- [ ] (a) 1.3 g
- [ ] (b) 1.3 cm^3
- [ ] (c) 0.75 g/cm^3
- [ ] (d) 1.3 g/cm^3
- [ ] (e) 48 000 g/cm^3

5 A statue is made from clay with density 1.4 g/cm. If it weighs 4 kg, what is its volume, given that density = $mass/volume$? Give the answer correct to 1 d.p.

- [ ] (a) 2857.1 cm^3
- [ ] (b) 2857.1 m^3
- [ ] (c) 2.86 cm^3
- [ ] (d) 2888.2 cm^3
- [ ] (e) 5.6 cm^3

6 The density of cork is 0.25 g/cm^3. Calculate the mass from a volume of 40 cm^3.

- [ ] (a) 10 g
- [ ] (b) 160 g
- [ ] (c) 1000 g
- [ ] (d) 1.01 kg
- [ ] (e) 10 kg

7 A tortoise moves at 25 cm/min. Convert this to metres/hour.

- [ ] (a) 0.15 metres/hour
- [ ] (b) 0.25 metres/hour
- [ ] (c) 0.25 metres/hour
- [ ] (d) 1.5 metres/hour
- [ ] (e) 15 metres/hour

8 A car travelled 200 km in 2½ hours. What was its average speed?

- [ ] (a) 0.125 km/h
- [ ] (b) 8 km/h
- [ ] (c) 80 km/h
- [ ] (d) 125 km/h
- [ ] (e) 500 km/h

9 A kangaroo hopped 3 km in 48 minutes. What was its average speed in metres/min?

- [ ] (a) 0.0625 metres/min
- [ ] (b) 3.75 metres/min
- [ ] (c) 62.5 metres/min
- [ ] (d) 625 metres/min
- [ ] (e) 3750 metres/min

10 A lion chases buffalo at a speed of 50 km/h for 1 minute. How far does he go? Give the answer correct to 2 s.f.

- [ ] (a) 0.83 km
- [ ] (b) 5 km
- [ ] (c) 8.3 km
- [ ] (d) 50 km
- [ ] (e) 300 km

11 A snake crosses a room of width 5 m in 30 seconds. Which one of the following correctly represents its speed?

- [ ] (a) 10 m/s
- [ ] (b) 10 m/min
- [ ] (c) 166 m/min
- [ ] (d) 166 m/s
- [ ] (e) 150 m/s

12 An eagle dives to catch a rabbit. It takes the eagle 3 seconds to catch the rabbit at a speed of 15 m/s. How far does it dive?

- [ ] (a) 5 m
- [ ] (b) 45 m
- [ ] (c) 50 m
- [ ] (d) 450 m
- [ ] (e) 450 cm

13 A prince gallops to the rescue of a princess in distress. He travels on horseback at 30 km/h for 20 minutes. How far does he go?

- [ ] (a) 30 km
- [ ] (b) 20 km
- [ ] (c) 50 m
- [ ] (d) 10 km
- [ ] (e) 6 km

14 A mountain rescue helicopter left its base at 11:00 hours and reached the accident at 11:15 hours. Its

85

average speed was 140 km/h. How far did it fly?

- (a) 15 km
- (b) 21 km
- (c) 35 km
- (d) 40 km
- (e) 140 km

15 A downhill skier has an average speed of 15 m/s. If a downhill slope is 500 m long, how long does it take the skier to ski down the slope? Give the answer correct to 3 s.f.

- (a) 3 seconds
- (b) 33.3 seconds
- (c) 75 seconds
- (d) 333.1 seconds
- (e) 7500 seconds

16 The Apollo manned flight reached a speed of 24 790 mph. How many miles would the Apollo have travelled in a day?

- (a) 24 790 miles
- (b) 596 940 miles
- (c) 594 960 miles
- (d) 594 969 miles
- (e) 1032.9 miles

17 A car goes at an average speed of 54 mph on the M1. How long does it take to travel a distance of 81 miles?

- (a) 40 minutes
- (b) 1 hour 30 minutes
- (c) 30 minutes
- (d) 1 hour 50 minutes
- (e) 1 hour 7 minutes

18 Thomas set off in his car at 9:00 am. He travelled a distance of 150 miles, arriving at noon. What was his average speed?

- (a) 75 mph
- (b) 50 mph
- (c) 37.5 mph
- (d) 45 mph
- (e) 25 mph

19 A coach manages 40 miles to the gallon, when it is travelling at 50 mph along the motorway. The coach travels for 4 hours at 50 mph. How many gallons of petrol does it use?

- (a) 10 gallons
- (b) 4 gallons
- (c) 3.2 gallons
- (d) 8 gallons
- (e) 5 gallons

20 A bus travels between two towns, which are 19 km apart. The journey usually takes 24 minutes. What is the average speed of the bus in km/h?

- (a) 47.5 km/h
- (b) 79 km/h
- (c) 7.6 km/h
- (d) 4.56 km/h
- (e) 45.6 km/h

21 Paul jogs 12 km in 1 hour 24 minutes. What is his average speed in km/h (correct to 1 d.p.)?

- (a) 14.9 km/h
- (b) 16.8 km/h
- (c) 9.7 km/h
- (d) 8.6 km/h
- (e) 10.3 km/h

QUESTIONS

Higher Level only

22 Two go-carts race each other over a distance of 580 km. The first cart has an average speed of 145 km/h, and the second one has an average speed of 124 km/h. By how many kilometres does the first one win?

- (a) 84 km
- (b) 21 km
- (c) 98.2 km
- (d) 31 km
- (e) 27.6 km

23 The density of cork is 0.23g/cm^3. The mass of a piece of cork is 172.5 g. Find the volume of the piece of cork.

- (a) 75 cm^3
- (b) 396.75 cm^3
- (c) 750 cm^3
- (d) 1.333 cm^3
- (e) 133 cm^3

24 A car travels at 65km/h for 7 hours and then at 85 km/h for 5 hours. Calculate the average speed for the whole journey, giving the answer to 1 d.p.

- (a) 76.7 km/h
- (b) 75.0 km/h
- (c) 73.3 km/h
- (d) 52.6 km/h
- (e) 75.9 km/h

Perimeter, area, and volume

KEY FACTS

• The perimeter of a shape is the distance round its outside.

• The area of a shape is the number of square units that it encloses.

• The volume of a solid shape is the number of cubic units that it contains.

• For a triangle, area = ½(base) × (perpendicular height).

• For a rectangle, area = length × width.

• For a parallelogram, area = (base) × (perpendicular height).

• For a trapezium, area = ½(sum of parallel sides) × (perpendicular distance between them).

• For a rhombus, area = ½(one diagonal × other diagonal).

• For a circle, circumference (perimeter) = 2 × π × radius.

• For a circle, area = π × (radius)(radius) or π × (radius)^2.

• For a cuboid, volume = length × width × height.

• For a prism, volume = (area of cross-section) × (length). Hence, volume of a cylinder = π × (radius)^2 × (length).

• For a sector of a circle of angle x, arc length = (^{x}⁄$_{360}$) × circumference of circle, and area of sector = (^{x}⁄$_{360}$) × area of circle.

• For two similar shapes, with enlargement scale factor k, then area scale factor = k^2 and volume scale factor = k^3.

QUESTIONS

1 "If a, b, and c are lengths, then (ab + bc + ac) could be the formula for an area." Is this statement true or false?

☐ (a) True
☐ (b) False

2 "The following diagram shows a cubical water tank of side 1 m. Ten rectangular bricks, each 5 cm × 10 cm × 20 cm, are immersed in the water. The water level rises 1 cm." Is this statement true or false?

☐ (a) True
☐ (b) False

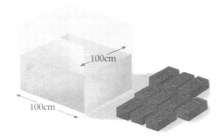

Q2

3 "The tea packet in the diagram below has a volume in cubic cm numerically equal to its surface area in square cm." Is this statement true or false?

☐ (a) True
☐ (b) False

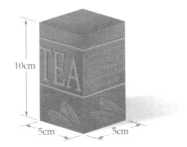

Q3

4 "Tom has a set of identical cubical bricks and, using all the bricks, has built a rectangular tower 24 bricks high, six bricks wide, and four bricks deep, as shown in the following diagram. He decides to rearrange the bricks and, again using all the bricks, builds instead a rectangular block on a square base that is nine bricks high. The base of the block is eight bricks wide." Is this statement true or false?

☐ (a) True
☐ (b) False

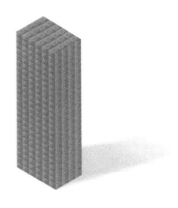

Q4

5 The diagram below shows a section of a worktop. Which of the following could be an expression for the volume?

☐ (a) 2h + 6r + πr
☐ (b) 6r + πr
☐ (c) 4r^2 + $^{πr^2}$⁄$_2$
☐ (d) 4r^{2}h + $^{πr^2h}$⁄$_2$
☐ (e) 4rh

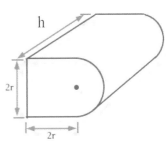

Q5, Q6, Q7

6 The diagram above shows a section of a worktop. Which of the following could be an expression for the area of the cross-section?

☐ (a) 4r^{2}h + $^{πr^2h}$⁄$_2$
☐ (b) 4r^2 + $^{πr^2}$⁄$_2$
☐ (c) 2h + 6r + πr
☐ (d) 4r^{2}h
☐ (e) 6r + πr

7 The diagram above shows a section of a worktop. Which of the following could be an expression for the perimeter of the front surface?

☐ (a) 4r^{2}h + $^{πr^2h}$⁄$_2$
☐ (b) 4r^2
☐ (c) 4r^2 + $^{πr^2}$⁄$_2$
☐ (d) 4rh
☐ (e) 6r + πr

8 Find the perimeter and area of the following shape.

☐ (a) 16 cm and 8 cm^2

- ☐ (b) 8 cm and 15 cm²
- ☐ (c) 16 cm and 15 cm²
- ☐ (d) 10 cm and 8 cm²
- ☐ (e) 15 cm and 15 cm²

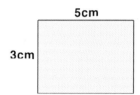

Q8

9 Find the perimeter of the L-shape shown below.

- ☐ (a) 44 cm
- ☐ (b) 50 cm
- ☐ (c) 28 cm
- ☐ (d) 40 cm
- ☐ (e) 60 cm

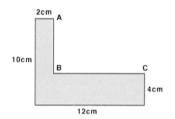

Q9

10 Find the perimeter of the T-shape shown below.

- ☐ (a) 13 m
- ☐ (b) 14.5 m
- ☐ (c) 20 m
- ☐ (d) 10 m
- ☐ (e) 12.75 m

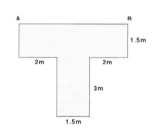

Q10

11 The following diagram shows two shapes. Find the area of shapes A and B respectively.

- ☐ (a) 64 cm², 54 cm²
- ☐ (b) 32 cm², 54 cm²
- ☐ (c) 24 cm², 36 cm²
- ☐ (d) 32 cm², 36 cm²
- ☐ (e) 64 cm², 27 cm²

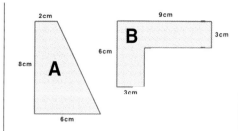

Q11

12 Find the area of the shape shown in the diagram below.

- ☐ (a) 72 cm²
- ☐ (b) 120 cm²
- ☐ (c) 84 cm²
- ☐ (d) 128 cm²
- ☐ (e) 96 cm²

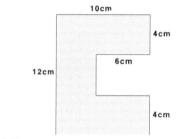

Q12

13 Find the area (to 1 d.p.) of the circle shown in the following diagram.

- ☐ (a) 15.7 cm²
- ☐ (b) 31.4 cm²
- ☐ (c) 39.3 cm²
- ☐ (d) 78.5 cm²
- ☐ (e) 157.1 cm²

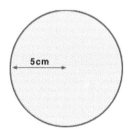

Q13

14 Find the circumference, (to 1 d.p.) of the circle shown in the following diagram.

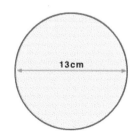

Q14

- ☐ (a) 265.5 cm
- ☐ (b) 20.4 cm
- ☐ (c) 40.8 cm
- ☐ (d) 132.7 cm
- ☐ (e) 66.4 cm

15 Find the circumference, (to 1 d.p.), of the circle shown in the following diagram.

- ☐ (a) 17.3 cm
- ☐ (b) 95.0 cm
- ☐ (c) 190.1 cm
- ☐ (d) 34.6 cm
- ☐ (e) 47.5 cm

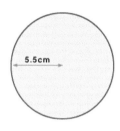

Q15

16 The diagram below shows a running track, which has two straight sections of 150 m. The ends of the track are semicircles, which have a diameter of 50 m. Find the perimeter, (to 1 d.p.), of the track.

- ☐ (a) 614.2 m
- ☐ (b) 400 m
- ☐ (c) 457.1 m
- ☐ (d) 378.5 m
- ☐ (e) 1281.7 m

Q16

17 Find the area of the parallelogram shown in the following diagram.

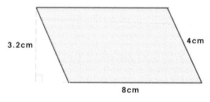

Q17

- ☐ (a) 25.6 cm²
- ☐ (b) 24 cm²

☐ (c) 12.8 cm²
☐ (d) 32 cm²
☐ (e) 51.2 cm²

18 A circus ring has a radius of 35 m. What is the circumference (to 1 d.p.) of the ring?

☐ (a) 438.8 m
☐ (b) 110 m
☐ (c) 1924.2 m
☐ (d) 240.5 m
☐ (e) 219.9 m

19 Mr Jolly is digging a hole in his garden in order to make a circular fish pond. He wants the area of the pond to be 20 m². What should the radius (to 1 d.p.) of the hole be?

☐ (a) 2.5 m
☐ (b) 3.2 m
☐ (c) 4.2 m
☐ (d) 5 m
☐ (e) 6.4 m

20 A farmer has 30 m of wire netting. He wants to make a circular enclosure to keep his hens in. What diameter (to 1 d.p.) should the enclosure have, if he intends to use up all of the wire?

☐ (a) 4.8 m
☐ (b) 9.5 m
☐ (c) 3.1 m
☐ (d) 4.4 m
☐ (e) 6.2 m

21 A goat is tethered by a 20 m chain to one corner of a rectangular field. The field measures 30 m by 50 m. Find the area of grass, over which the goat can graze. Give the answer correct to 1 d.p.

☐ (a) 714 m²
☐ (b) 314.2 m²
☐ (c) 157.1 m²
☐ (d) 628.3 m²
☐ (e) 1256.6 m²

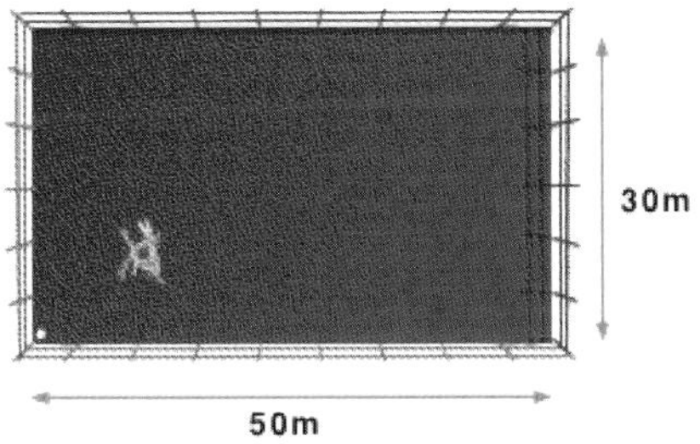

Q21

22 The following diagram shows a triangular prism. Find the area of the net of the prism.

☐ (a) 150 cm²
☐ (b) 144 cm²
☐ (c) 164 cm²
☐ (d) 156 cm²
☐ (e) 360 cm²

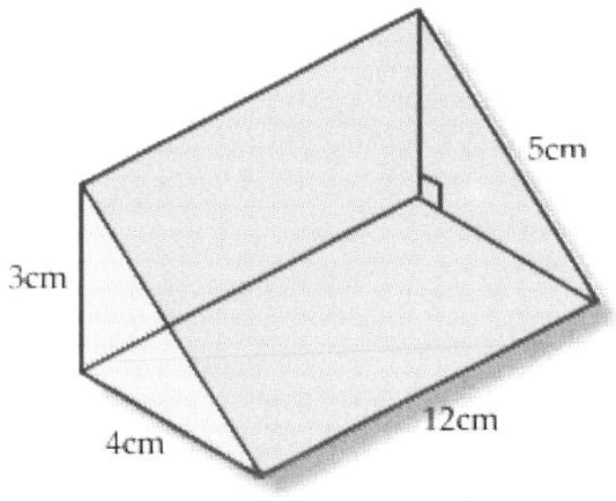

Q22

23 Find the area of the shape shown in the following diagram. Give the answer correct to 2 d.p.

☐ (a) 38.03 m²
☐ (b) 22.95 m²
☐ (c) 27.97 m²
☐ (d) 25.96 m²
☐ (e) 50.09 m²

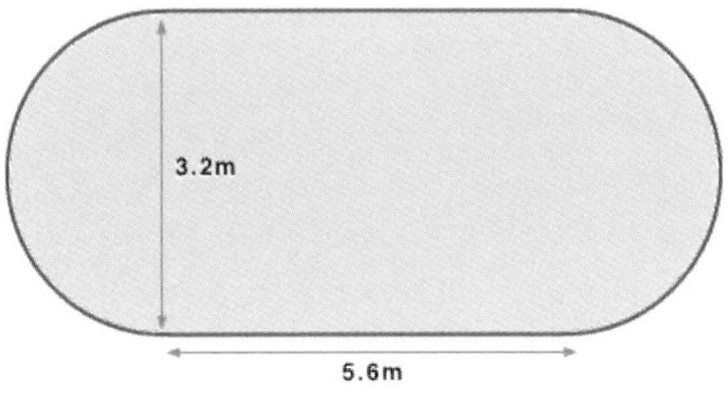

Q23

24 The diagram below shows rhombus ABCD. AC = 16 cm. BD = 12 cm. Find the area of the rhombus.

☐ (a) 24 cm²
☐ (b) 192 cm²
☐ (c) 96 cm²
☐ (d) 48 cm²
☐ (e) 120 cm²

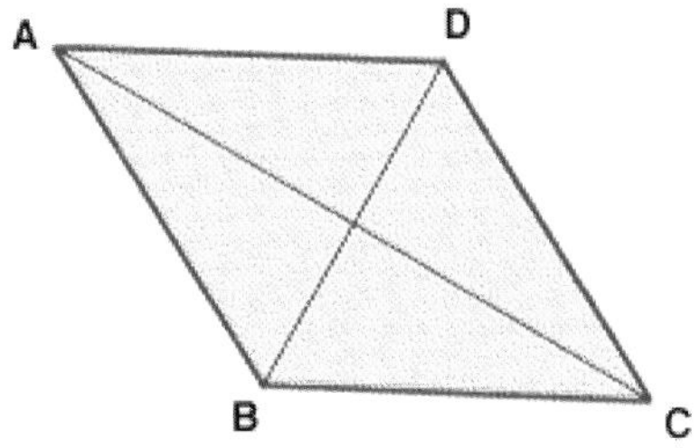

Q24

25 Find the volume of the solid shown in the following diagram by counting the cubes, where one cube has the volume of 1 cm³.

☐ (a) 26 cm³
☐ (b) 36 cm³
☐ (c) 29 cm³
☐ (d) 22 cm³
☐ (e) 44 cm³

Q25

26 Find the volume of the cuboid shown in the diagram below.

☐ (a) 49 cm³
☐ (b) 35 cm³
☐ (c) 175 cm³
☐ (d) 25 cm³
☐ (e) 245 cm³

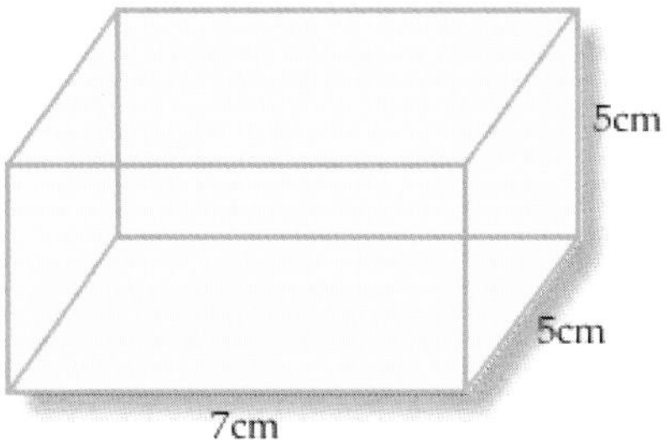

Q26

27 The following diagram shows the net of a cuboid. Find the volume of the cuboid.

☐ (a) 280 cm³
☐ (b) 21 cm³
☐ (c) 490 cm³
☐ (d) 160 cm³
☐ (e) 400 cm³

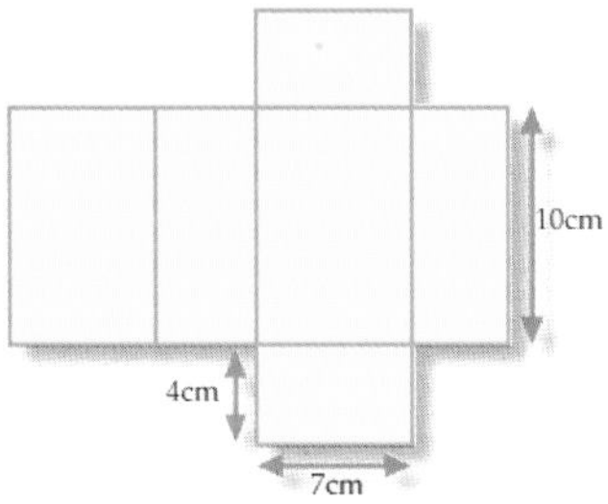

Q27

28 A drip tray in a fridge is 45 cm long, 30 cm wide, and 8 cm deep, as shown in the following diagram. How many litres of water does the tray contain when it is full?

☐ (a) 108 litres
☐ (b) 10.8 litres
☐ (c) 36 litres

(d) 3.6 litres
(e) 1.08 litres

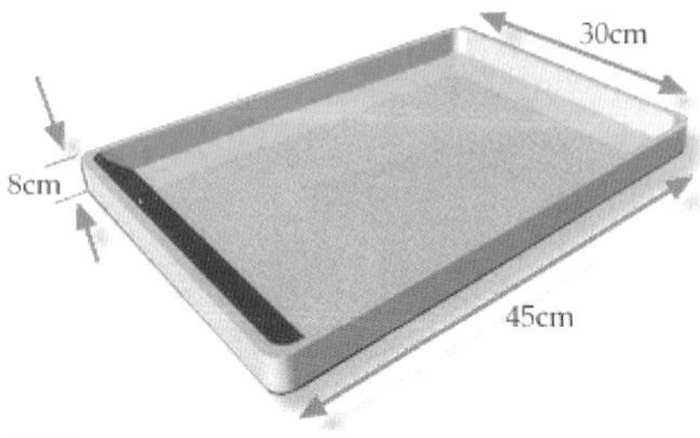

Q28

29 A paving stone has a square surface of side 600 mm, and is 50 mm deep. Find the volume of a stone. Give the answer in cubic centimetres.

(a) 18 000 cm³
(b) 300 cm³
(c) 1800 cm³
(d) 3000 cm³
(e) 18 000 000 cm³

30 A skip is in the shape of a cuboid with a volume of 9 m³. The skip is 3 m long and 2 m wide. How high is it?

(a) 3 m
(b) 1 m
(c) 1.5 m
(d) 2 m
(e) 0.5 m

31 A paddling pool is rectangular, measuring 12 m by 7 m. The water is 60 cm deep throughout. Find the volume of the water. Give your answer in cubic metres.

(a) 54 m³
(b) 504 m³
(c) 50.4 m³
(d) 5.04 m³
(e) 5.4 m³

32 Find the volume of the solid shown in the diagram below.

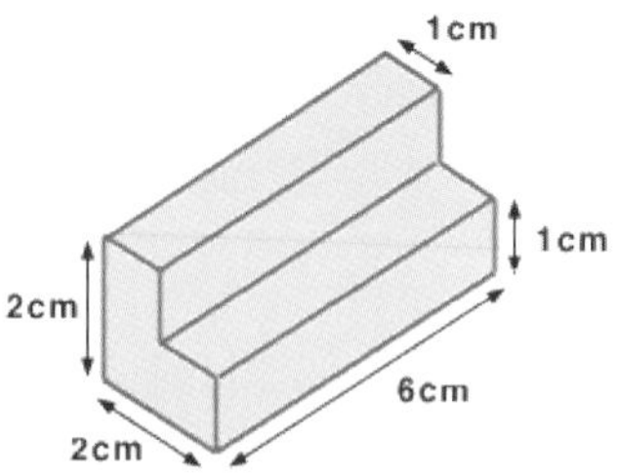

Q32

(a) 10 cm³
(b) 24 cm³
(c) 12 cm³
(d) 18 cm³

(e) 30 cm³

33 Jack has some toy building bricks, which are cubes with sides of length 5 cm. He has a wooden box to keep the bricks in. The box is a cuboid with dimensions 40 cm by 25 cm by 15cm. How many bricks fit into the box?

(a) 12
(b) 40
(c) 400
(d) 1200
(e) 120

34 A rectangular water tank measures 2 m by 3 m by 4 m. What is its capacity in litres?

(a) 24 000 litres
(b) 240 litres
(c) 2400 litres
(d) 2.4 litres
(e) 24 litres

35 Salt is sold in boxes that have a volume of 720 cm³. Each box is a cuboid, 18 cm high, and 4 cm deep. Find the width of the box.

(a) 1 cm
(b) 100 cm
(c) 16 cm
(d) 10 cm
(e) 1.6 cm

36 The diagram below shows a hexagonal prism, which has a cross-sectional area of 30 cm². Calculate the volume of the prism.

(a) 1080 cm³
(b) 270 cm³
(c) 540 cm³
(d) 810 cm³
(e) 8100 cm³

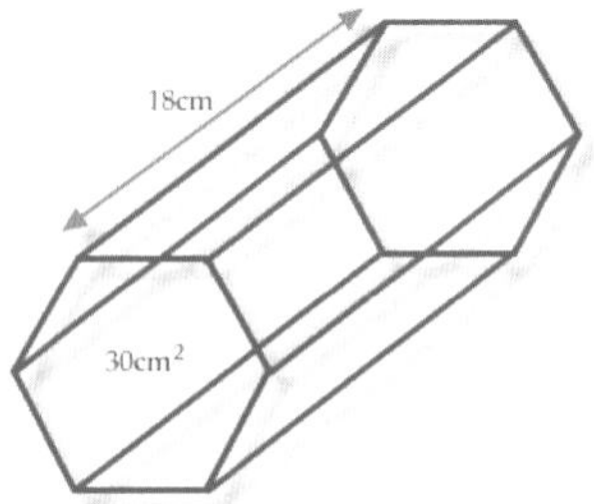

Q36

37 The following diagram shows a triangular prism. Calculate the volume of the prism.

(a) 377 cm³
(b) 188.5 cm³
(c) 462 cm³
(d) 231 cm³

(e) 115.5 cm³

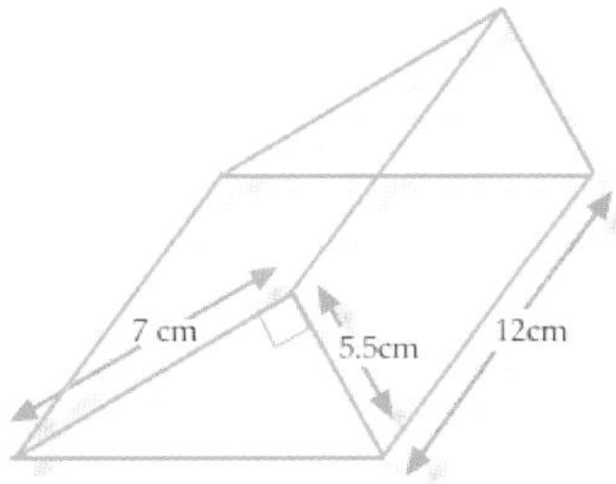

Q37

38 A cylindrical water tank has a radius of 65 cm and a height of 245 cm. Find the capacity of the tank in litres to 1 d.p.

(a) 50 litres
(b) 13 007.8 litres
(c) 3251.9 litres
(d) 431 101 001 litres
(e) 325.2 litres

39 Oil fills an inverted metal cone to depth of 30 cm. The radius of the surface of the oil is 18 cm. Calculate the volume of the oil in the cone (to the nearest integer).

(a) 43 130 536 cm³
(b) 10 179 cm³
(c) 43 565 cm³
(d) 43 113 393 cm³
(e) 16 965 cm³

QUESTIONS

Higher Level only

40 In the following diagram, the height of the trapezium XYCB is one third of the height of the triangle ABC. The area of trapezium XYCB is greater than the area of triangle AXY. Is this statement true or false?

(a) True
(b) False

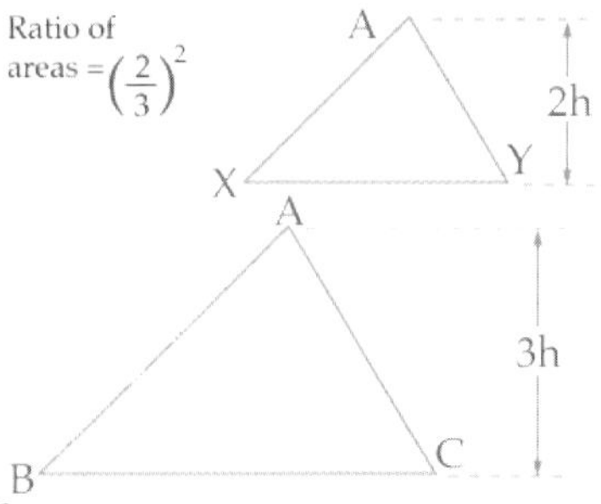

Ratio of areas $= \left(\frac{2}{3}\right)^2$

Q40

41 If the sides of a rectangle are

increased by 10%, the area is increased by 20%. Is this statement true or false?

☐ (a) True
☐ (b) False

42 A metal bar is in the form of a cuboid, 60 cm by 15 cm by 8 cm. A cubic centimetre of the metal has a mass of 6 g. Find the mass of the bar, in kilograms.

☐ (a) 432 kg
☐ (b) 7.2 kg
☐ (c) 72 kg
☐ (d) 4.32 kg
☐ (e) 43.2 kg

43 The circle in the following diagram has a radius of 6 cm. Find the length of the arc AB which subtends an angle of 130° at the centre of the circle, giving the answer to 1 d.p.

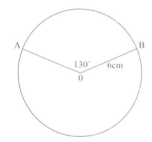

Q43

☐ (a) 40.8 cm
☐ (b) 13.6 cm
☐ (c) 27.2 cm
☐ (d) 4316.8 cm
☐ (e) 420.4 cm

44 The dimensions of a greenhouse are shown in the following diagram. Calculate the surface area of the greenhouse (to 1 d.p.)

☐ (a) 4103.9 m²
☐ (b) 100.0 m²
☐ (c) 126.6 m²
☐ (d) 43 107.5 m²
☐ (e) 108.4 m²

Q44

45 A steel cuboid measuring 60 mm by 25 mm by 12 mm is melted down and cast into ball bearings of radius 3 mm. How many ball bearings are cast?

☐ (a) 1273
☐ (b) 159

☐ (c) 477
☐ (d) 419
☐ (e) 63

46 The volume of a sphere is 600 cm³. Calculate the diameter of the sphere, giving the answer to 1 d.p.

☐ (a) 10.5 cm
☐ (b) 23.9 cm
☐ (c) 5.2 cm
☐ (d) 13.8 cm
☐ (e) 7.3 cm

47 The diagram below shows a sector of a circle. The area of the sector equals 75 cm². The angle AOB equals 50°. Calculate the perimeter of the sector, giving the answer correct to 1 d.p.

☐ (a) 11.4 cm
☐ (b) 13.1 cm
☐ (c) 37.7 cm
☐ (d) 39.3 cm
☐ (e) 26.2 cm

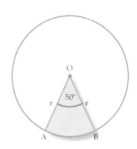

Q47

91

ANSWERS

Representation of 2D and 3D shapes

☐ 1 *(b)*
False. The edges of the net given will not join up satisfactorily to form a triangular prism. If the edges were brought together, the resulting solid would be a square-based pyramid.

☐ 2 *(a)*
True. If the edges of the net given are brought together, the resulting solid will be a regular triangular-based pyramid or a tetrahedron.

☐ 3 *(b)*
False. If the net given is folded up to form a box, the ends would be found to be too big.

☐ 4 (d)
A prism is a solid that has a constant cross-section.

☐ 5 *(e)*
A regular shape has equal sides and equal angles. A square has four angles of 90° and four equal sides.

☐ 6 *(d)*
Shape 1 is a cuboid, which has six rectangular faces. Shape 2 is a prism, which is a solid that has a constant cross-section. This cross-section is a triangle. Shape 3 is a cone, which has a circular base and one vertex at the top.

☐ 7 *(a)*
The net should fold together without overlapping. There should be no gaps.

☐ 8 *(a)*
The net should fold together without overlapping. There should be no gaps.

☐ 9 *(d)*
The net should fold together without overlapping. There should be no gaps. Nets W and X will form prisms, and not pyramids.

☐ 10 *(e)*
A cuboid is a solid that has six rectangular faces. A triangular prism has a constant cross-section, which is a triangle. A square-based pyramid has one top vertex joined to the four vertices of a square.

☐ 11 *(a)*
When the net of the cube is folded, Square B would be opposite square D, so it would be yellow. Square E would

be opposite square A, and therefore it would be green.

☐ 12 *(d)*
A prism is a solid that has a constant cross-section. This cross-section is triangular.

Classification of polygons

☐ 1 *(b)*
False. In any triangle, an exterior angle equals the sum of the interior opposite angles. So, x = a + b. Note that c = 180° – x and a + b + c = 180° (angles in a triangle add up to 180°). Therefore, a + b + (180° – x) = 180° and x = a + b.

☐ 2 *(b)*
False. In a polygon, the number of sides and the number of interior angles are the same.

☐ 3 *(a)*
True. The sum of the interior angles of a polygon with n sides is (n – 2) × 180°. Therefore, the sum of the interior angles of a hexagon is 4 × 180 = 720°. Five right angles add up to 450°, which leaves 270° for the sixth angle.

☐ 4 *(a)*
True. The sum of the angles of a quadrilateral is always 360°. If two of them add up to 180°, then so must the remaining two.

☐ 5 *(b)*
False. PQRS is a parallelogram where the opposite angles are equal, but not right angles.

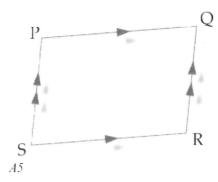

A5

☐ 6 *(a)*
True. The rhombus is a parallelogram where all four sides are equal and the opposite angles are equal. If the angles were 90° the shape would be a special kind of a rhombus, known as a square.

☐ 7 *(b)*
False. If the equal sides are opposite each other, then the quadrilateral is a parallelogram, but if they are adjacent

(next to one another) then the quadrilateral is a kite.

☐ 8 *(b)*
False. Since the angles of a quadrilateral add up to 360°, the other pair of angles add up to 180°, but they are not necessarily both 90°. (When the opposite angles are supplementary, the quadrilateral is said to be cyclic because it is possible to draw a circle through all four corners or vertices. When two opposite angles are both 90°, the diagonal opposite the two right angles is the diameter of the circle.)

☐ 9 *(b)*
False. Each angle of an equilateral triangle is 60°, and each angle of a square is 90°. Therefore, angle DAX = 90 – 60 = 30°. AX = AB (the sides of an equilateral triangle are an equal length). AB = AD (the sides of a square are an equal length). Therefore, AX = AD and triangles AXD and BXC are isosceles with angles 30°, 75°, and 75°. Angles at X total 360°. So, angle DXC = (60 + 75 + 75) – 360 = 150°.

☐ 10 *(a)*
True. The rhombus has four equal sides and the diagonals bisect each other. Therefore, the four triangles have the same length sides (and are all right-angled triangles).

☐ 11 *(c)*
The sum of the angles of a triangle is 180°. An isosceles triangle has two equal angles. Therefore, 2a + 100° = 180°. 2a = 80°. So, a = 40°.

☐ 12 *(c)*
a = 180° – 65° = 115° (angles on a straight line add up to 180°). b = 115° (opposite angles of a parallelogram are equal). c = 180° – b = 65° (angles on a straight line add up to 180°).

☐ 13 *(a)*
Angle AOB = 90° (the diagonals of a rhombus cross at right angles). Angle ABO = 180° – 90° – 70° = 20° (the sum of the angles in a triangle is 180°). Angle BDC = angle ABO (alternate angles are equal). So, angle BDC = 20°.

☐ 14 *(c)*
The first shape is a hexagon, which has six sides. The second shape is a parallelogram, which has two sets of parallel sides. The third shape is a trapezium, which has one pair of parallel sides.

☐ 15 *(b)*
The first line is the diameter, which

passes through the centre of a circle. The second line is a chord, which passes through two points on the circumference of a circle. The third line is a tangent, which touches a point on the circumference of a circle.

☐ **16** *(a)*
A kite has two sets of equal sides that are adjacent.

☐ **17** *(d)*
A rhombus has four equal sides and two lines of symmetry.

☐ **18** *(e)*
Some types of trapezium only have two parallel sides.

☐ **19** *(a)*
The sum of the angles in a quadrilateral is 360°. Therefore, to find the missing angle, subtract the given angles from 360°. 360° – 103° – 81° – 102° = 74°.

☐ **20** *(d)*
The diagonals of a square and a rhombus cross at 90°.

☐ **21** *(b)*
The diagonals of a rectangle and a square are equal in length.

☐ **22** *(a)*
Angles on a straight line add up to 180°. Therefore, three of the interior angles can be found by subtracting the given angles from 180°. These are 66° (180° – 114°), 108° (180° – 72°), and 106° (180° – 74°). The sum of the angles in a quadrilateral is 360°. The fourth interior angle = 360° – 66° – 108° – 106° = 80°. So, a = 180° – 80° = 100° (angles on a straight line add up to 180°).

☐ **23** *(e)*
Angle EAB = 60° (angles of an equilateral triangle are 60°). Angle DAB is a right angle (angles of a square are 90°). Therefore, angle DAE = 90° – 60° = 30°. The triangle ADE is isosceles so the lines AD and AE are the same and angle ADE equals angle AED. Angles ADE + AED = 180° – 30° = 150°. Angle ADE = 150° ÷ 2 = 75°. So, angle ADE = angle AED = 75°.

☐ **24** *(a)*
s = 180° – 108° – 38° = 34° (the sum of the angles in a triangle is 180°). The angle next to the angle of 101° = 79° (angles on a straight line add up to 180°). Therefore, t = 180° – 79° – 44° = 57° (the sum of the angles in a triangle is 180°).

☐ **25** *(d)*
The exterior angles of a polygon add up

to 360°. One exterior angle of a regular nonagon = 360° ÷ 9 = 40°. The interior and exterior angles have a sum of 180° (angles on a straight line add up to 180°). Therefore, an interior angle = 180° – 40° = 140°.

☐ **26** *(c)*
The sum of the angles of a triangle is 180°. Therefore, the third angle of the triangle = 180° – 55° – 56° = 69°. Angles on a straight line add up to 180°. Therefore, 69° + 42° + e = 180°. So, e = 180° – 111° = 69°.

☐ **27** *(d)*
W and Z are similar because they have equal angles of 40°, 50°, and 90°.

☐ **28** *(c)*
The ratio of the sides of the triangles is 15 cm:9 cm = 5:3. X = 8 × ³⁄₅ = 4.8 cm.

☐ **29** *(e)*
Corresponding sides of similar triangles are opposite equal angles. The ratio of the sides = 50 mm:30 mm = 5:3. LM = 55 × ³⁄₅ = 33 mm, MN = 40 × ³⁄₅ = 24 mm.

☐ **30** *(a)*
Corresponding sides of similar triangles are opposite equal angles. The ratio of the sides is 12 cm:15 cm = 4:5. DF = ²⁰⁄₄ × 5 = 16 mm. LN = ¹⁸⁄₅ × 4 = 22.5 mm.

Symmetry

☐ **1** *(b)*
False. This statement does not apply when, for example, the parallelogram or the following symbol is considered.

A1

☐ **2** *(b)*
False. Equilateral triangles have both reflectional symmetry and rotational symmetry, but isosceles triangles also have reflectional symmetry.

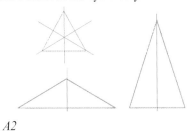

A2

☐ **3** *(b)*
An isosceles triangle has two equal sides, two equal angles, and one line of symmetry.

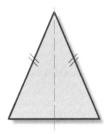

A3

☐ **4** *(a)*
A line of symmetry divides a shape into two equal halves. A parallelogram does not have a line of symmetry. If the parallelogram is rotated through 180° about its centre it looks exactly the same, which means that it has rotational symmetry of order 2. A shape that has rotational symmetry of order 2 can be rotated through 180° about its centre and still look the same and occupy the same space.

☐ **5** *(b)*
A plane of symmetry divides a solid into two halves, which are the mirror images of each other. The pyramid has four planes of symmetry that pass through the four lines of symmetry of the base.

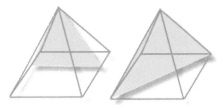

A5

☐ **6** *(a)*
A plane of symmetry divides a solid into two equal halves, which are the mirror images of each other. A cuboid has three planes of symmetry, each of which is parallel to two of the faces of the cuboid.

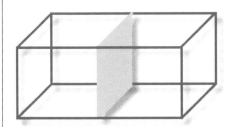

A6

☐ **7** *(c)*
A plane of symmetry divides a solid into two halves, which are the mirror images of each other. X and Y are planes of symmetry of the cylinder.

☐ **8** *(d)*
A plane of symmetry divides a solid into two equal halves, which are the mirror images of each other. A cube has three planes of symmetry that are parallel to its faces, and six planes that pass through two parallel edges.

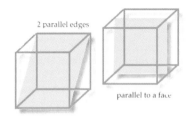

A8

☐ **9** *(e)*
A plane of symmetry divides a solid into two halves, which are the mirror images of each other. Each prism has planes of symmetry that pass through the lines of symmetry of its cross-section, and a plane that cuts it in half lengthwise.

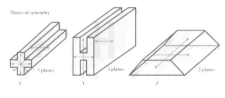

A9

☐ **10** *(c)*
The order of rotational symmetry of a shape is the number of times the original appearance is repeated in a full turn. The diagram with flag X added has rotational symmetry of order 2. A shape that has rotational symmetry of order 2 can be rotated through 180° about its centre, and still look the same and occupy the same space.

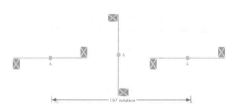

A10

☐ **11** *(e)*
The order of rotational symmetry of a shape is the number of times the

original appearance is repeated in a full turn. Diagram A, with Z added, has rotational symmetry of order 4. A shape that has rotational symmetry of order 4 can be rotated through 90° about its centre and still look the same and occupy the same space.

☐ **12** *(d)*
The order of rotational symmetry of a shape is the number of times the original appearance is repeated in a full turn. Diagram A, with Y added, has rotational symmetry of order 3. A shape that has rotational symmetry of order 3 can be rotated through 120° about its centre and still look the same and occupy the same space.

☐ **13** *(d)*
The order of rotational symmetry of a shape is the number of times the original appearance is repeated in a full turn. When a regular hexagon is rotated through 360°, the appearance of the hexagon is repeated six times. A shape that has rotational symmetry of order 6 can be rotated through 60° about its centre and still look the same and occupy the same space.

☐ **14** *(d)*
A line of symmetry divides a shape into two equal halves, which are reflections of each other. A regular hexagon has six lines of symmetry.

Regular hexagon

A14

☐ **15** *(d)*
A line of symmetry divides a shape into two halves, which are the mirror images of each other. A regular pentagon has five lines of symmetry, each of which passes through a vertex and the middle of the opposite side.

Pentagon

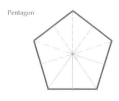

A15

☐ **16** *(a)*
The order of rotational symmetry is the number of positions in which the shape looks identical when it is rotated through 360° about its centre. A shape

that has rotational symmetry of order 3 can be rotated through 120° about its centre and still look the same and occupy the same space.

☐ **17** *(c)*
The order of rotational symmetry of a shape is the number of positions in which the shape looks identical when it is rotated through 360° about its centre. A shape that has rotational symmetry of order 4 can be rotated through 90° about its centre and still look the same and occupy the same space.

☐ **18** *(e)*
The order of rotational symmetry of a shape is the number of positions in which the shape looks identical when it is rotated through 360° about its centre. Shape W has rotational symmetry of order 4, shape Y has rotational symmetry of order 2, and shape Z has rotational symmetry of order 3.

v W X y z

A18

☐ **19** *(a)*
The order of rotational symmetry of a shape is the number of positions in which the shape looks identical when it is rotated through 360° about its centre. A shape that has rotational symmetry of order 7 can be rotated through 51.4° (correct to 1 d.p.) about its centre and still look the same and occupy the same space.

☐ **20** *(d)*
A line of symmetry divides a shape into two halves, which are mirror images of each other. The tile pattern has four lines of symmetry.

A20

Angles

☐ 1 (a)

True. The two angles marked x are vertically opposite, and the two angles marked y are alternate. So x, y, and z can be seen to be equal to the angles of the triangle PQR and the angles of a triangle always add up to 180°.

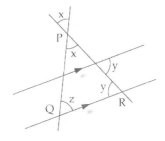

A1

☐ 2 (b)

False. The sum of the two angles marked is 181°. If the sum was 180°, lines p and q would be parallel. But, because the sum is greater than 180°, the lines will meet to the left.

A2

☐ 3 (a)

True. A polygon of n sides can be divided into (n – 2) triangles, each of which has an angle sum of 180°.

A3

☐ 4 (a)

True. Since each interior angle of a regular polygon is 144°, each exterior angle is 180° – 144° = 36°. Travelling once round the perimeter of the polygon you must turn through 360°;

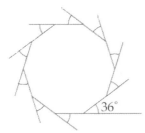

A4

this is equivalent to 10 corners of 36°. So, there are 10 sides of the polygon.

☐ 5 (a)

True. Ignore the middle one of the three parallel lines. Angle x = angle z (corresponding angles are equal). Angles y and z are angles on a straight line. So, x + y = 180° (angles in a straight line add up to 180°).

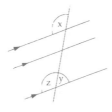

A5

☐ 6 (b)

False. To be congruent, the parallelograms must be exactly the same size and shape. Although they have sides of the same length, the angles may be different. Therefore, we cannot assume that the parallelograms are congruent.

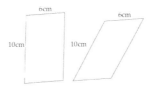

A6

☐ 7 (a)

The exterior angles of a polygon add up to 360°. A pentagon has five sides and five exterior angles. Therefore, each exterior angle is 72° (360 ÷ 5 = 72). Each interior angle is 108° as 180° – 72° = 108° (angles on a straight line add up to 180°).

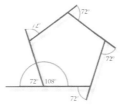

A7

☐ 8 (c)

Three hexagons meet at each vertex of a honeycomb. Therefore, each interior angle equals 120° (360° ÷ 3 = 120°).

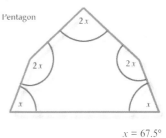

A8

☐ 9 (b)

The exterior angles of a polygon add up to 360°. In a regular polygon, the exterior angles are equal. Therefore, 360° ÷ 60° = 6. So, the polygon has six sides, which is a hexagon.

A9

☐ 10 (a)

The sum of the angles at a point is 360°. Therefore, 90° + 55° + 80° + 75° + 2x = 360°. 2x = 360° – 300° = 60°. 2x = 60°. So, x = 30°.

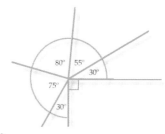

A10

☐ 11 (d)

The sum of the angles of a triangle is 180°. Therefore, q = 180° – 110° – 40° = 30°. r = q = 30° (alternate angles are the same). Therefore, p = 180° – 90° – r (angles in a triangle add up to 180°). So, p = 60°.

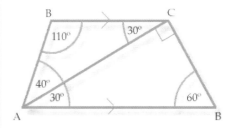

A11

☐ 12 (d)

The sum of the interior angles of a polygon = (n – 2)180°, where n is the number of sides. Therefore, (5 – 2)180° = 540°. x + 2x + 2x + 2x + x = 8x. Therefore, 8x = 540°. So, x = 540° ÷ 8 = 67.5°.

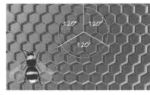

A12

13 *(c)*
a = 58° (corresponding angles are equal). b = 180° – 58° = 122° (angles on a straight line add up to 180°). c = b = 122° (vertically opposite angles are equal).

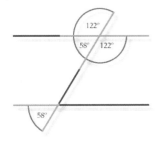

A13

14 *(d)*
Angle DBC = 54° as this angle is alternate to angle ADB (alternate angles are equal). Angle DAB equals angle ABD as the triangle ABD is isosceles. Therefore, angles DAB + ABD = 180° – 54° = 126° (angles in a triangle add up to 180°). So, angle ABD = 126° ÷ 2 = 63°. Angle ABC = ABD + DBC = 54° + 63° = 117°.

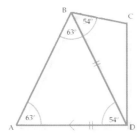

A14

15 *(c)*
Angle ABC = 60° as the triangle ABC is equilateral. Angle CBD = angle BDC as the triangle BCD is isosceles. Therefore, angles CBD + BDC = 180° – 140° = 40°. So, angle CBD = 40° ÷ 2 = 20°. Angle ABD = ABC – CBD = 60° – 20° = 40°.

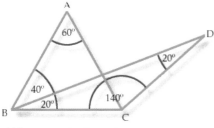

A15

16 *(c)*
Angle DBC is 60° as the triangle BCD is equilateral. Angle ABC = angle ACB as the triangle ABC is isosceles. Therefore, angles ABC + ACB = 180° – 90° = 90°. So, angle ABC = 90 ÷ 2 = 45°. Angle ABD = ABC + CBD = 60° + 45° = 105°.

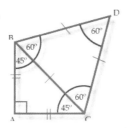

A16

17 *(d)*
q = 25° as triangle ABD is isosceles. r = 180° – 25° – 25° = 130° (angles in a triangle add up to 180°). r + s = 180° (angles on a straight line add up to 180°). So, s = 180° – 130° = 50°. p = t as triangle BCD is isosceles. Therefore, p + s + t = 180° (angles in a triangle add up to 180°). p + t = 180° – 50° = 130°. So, p = t = 130° ÷ 2 = 65°.

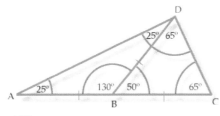

A17

18 *(d)*
The isosceles triangle has two equal angles of 47°. Therefore, c + 47° + 47° = 180° (angles of a triangle add up to 180°). So, c = 86°. b = 47° (alternate angles are equal). Therefore, a + 47° = 180° (angles on a straight line add up to 180°). So, a = 133°.

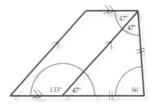

A18

19 *(e)*
The exterior angles of a polygon add up to 360°. Therefore, 360° ÷ 72° = 5. A polygon with five sides is called a pentagon.

A19

20 *(e)*
The exterior angle at each vertex of the regular polygon = 180° – 170° = 10° (angles on a straight line add up to 180°). 360° ÷ 10° = 36 (exterior angles of a polygon add up to 360°). Therefore, the polygon has 36 sides.

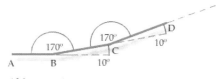

A20

21 *(b)*
One exterior angle of a regular hexagon, b = 360° ÷ 6 = 60° (exterior angles of a polygon add up to 360°). Angle FAB = 180° – b = 120° (angles on a straight line add up to 180°). Triangle FAB is isosceles with two equal angles at F and B, which is 2a. 2a = 180° – 120° = 60° (angles in a triangle add up to 180°). So, a = 30°.

A21

22 *(d)*
Angle BCA = 30° (vertically opposite angles are equal). Triangle ABC is isosceles, and so angle ABC = angle a. 2a + 30° = 180° (angles of a triangle add up to 180°). Therefore, 2a = 150°, so a = 75°. b = a = 75° (alternate angles are equal).

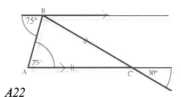

A22

23 *(d)*
The sum of the interior angles of a polygon = (n – 2)180°, where n is the number of sides. Therefore the sum of the interior angles of a pentagon = (5 – 2)180° = 3 × 180° = 540°. Each interior angle of a regular pentagon = x. Therefore, 5x = 540°, so x = 108°.

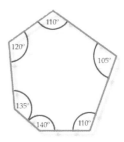

A24

24 *(e)*
The sum of the interior angles of a polygon = (n – 2)180°, where n is the

number of sides. So, the sum for a hexagon = (6 – 2)180° = 4 × 180° = 720°. Therefore, 120° + 135° + 140° + 105° + a = 720°. 610 + a = 720°. So, a = 110°.

□ **25** *(d)*
a = 180° – 115° = 65° (angles on a straight line add up to 180°). b = 180° – 100° = 80° (angles on a straight line add up to 180°). The sum of the angles of a quadrilateral is 360°. Therefore, d = 360° – 65° – 80° – 125°. So, d = 90°.

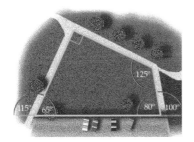

A25

□ **26** *(c)*
The triangle formed by the open stepladder is isosceles, so two angles are the same. Therefore, 180° – 40° = 140° (the sum of the angles in a triangle is 180°). So, each of the other two angles of the triangle = 140° ÷ 2 = 70°.

A26

□ **27** *(e)*
An obtuse angle is an angle that is between 90 and 180°.

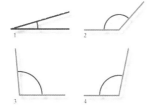

A27

□ **28** *(c)*
A right angle is equal to 90°. An obtuse angle is between 90 and 180°. An acute angle is less than 90°.

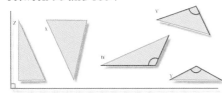

A28

□ **29** *(d)*
The hour hand turns through one twelfth of a rotation each hour. Each rotation is 360°, therefore each hour is a turn of 360° ÷ 12 = 30°. In 3 hours, the hour hand turns through 3 × 30 = 90°.

□ **30** *(b)*
The sum of the angles of a triangle is 180°. Therefore, 180° – 90° – 63° = 27°.

A30

□ **31** *(d)*
The sum of the angles on a straight line is 180°. Therefore, 4e = 180°. So, e = 180° ÷ 4 = 45°.

Angles

Higher Levels

□ **32** *(a)*
True. Angle ATC = 90° (tangent is perpendicular to the radius). Angle TBC = 90° (angle in a semicircle is a right angle). So, angle BTC is both (90 – y) and (90 – x) (angles in a triangle add up to 180°). Therefore, x = y.

□ **33** *(b)*
a = 53° and b = 42° (angles in the same segment are equal).

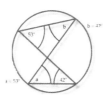

A33

□ **34** *(b)*
In triangle OAB, angle OBA = 35° (two angles in an isosceles triangle are equal). Angle AOB = 180° – 35° – 35° = 110°. Angle AOB = 2ACB (angle at the centre is twice the angle at the circumference). Therefore, angle ACB = 55°.

A34

□ **35** *(e)*
p = 84° (angle at the centre is twice the angle at the circumference). Angle OBC = angle OCB (two angles in an isosceles triangle are equal). 180° – 84° = 96° and 96° ÷ 2 = 48°. So, q = 48°.

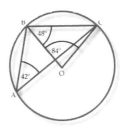

A35

□ **36** *(c)*
s = 52° (angle at the centre is twice the angle at the circumference). Triangle OMN is isosceles where two angles are equal. 180° – 104° = 76° and 76° ÷ 2 = 38°. So, t = 38°.

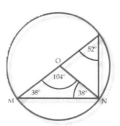

A36

□ **37** *(c)*
Angle POR = 90° (angle in a semicircle is a right angle). x + 2x + 90° = 180° (the sum of the angles of a triangle is 180°). 3x = 90°. So, x = 30°.

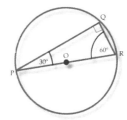

A37

□ **38** *(c)*
q = 90° (angle in a semicircle is a right angle). p + 50° + 90° = 180° (the sum of the angles of a triangle is 180°). 180° – 140° = 40°. So, p = 40°.

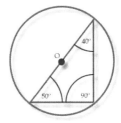

A38

39 *(d)*
Mark point D onto the circumference of the circle and draw the lines AD and CD. Angle AOC = 2ADC (angle at the centre is twice the angle at the circumference). Angle ADC = 150° ÷ 2 = 75°. Angle ABC = 180° – 75° = 105° (opposite angles of a cyclic quadrilateral add up to 180°).

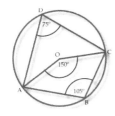

A39

40 *(e)*
a = 66° (alternate segment theorem). a + b + 50° = 180° (angles in a triangle add up to 180°). So, angle b = 180° – 50° – 66° = 64°.

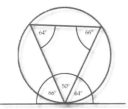

A40

41 *(c)*
Angle CAB = 75° (alternate segment theorem). Triangle ABC is isosceles, so angle ABC = angle CAB = 75°. Therefore, p = 180° – 75° – 75° = 30° (angles in a triangle add up to 180°).

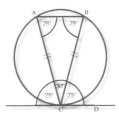

A41

42 *(c)*
Triangle PQR is isosceles (tangents from external point are equal). Therefore angle RPQ = m. 2m = 180° – 76° = 104°. So, m = 104° ÷ 2 = 52°. OP is perpendicular to PQ (tangent is perpendicular to radius).Therefore, n + 52° = 90°. So, n = 90° – 52° = 38°.

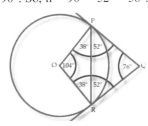

A42

43 *(c)*
q = angle PMQ = 66° (alternate segment theorem). Triangle PQR is isosceles, so angle QPR = q. Therefore, r + 2q = 180° (angle sum of triangle PQR). So, r = 180° – 132° = 48°.

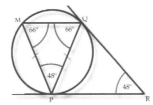

A43

44 *(b)*
Angle ABC = 53° (alternate angles are the same). a = angle ABC = 53° (alternate segment theorem). At point A, a + b + 53° = 180°. So, b = 180° – 53° – 53° = 74°.

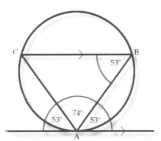

A44

45 *(a)*
Draw the line RO. Triangle SOR is isosceles, therefore angle SRO = 28°. Angle SRT = 63° (angle at the centre is twice the angle at the circumference). Therefore, angle ORT = 63° – 28° = 35°. Triangle ORT is isosceles. So, t = angle ORT = 35°.

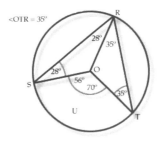

A45

46 *(a)*
Angle AED = 116° (vertically opposite angles are the same). Therefore, a + 116° + 35° = 180° (angle sum of triangle AED). So, a = 180° – 151° = 29°. b = a = 29° (angles in the same segment are equal). Angle BAD = 180° – 75° – 29° = 76° (angle sum of triangle ABD). Angle BAE = 76° – 35° = 41°. So, c = angle BAE = 41° (alternate segment theorem).

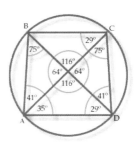

A46

47 *(c)*
The exterior angles of a polygon have a sum of 360° and the sum of the interior and exterior angles equals 180°. If the interior angle equals 130°, then the external angle equals 50° (180° – 130° = 50°). This is not a factor of 360°. Therefore, 130° cannot be the interior angle of a regular polygon. All of the other exterior angles are factors of 360°.

48 *(b)*
The sum of the interior angles of a regular octagon = (8 – 2)180° = 6 × 180° = 1080°. The interior angle CDE = 1080° ÷ 8 = 135°. DH is a line of symmetry and bisects the interior angle CDE. Therefore, angle HDE = 135° ÷ 2 = 67.5°. Angle EDA = 90° as DE is parallel to AH. Angle HDE + angle ADH = angle EDA. 67.5° + angle ADH = 90°. So, angle ADH = 22.5°.

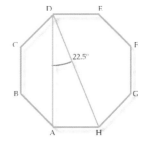

A48

Trigonometry and Pythagoras

1 *(b)*
False. The hypotenuse (the side opposite the right angle) is always the longest side in a right-angled triangle and therefore must always be on its own in the equation of Pythagoras. In this case, the hypotenuse is b and $a^2 + c^2 = b^2$.

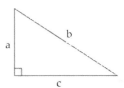

A1

☐ **2** *(a)*
True. The squares of the sides are 64, 225, and 289. Since 64 + 225 = 289, by Pythagoras' theorem, the triangle does have a right angle opposite the side of length 17.

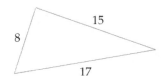

A2

☐ **3** *(a)*
True. The bearing of P from Q = 123° + 180° = 303°.

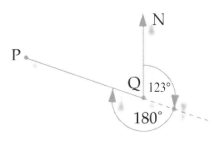

A3

☐ **4***(d)*
In triangle BCD, $BD^2 = 5^2 + 5^2 = 50$ (Pythagoras' theorem). In triangle BDE, $BE2 = BD^2 + 5^2 = 50 + 25 = 75$ (Pythagoras' theorem). BE = $\sqrt{75}$ = 8.7 cm (correct to 1 d.p.).

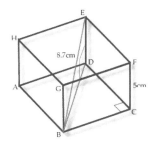

A4

☐ **5** *(b)*
$PR^2 = PQ^2 + QR^2$ (Pythagoras' theorem). $PR^2 = 9^2 + 12^2 = 81 + 144 = 225$. So, PR = $\sqrt{225}$ = 15 cm.

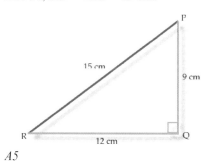

A5

☐ **6** *(b)*
$a^2 = b^2 + c^2$ (Pythagoras' theorem). $a^2 = 2.5^2 + 6^2 = 6.25 + 36 = 42.25$. So, a = $\sqrt{42.25}$ = 6.5 cm.

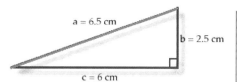

A6

☐ **7** *(c)*
$x^2 = y^2 + z^2$ (Pythagoras' theorem). $x^2 = 4.3^2 + 5.2^2 = 18.49 + 27.04 = 45.53$. So, x = $\sqrt{45.53}$ = 6.7 cm (correct to 1 d.p.).

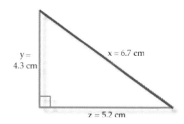

A7

☐ **8** *(b)*
$RT^2 = SR^2 + ST^2$ (Pythagoras' theorem). 169 = 144 + ST^2. Therefore, ST^2 = 169 – 144 = 25. So, ST = $\sqrt{25}$ = 5 cm.

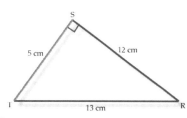

A8

☐ **9** *(a)*
$x^2 = y^2 + z^2$ (Pythagoras' theorem). 39 = 36 + z^2. Therefore, z^2 = 1521 – 1296 = 225. So, x = $\sqrt{225}$ = 15 cm.

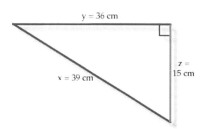

A9

☐ **10** *(d)*
$L^2 = 12^2 + 7^2$ (Pythagoras' theorem). $L^2 = 144 + 49 = 193$. So, L = $\sqrt{193}$ = 13.9 cm (correct to 1 d.p.).

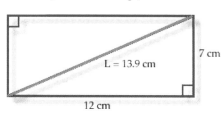

A10

☐ **11** *(e)*
AD divides the triangle into two equal halves, so BD = 4 cm. $15^2 = 4^2 + h^2$ (Pythagoras' theorem). Therefore, h^2 = 225 – 16 = 209. So, h= $\sqrt{209}$ = 14.5 cm (correct to 1 d.p.).

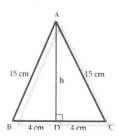

A11

☐ **12** *(d)*
$11.5^2 = a^2 + a^2$ (Pythagoras' theorem). $132.25 = a^2 + a^2 = 2a^2$. Therefore, a^2 = 132.25 ÷ 2 = 66.125. So, a = $\sqrt{66.125}$ = 8.1 cm (correct to 1 d.p.).

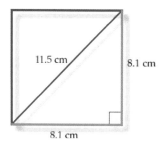

A12

☐ **13** *(d)*
The triangle is isosceles, so it can be divided into two equal halves. Half of the base equals 6 cm. $12^2 = h^2 + 6^2$. Therefore, h^2 = 144 – 36 = 108. So, h= $\sqrt{108}$ = 10.4 cm (correct to 1 d.p.).

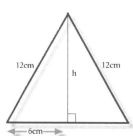

A13

☐ **14** *(d)*
$d^2 = 24^2 + 18^2$ (Pythagoras' theorem). $d^2 = 576 + 324 = 900$. So, d = $\sqrt{900}$ = 30 km.

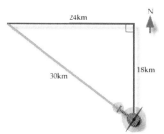

A14

☐ **15** *(d)*

The triangle is isosceles, so it can be divided into two equal halves. Half the base is 8 cm. Hypotenuse^2 = 6^2 + 8^2 = 36 + 64 = 100 (Pythagoras' theorem). Therefore, hypotenuse = √100 = 10 cm. So, the total length of wire = 10 + 10 + 16 = 36 cm.

A15

☐ **16** *(b)*

3^2 = d^2 + 1.4^2 (Pythagoras' theorem). 9 = d^2 + 1.96. Therefore, d^2 = 9 – 1.96 = 7.04. So, d = √7.04 = 2.7 m (correct to 1 d.p.).

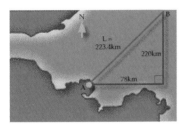

A16

☐ **17** *(b)*

L^2 = 220^2 + 78^2 (Pythagoras' theorem). L^2 = 48 400 + 6084 = 54 484. So, L = √54 484 = 233 km (to the nearest metre).

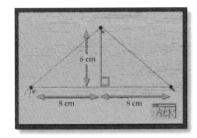

A17

☐ **18** *(d)*

Sin x = $^{opposite}/_{hypotenuse}$ = $^7/_{10}$ = 0.7. So, x = sin^{-1} (0.7) = 44° (to the nearest degree).

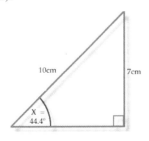

A18

☐ **19** *(d)*

Tan x = $^{opposite}/_{adjacent}$ = $^{7.6}/_4$ = 1.9. So, x = tan^{-1} (1.9) = 62.2° (correct to 1 d.p.).

A19

☐ **20** *(a)*

Cos x = $^{adjacent}/_{hypotenuse}$ = $^{7.2}/_9$ = 0.8. So, x = cos^{-1} (0.8) = 36.9° (correct to 1 d.p.).

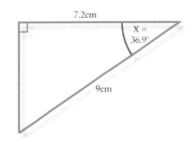

A20

☐ **21** *(c)*

The triangle is isoceles so it can be split into two halves by the line AD. Therefore, BD = 8 cm and angle ADB = 90°. Cos ABD = $^{adjacent}/_{hypotenuse}$ = $^8/_{11}$ = 0.727272 ... So, angle ABD = cos^{-1} (0.72) = 43.3° (correct to 1 d.p.).

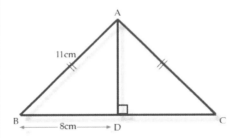

A21

☐ **22** *(c)*

The triangle is isoceles so it can be split into two halves by the line AD. Therefore, BD = 9 cm and angle BAD = 130 ÷ 2 = 65°. Sin 65° = $^{opposite}/_{hypotenuse}$ = $^9/_{AB}$. So, AB = $^9/_{sin 65°}$ = 9.9 cm.

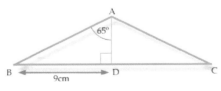

A22

☐ **23** *(b)*

Cos X = $^{adjacent}/_{hypotenuse}$ = $^{1.2}/_4$ = 0.3. So, X = cos^{-1} (0.3) = 72° (to the nearest degree).

A23

☐ **24** *(d)*

Cos 60° = $^{adjacent}/_{hypotenuse}$ = $^X/_{1.8}$. So, X = 1.8 cos 60° = 0.90 m (correct to 2 d.p.).

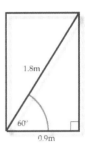

A24

☐ **25** *(a)*

A bearing is the angle, measured in a clockwise direction, between north and the direction described. Tan QPR = $^{opposite}/_{adjacent}$ = $^{17}/_{25}$ = 0.68. So, angle QPR = tan^{-1} (0.68) = 34° (correct to the nearest degree).

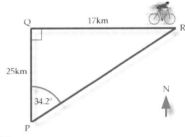

A25

☐ **26** *(c)*

In the triangle, tan ABC = $^{opposite}/_{adjacent}$ = $^{115}/_{63}$ = 1.825397. Therefore, angle ABC = tan^{-1} (1.825397) = 61.3° (correct to 1 d.p.). The bearing is the clockwise angle between north and the line AB. So, the bearing of A from B = 360° – 61.3° = 298.7° (to 1 d.p.).

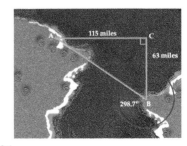

A26

☐ **27** *(d)*

If a north-south line is drawn at Q, the

angle between the line and PQ is 55° (alternate angles are equal). A bearing is the clockwise angle between north and the direction being described. The bearing of P from Q = 180° + 55°, which equals 235°.

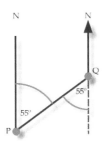

A27

□ **28** *(c)*
The acute angle between the north line and AB = 360° – 310° = 50°. A bearing is the clockwise angle between north and the direction being described. If a north-south line is drawn at B, the acute angle between the south line and BA = 50° (alternate angles are equal). So, the bearing of A from B = 180° – 50° = 130° (angles in a straight line add up to 180°).

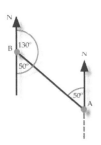

A28

□ **29** *(c)*
The smallest angle of a triangle is opposite the smallest side. Therefore, N is the smallest angle. Cos N = $\frac{l^2 + m^2 - n^2}{2lm}$ (cosine formula). Cos N = $\frac{5.14^2 + 4.83^2 - 3.59^2}{2 \times 5.14 \times 4.83}$ = 0.7423689. So, angle N = cos⁻¹ (0.7423689) = 42.1° (correct to 1 d.p.).

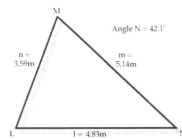

A29

□ **30** *(b)*
In triangle AXB, angle B can be found using the sine formula: $\frac{\sin B}{b} = \frac{\sin X}{x}$. $\frac{\sin B}{65} = \frac{\sin 97°}{250}$. Sin B = $\frac{65 \sin 97°}{250}$ = 0.258062. Angle B = sin⁻¹ (0.258062) = 14.955°. So, angle A = 180° – 97° – 14.955° = 68.0° (correct to 1 d.p.).

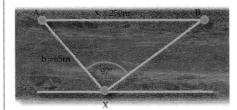
Angle XAB = 68.0°

A30

□ **31** *(d)*
ABC = 180° – 115° – 40° = 25°. $\frac{c}{\sin A}$ = $\frac{a}{\sin C}$. $\frac{a}{\sin 115°}$ = $\frac{9}{\sin 25°}$ = 19.3 km (correct to 1 d.p.).

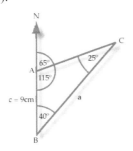

A31

□ **32** *(c)*
A bearing is the angle, measured in a clockwise direction, between north and the direction being described.

□ **33** *(d)*
A bearing is measured in a clockwise direction, between north and the direction being described. In the diagram, there are alternate angles of 30°. Therefore, the bearing is 330°.

Trigonometry and Pythagoras

Higher Levels

□ **34** *(c)*
In triangle ABC, AC² = 8² + 8² = 128 (Pythagoras' theorem). AC = √128 = 11.3137 cm. AO = AC ÷ 2 = 5.6569 cm. In triangle TOC, TO² = 12² – 5.6569² = 112 (Pythagoras' theorem). TO = √112 = 10.6 cm (correct to 1 d.p.).

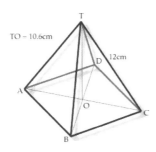
TO = 10.6cm

A34

□ **35** *(d)*
Angle PMN = 90° (Alternate angles of

33° at M, and 57° because of the straight angle at M). Therefore, in triangle PMN, PN² = 10² + 12² = 100 + 144 = 244. PN = √244 = 15.6 km (correct to 3 s.f.).

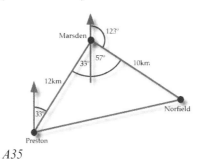

A35

□ **36** *(d)*
In triangle LMN, LN² = 7.4² + 8.6² = 128.72 (Pythagoras' theorem). LN = √128.72 = 11.3458 cm. In triangle LNS, SN² = 5.3² + LN² = 156.81 (Pythagoras' theorem). SN = √156.81 = 12.5 cm (correct to 3 s.f.).

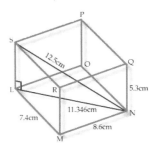

A36

□ **37** *(b)*
In triangle SUT, tan 11° = $\frac{TU}{SU}$ = $\frac{TU}{80}$. Therefore, TU = 80 × tan 11° = 15.5504 m. In triangle TUV, tan TVU = $\frac{TU}{VU}$ = $\frac{15.5504}{105}$ = 0.148099283. Therefore, TVU = tan⁻¹ (0.148099283) = 8.4° (correct to 1 d.p.).

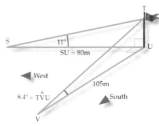

A37

□ **38** *(b)*
In triangle AXB, sin 38° = $\frac{BX}{AB}$. Therefore, BX = AB × sin 38° = 20 × sin 38° = 12.31323km. In triangle BCY, cos 20° = $\frac{BY}{BC}$. Therefore, BY = BC × cos 20° = 35 × cos 20° = 32.88924 km. XY = BY – BX = 20.6 km (correct to 3 s.f.).

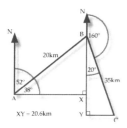

A38

☐ **39** *(d)*
In triangle ABE, cos 15° = $^{EA}\!/_{15}$. Therefore, EA = 15 × cos 15° = 14.488887 km. In triangle BFC, cos 42° = $^{BF}\!/_{18}$. Therefore, BF = 18 × cos 42° = 13.376607 km. AD = EA + DE. DE = BF (opposite lines of a rectangle are equal length). So, AD = EA + BF = 27.9 km (correct to 1 d.p.).

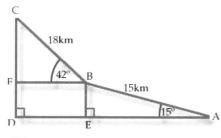

A39

☐ **40** *(b)*
$p^2 = q^2 + r^2 - 2qr \cos P$ (cosine formula). $p^2 = 8^2 + 5^2 - 2 × 8 × 5 × \cos 73° = 64 + 25 - 80 \cos 73° = 65.61026$. So, p = √65.61026 = 8.1 cm (correct to 1 d.p.).

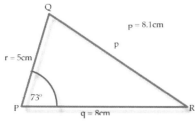

A40

☐ **41** *(d)*
$b^2 = \frac{b^2 + c^2 - a^2}{2bc}$ (cosine formula). $b^2 = 11.4^2 + 7.5^2 - 2 × 11.4 × 7.5 × \cos 115° = 258.4777$. So, b = √258.4777 = 16.1 mm (correct to 1 d.p.).

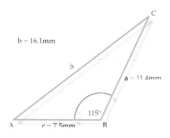

A41

☐ **42** *(a)*
$\cos A = \frac{b^2 + c^2 - a^2}{2bc}$ (cosine formula). $\cos A = \frac{2.9^2 + 3.8^2 - 2.2^2}{2 × 2.9 × 3.8} = 0.8171506$. So, angle A = cos⁻¹

(0.8171506) = 35.2° (correct to 1 d.p.).

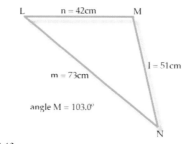

A42

☐ **43** *(c)*
$\cos M = \frac{L^2 + n^2 - m^2}{2Ln}$ (cosine formula). $\cos M = \frac{42^2 + 51^2 + 73^2}{2 × 42 × 51} = -0.2250223$. So, angle M = cos⁻¹ (−0.2250223) = 103.0° (correct to 1 d.p.).

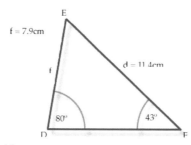

A43

☐ **44** *(c)*
$^f\!/_{\sin F} = {^d\!/_{\sin D}}$ (sine formula). $^f\!/_{\sin 43°} = {^{11.4}\!/_{\sin 80}}$. So, f = $\frac{11.4 \sin 43°}{\sin 80°}$ = 7.9 cm (correct to 1 d.p.).

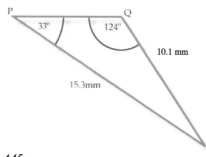

A44

☐ **45** *(b)*
$^p\!/_{\sin P} = {^q\!/_{\sin Q}}$ (sine formula). $^p\!/_{\sin 33°} = {^{15.3}\!/_{\sin 124°}}$. So, p = $\frac{15.3 \sin 33°}{\sin 124°}$ = 10.1 mm (correct to 1 d.p.).

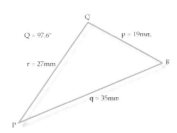

A45

☐ **46** *(a)*
$\frac{\sin A}{a} = \frac{\sin C}{c}$ (sine formula). $^{\sin A}\!/_{8.5} = {^{\sin 63°}\!/_{9.4}}$. Sin A = $\frac{8.5 \sin 63°}{9.4}$ = 0.80956974. So, angle A = sin⁻¹ (0.80956974) = 53.7° (correct to 1 d.p.).

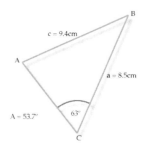

A46

☐ **47** *(c)*
The largest angle of a triangle is opposite the largest side. Therefore, Q is the largest angle. Cos Q = $\frac{p^2 + r^2 - q^2}{2pr}$ (cosine formula). Cos Q = $\frac{19^2 + 27^2 - 35^2}{2 × 19 × 27} = -0.1315789$. So, angle Q = cos⁻¹ (−0.1315789) = 97.6° (correct to 1 d.p.).

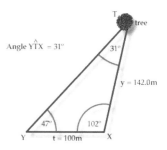

A47

☐ **48** *(e)*
In triangle TYX, angle YTX = 180 – 47 – 102 = 31°. $^y\!/_{\sin Y} = {^t\!/_{\sin T}}$ (sine formula). $^y\!/_{\sin 47°} = {^{100}\!/_{\sin 31°}}$. So, y = $\frac{100 \sin 47°}{\sin 31°}$ = 142.0 m (correct to 1 d.p.).

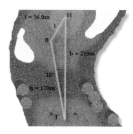

A48

☐ **49** *(b)*
$t^2 = b^2 + h^2 - 2bh \cos 10$ (cosine formula). $t^2 = 215^2 + 170^2 - 2 × 215 × 170 × \cos 10° = 3135553$. So, t = √3135553 = 56.0 m (correct to 1 d.p.).

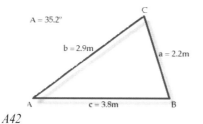

A49

☐ **50** *(d)*
$^d\!/_{\sin D} = {^b\!/_{\sin B}}$. $^d\!/_{\sin 18°} = {^{400}\!/_{\sin 13}}$. d = $\frac{400 \sin 18°}{\sin 13°}$ = 549.483. $^h\!/_d$ = sin 31°. h = d sin 31° = 283 m (correct to the nearest metre).

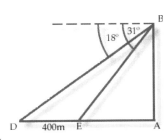

A50

☐ **51** *(c)*
Angle ATB = 180° − 155° − 18° = 7°.
In triangle ABT, $\frac{a}{\sin A} = \frac{t}{\sin T}$. $\frac{a}{\sin 18°} = \frac{20}{\sin 7°}$. a = $\frac{20 \sin 18°}{\sin 7°}$ = 50.7128 m. In triangle TBD, $\frac{h}{a}$ = sin 25°. So, h = a × sin 25° = 50.7128 × sin 25° = 21 m (correct to the nearest metre).

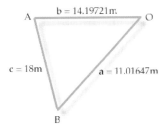

A51

☐ **52** *(d)*
In triangle AOC, sin 25° = $\frac{60}{AC}$. AC = $\frac{60}{\sin 25°}$ = 141.972 m. In triangle BOC, sin 33° = $\frac{60}{BC}$. BC = $\frac{60}{\sin 33°}$ = 110.1647 m. So, cos C = $\frac{(110.16)^2 + (141.97)^2 - (180)^2}{2 \times 110.16 \times 141.97}$ = −0.0035. So, angle C = cos⁻¹(−0.0035) = 90° (correct to the nearest degree).

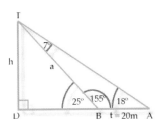

A52

Co-ordinates and transformations

☐ **1** *(b)*
False. In a mathematical enlargement, the object and the image are certainly similar, but also the sides remain parallel to their original directions, which in this case they do not.

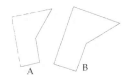

A1

☐ **2** *(a)*
True. Angle C in triangle ABC is equal to (90 − A) (angles in a triangle add up to 180°). So, each of the triangles ABC, ADB, and BDC have angles equal to 90°, A, and (90 − A). Therefore, the triangles are equiangular – hence they are similar.

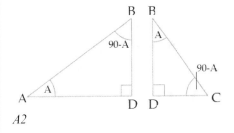

A2

☐ **3** *(a)*
True. The transformed position of P is shown in the following diagram, as P' (−4, 7).

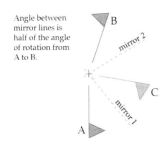

A3

☐ **4** *(a)*
True. Two mirror lines through the centre of rotation separated by an angle equal to half the angle of rotation will achieve the result. Flag A is reflected into intermediate position C by the first mirror (note that flag C is the wrong way up); C is then reflected into B by the second.

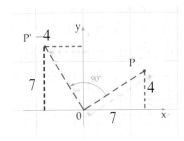

A4

☐ **5** *(a)*
True. The following diagram shows the equivalence of the two transformations. The reflection in the x-axis maps the point (x, y) on to the point (x, −y), while rotation through 90° anticlockwise about the origin maps (x, −y) on to (y, x). Reflection in the line y = x maps the point (x, y) directly on to the point (y, x).

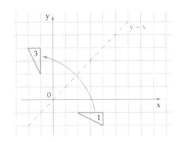

A5

☐ **6** *(b)*
False. Following through the two sequences shows that you finish up at different points, confirming that the statement is false.

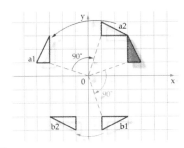

A6

☐ **7** *(a)*
True. The two mirror lines must be parallel to each other and both at right angles to the direction of the translation (the distance apart is half the distance of the translation). The diagram below shows how the translation is achieved.

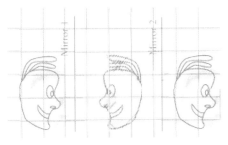

A7

☐ **8** *(a)*
True. If two plane figures are similar then one is an enlargement of the other (possibly rotated) and all the lengths in one are multiplied by the scale factor to produce the lengths in the other. In the following diagram, the ratios p':p, q':q, d':d etc. are all the same (approximately 0.5 in this case).

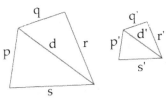

$$\frac{p'}{p} = \frac{q'}{q} = \frac{r'}{r} = \frac{s'}{s} = \frac{d'}{d}$$

A8

103

☐ **9** *(a)*
True. A single rotation through 90°
anticlockwise about the centre (2, 4), as
shown in the following diagram, will
achieve the required result.

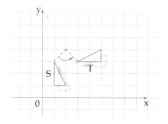

A9

☐ **10** *(b)*
False. After reflection in the line y = –x,
the x co-ordinate of the transformed
point is the opposite sign of the original
y co-ordinate, and the y co-ordinate of
the transformed point is the opposite
sign of the original x co-ordinate. Point
P is (7, 4), so after this reflection the
co-ordinates are (–4, –7).

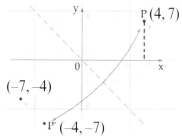

A10

☐ **11** *(b)*
False. The centre of enlargement can be
found by drawing lines to join the
corresponding points of A and B and
extending them until they meet. In this
case, the lines meet at point C, and not
point O.

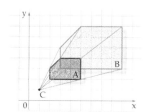

A11

☐ **12** *(b)*
False. Triangle OXY is an enlargement
of triangle OAB, but the ratio of
corresponding sides is 3:1, so the scale
factor is 3.

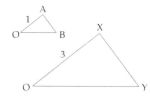

A12

☐ **13** *(b)*
False. In an enlargement, lengths
become multiplied by the scale factor
but the size of the angles remains the
same. In this case, the angle of the
sector has doubled as well as the radius,
(and the arc has been multiplied by 4).

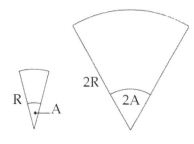

A13

☐ **14** *(b)*
False. When a point is reflected in the
y-axis, the x co-ordinate changes sign
and the y co-ordinate stays the same. P
is the point (b, a), so the correct answer
is (–7, 4). The point (7, –4) is the
reflection of P in the x-axis.

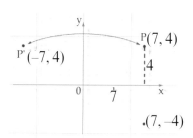

A14

☐ **15** *(a)*
True. The following diagram shows a
parallelogram divided into two pieces by
a straight line through its centre. The
angles and the lengths of the two pieces
are exactly the same. Therefore, the two
pieces are congruent.

A15

☐ **16** *(a)*
The co-ordinates of a point are written
in the form (x, y), where x is the
horizontal distance of the point from
the origin (0, 0) and y is the vertical
distance. To complete the parallelogram,
D will be to B as C is to A. As we have
to move 4 to the right and 1 up to get to
A from C, we do the same to get from B
to D.

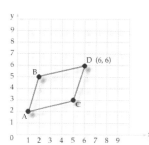

A16

☐ **17** *(b)*
The co-ordinates of a point are written
in the form (x, y). x is the horizontal
distance of the point from the origin
(0, 0) and y is the vertical distance. The
points A, B, C, and D must follow in
order to make ABCD. To complete the
square, D will be to C as A is to B. As
we have to move 5 to the left and 2
down to get to A from B, we do the
same to get from C to D.

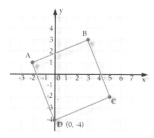

A17

☐ **18** *(d)*
Congruent shapes are exactly the same
shape and size.

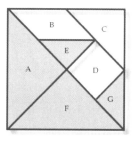

A18

☐ **19** *(b)*
The order of rotational symmetry of a
shape is the number of times the
original appearance is repeated in a full
turn. A shape that has rotational
symmetry of order 2 can be rotated
through 180° about its centre and still
look the same and occupy the same
space.

A19

☐ **20** *(c)*
The translation of 1 unit left and 4 units down can be described by the column vector

$\begin{pmatrix} -1 \\ -4 \end{pmatrix}$.

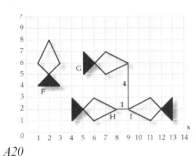

A20

☐ **21** *(e)*
A is transformed to A' by an enlargement. B is transformed to B' by a reflection. C is transformed to C' by a translation.

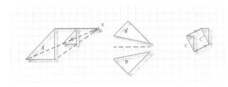

A21

☐ **22** *(b)*
The transformation from S to T is 2 squares across and 5 up, and from T to R is 3 across and 3 down. These can be described by the column vectors.

$\begin{pmatrix} 2 \\ 5 \end{pmatrix} \begin{pmatrix} 3 \\ -3 \end{pmatrix}$

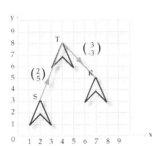

A22

☐ **23** *(d)*
T is transformed to T1 by a reflection in the vertical line x = 2, to T2 by a translation of (–7, 0), and to T3 by a rotation of 90° anti-clockwise about (0, 0).

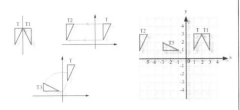

A23

☐ **24** *(c)*
Triangle B is a mirror image of A in the line y = x.

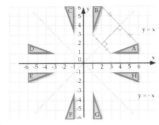

A24

☐ **25** *(a)*
B is the mirror image of triangle E in the line y = –x.

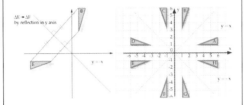

A25

☐ **26** *(b)*
A half turn about the origin will transform triangle C to G.

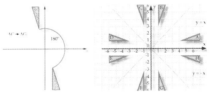

A26

☐ **27** *(a)*
D is the point (2, 3). If D is reflected in the x-axis, the co-ordinates of the new point will be (2, –3)

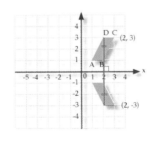

A27

☐ **28** *(e)*
A reflection in the y-axis will transform B to C and A to D.

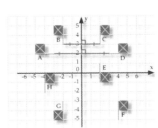

A28

☐ **29** *(b)*
A rotation of 180° about the point (–3, –2.5) will transform G to H.

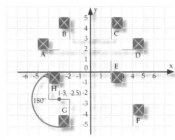

A29

☐ **30** *(a)*
When a shape is enlarged so that each length becomes three times the original length, the scale factor is 3.

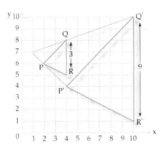

A30

☐ **31** *(a)*
The odd one out has a scale factor of 1.5. The scale factor is the ratio of the lengths of the sides of Q to the corresponding sides of P.

☐ **32** *(c)*
The centre of the enlargement is the point X (4, 4). The new positions of P and Q are twice as far from X as the original positions.

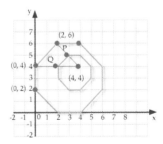

A32

Scale

☐ **1** *(d)*
Since the scale is 1:40 000, 5 cm represents 5 × 40 000 = 200 000 cm. 200 000 cm is equal to 2000 m (100 cm equals 1 m). 2000 m equals 2 km (1000 m equals 1 km).

105

☐ **2** *(e)*
Scale = 1:15 000, so 6 cm on the map equals 6 × 15 000 = 90 000 cm. 100 cm = 1 m, and 90 000 cm = 90 000 ÷ 100 m = 900 m.

☐ **3** *(a)*
3 km is equal to 300 000 cm (1 km = 1000 m, 1m = 100 cm). 300 000 ÷ 15 000 = 20 cm.

☐ **4** *(b)*
17 cm represents 17 × 6000 = 102 000 cm. 102 000 cm is equal to 1.02 km (100 cm = 1 m, 1000 m = 1 km).

☐ **5** *(b)*
Since the angle made by the sun is the same for the pole and the building, the triangles are similar. h ÷ 36 = 5 ÷ 7.5. h = 5 × 36 ÷ 7.5 = 24 m.

☐ **6** *(d)*
The ratio of the width of the photo to the real width is: 10.5 cm:7 m = 10.5 cm:700 cm = 3:200. Real height = 13.5 × 200 ÷ 3 = 900 cm = 9 m.

☐ **7** *(c)*
The ratio of the two photographs is 10.5 cm:14.7 cm = 105:147 = 5:7. The height of the new photo = 16 x ⅞ = 22.4 cm.

Loci

☐ **1** *(a)*
True. The locus of a point equidistant (the same distance) from two fixed points is the perpendicular bisector of the line joining the points.

☐ **2** *(a)*
True. OC = OS. So, triangle OCS is isosceles and O lies on the perpendicular bisector of CS, however far O is from the line CS. Therefore, the path, or locus, of O is the perpendicular bisector of CS.

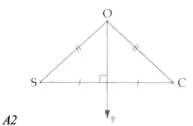

A2

☐ **3** *(a)*
The points on the circumference of the circle are all 5 cm from the centre, A.

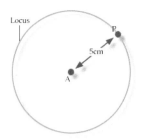

A3

☐ **4** *(b)*
The points on the perpendicular bisector of AB are all equidistant from A and B, by symmetry.

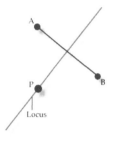

A4

☐ **5** *(d)*
The bisectors of the angles between the two lines contain all the points that are equidistant from AB and CD, by symmetry.

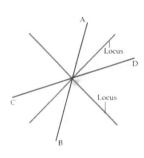

A5

☐ **6** *(e)*
At each end of the locus the two semicircles have points that are 5 cm from A and B. The two line segments, parallel to AB, contain points that are 5 cm from the line segment AB.

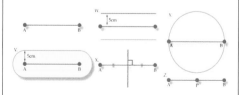

A6

☐ **7** *(a)*
The grass grows well in the area that is more than 1.5 m from the hedge. The area that is not shaded green contains the points that are within 1.5 m of the hedge.

☐ **8** *(b)*
The cows can graze to the right of the perpendicular bisector of AD and BC, and within a circle, centre D, with radius 40 m.

☐ **9** *(c)*
The region in which both stations can be received must lie inside the circle centre A with radius 30 km and also inside the circle centre B with radius 20 km.

Standard units of measure

☐ **1** *(b)*
False. 5 kg is equivalent to 11 lb but 0 kg is equivalent to 0 lb, and not to 5 lb as the following graph shows.

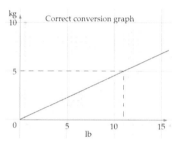

A1

☐ **2** *(b)*
False. 270 m = 27 000 cm. To convert 27 000 cm to feet, divide by 30. So, 27 000 ÷ 30 = 900 feet.

☐ **3** *(a)*
True. 1 inch = 2.5 cm. So, 2.8 inches = 2.8 × 2.5 = 7 cm.

☐ **4** *(a)*
319 miles = 319 × 1.6 km = 510.4 km. Therefore, speed = 319 mph = 510.4 km/h.

☐ **5** *(b)*
9 cm = 90 mm. 90 – 32 = 58 mm.

☐ **6** *(b)*
1 cm = 10 mm. Therefore, 25.87 cm = 25.87 × 10 = 258.7 mm.

☐ **7** *(a)*
100 cm = 1 m. Therefore, 1267 cm = 1267 cm ÷ 100 = 12.67 m.

☐ **8** *(b)*
1000 kg = 1 tonne. Therefore, 4560 kg = 4560 ÷ 1000 = 4.56 tonnes.

☐ **9** *(e)*
100 cm = 1 m. 1000 m = 1 km. So, 100 000 cm = 1 km. Therefore, 60 500 cm = 60 500 ÷ 100 000 =

0.605 km.

☐ **10** *(c)*
34 × 5 = 170 cm. 170 cm = 170 ÷ 100 = 1.7 m.

☐ **11** *(b)*
9 m = 9000 mm. Therefore, 9000 ÷ 45 = 200 jumps.

☐ **12** *(c)*
1000 ml = 1 litre. 45 000 ml = 45 000 ÷ 1000 = 45 litres.

☐ **13** *(b)*
1000 g = 1 kg. 45 360 g = 45 360 ÷ 1000 = 45.36 kg.

☐ **14** *(c)*
750 × 4 = 3000 g. 3000 g = 3000 ÷ 1000 = 3 kg.

☐ **15** *(a)*
1 kg = 1000 g. 1.43 kg = 1430 g. 1430 − 650 = 780 g.

☐ **16** *(d)*
28 × 20 = 560 seconds. 60 seconds = 1 minute. Therefore, 560 ÷ 60 = 9 minutes 20 seconds.

☐ **17** *(a)*
10.6 × 100 = 1060 cm. 1060 cm = 1060 ÷ 100 = 10.6 m.

☐ **18** *(d)*
1 foot = 0.30 m. 10 feet = 3 m (multiply by 10). 100 feet = 30 m. Therefore, 1000 feet = 300 m.

☐ **19** *(d)*
1 m = 3.3 feet. 6 m = 19.8 feet (multiply by 6).

☐ **20** *(d)*
1 m = 100 cm = 3.3 feet. 1 cm = 0.033 feet (divide by 100). Therefore, 95 cm = 3.135 feet (multiply by 95).

☐ **21** *(c)*
1000 cm = 1 litre. 700 000 cm = 700 litres (multiply by 700). Therefore, rate = 700 000 cm^3/minute = 700 litres/minute.

☐ **22** *(b)*
1 gallon = 8 pints. So, 5 gallons = 40 pints (multiply by 5).

☐ **23** *(b)*
1 inch = 25.4 mm. So, 0.5 inch = 12.7 mm (divide by 2).

☐ **24** *(b)*
4.55 litres = 1 gallon. 1 litre = 0.2198 gallons (divide by 4.55). Multiply by 3, so 3 litres = 0.66 gallons (correct

☐ **25** *(c)*
1 litre = 1000 ml = 1.76 pints. 100 ml = 0.176 pints (divide by 10). So, 400 ml = 0.704 pints (multiply by 4).

☐ **26** *(c)*
1 oz = 28 g. Hence, 6 oz = 168 g (multiply by 6).

☐ **27** *(c)*
160 ÷ 5 = 32 miles/gallon.

☐ **28** *(d)*
1 kg = 1000 g. 0.6 kg = 600 g (divide by 0.6). $\frac{\text{weight of box}}{\text{weight of one matchstick}}$ = number of matchsticks in the box. Therefore, $\frac{600}{1.2}$ = 500 matchsticks.

☐ **29** *(e)*
1 km = 1000 m. 25 km = 25 000 m (multiply by 25). $\frac{\text{length of race}}{\text{length of pool}}$ = number of lengths in the race. Therefore, $\frac{25\,000}{50} = \frac{2500}{5}$ = 500 lengths.

☐ **30** *(c)*
1 kg = 1000 g. 1.1 kg = 1100 g (multiply by 1.1). 4560 − 1100 = 3460 g.

☐ **31** *(a)*
500g takes 20 minutes. 25g takes 1 minute (divide by 20). 2.75 kg = 2.75 × 1000 = 2750 g. Therefore, 2750 g takes 110 minutes ($\frac{2750}{25}$ = 110).

☐ **32** *(c)*
A gallon is approximately 4.5 litres.

☐ **33** *(d)*
A metre is slightly larger than 3 feet.

☐ **34** *(e)*
A foot is approximately 30 cm.

☐ **35** *(a)*
1.5 km is equal to 150 000 cm (1 km = 1000 m, 1 m = 100 cm). 150 000 ÷ 75 = 2000 paces.

☐ **36** *(d)*
8km is approximately 5 miles. 560 km ÷ 8 = 70, so, 70 × 5 miles = 350 miles.

☐ **37** *(b)*
5 × 175 = 875 ml. 1 litre equals 1000 ml. 1000 − 875 = 125 ml.

☐ **38** *(e)*
A kilogram is approximately equal to 2.2 lbs. Therefore, 30 kg is equal to 2.2 × 30 = 66 lbs.

☐ **39** *(c)*
One hour after 10:38 is 11:38. Another 22 minutes takes the time to 12:00. This leaves 26 minutes. Therefore, the time of

arrival is 12:26.

☐ **40** *(d)*
1 foot is equal to 12 inches. Therefore, 6 feet 4 inches is equal to 76 inches. 76 ÷ 39 = 1.95 m.

☐ **41** *(b)*
On scale A, each mark represents 0.1 cm. The reading is halfway between 8.6 and 8.7, which is 8.65. On scale B, each mark represents 12.5, so the reading is 162.5. On scale C, each mark represents 0.5. The reading is halfway between 7.5 and 8.0, which is 7.75.

☐ **42** *(b)*
10 m/s is equal to 10 × 60 = 600 m/min (60 seconds = 1 minute). 600 m/min = 600 × 60 = 36 000 m/h (60 mins = 1 hour). 36 000 m/h = 36 000 ÷ 1000 = 36 km/h (1000 m = 1 km).

☐ **43** *(d)*
1 8 cm^3 of gold weighs 231.6 ÷ 12 = 19.3 g. The volume of the second piece = 328.1 ÷ 19.3 = 17 cm^3.

☐ **44** *(c)*
πr^2(l + d) is number × length^2 × length, which has dimension L^3. Area has dimension L^2.

Standard units of measure

Higher Levels

☐ **45** *(a)*
A perimeter has the dimension length (L). (π + 2) has no dimension. r(π + 2) is number × length and has dimension L. The other options have dimensions of either L^2 or L^3.

☐ **46** *(b)*
A perimeter has the dimension length (L). (a + b + c) has dimension L. 4(a + b + c) is number × length, and so has dimension L. The other options have dimensions of either L^2 or L^3.

☐ **47** *(e)*
Area has dimension length × length, which is L^2. $\frac{ab}{2}$ is $\frac{\text{length} \times \text{length}}{\text{number}}$, which has dimension L^2. The other expressions do not have the correct dimensions.

☐ **48** *(b)*
Volume is length × length × length, which has dimension L^3. πr^{2}h is number length^2 × length, which has dimension L^3. $\frac{\pi r^3}{3}$ is number × length^2 × $\frac{\text{length}}{\text{number}}$, which has dimension L^3. The other expressions do not have the correct dimensions.

☐ **49** *(b)*
Volume is length × length × length, which has dimension L^3. $\pi r^2 d/6$ is number × length^2 × length/number, which has dimension L^3. The other expressions do not have the correct dimensions.

☐ **50** *(a)*
Surface area is length × length, which has dimension L^2. 2hr is number × length × length, which has dimension L^2. $\pi rh/4$ is number × length^2/number, which has dimension L^2. $\pi rh/4$ is number × length × length/number. The other expressions do not have the correct dimensions.

☐ **51** *(e)*
Volume is length × length × length, which has dimension of L^3. $(R^2 - r^2)$ has dimension L^2 and l has dimension L so $(R^2 - r^2)l$ has dimension $L^2 \times L = L^3$. π has no effect on the dimensions since numbers have no dimensions. The other expressions do not have the correct dimensions for a volume.

☐ **52** *(c)*
The minimum length of a side of a quadrangle = 43 – ½(1 m) = 42.5 m. Lower bound of area = 42.5 × 42.5 = 1806 m^2 (to the nearest integer).

Discrete and continuous measure

☐ **1** *(b)*
False. Since the length of the running track is accurate to the nearest half metre, its true value is nearer to 100 m than it is to the points half a metre on either side of 100 m, that is to 99.5 m or to 100.5 m. The length must therefore lie in the range 99.75 m to 100.25 m.

☐ **2** *(b)*
False. At exactly 10:30, the clock will read 10:30, but 31 seconds later it will still read 10:30. However, to the nearest minute, the time would then be 10:31.

☐ **3** *(a)*
True. 1 m = 100 cm. So, 1 m^3 = 100 × 100 × 100 = 1 000 000 cm^3.

☐ **4** *(b)*
False. The following diagram shows a square of side 1 m. Each side can be subdivided into 100 cm and therefore the whole square will contain 100 rows of 100 squares of side 1 cm, which is a total of 10 000 small squares.

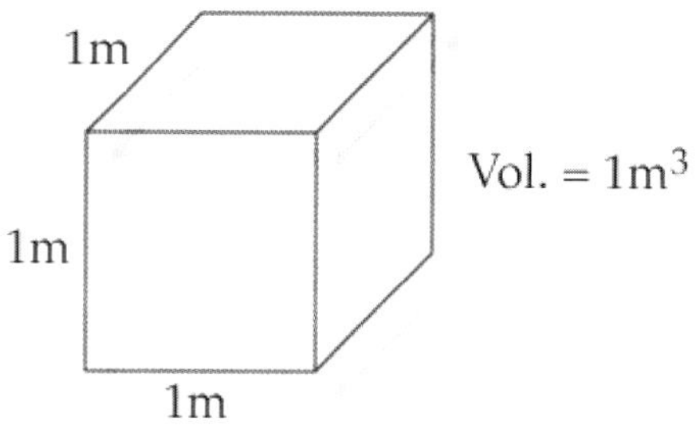

A4

☐ **5** *(b)*
If a number is correct to the nearest 10, it can vary by 5 either side of the value. Therefore, the least number of people employed = 1200 – 5 = 1195.

☐ **6** *(b)*
The variation in the length of the pencil can be as much as 0.5 mm either side of 173 mm. This gives a range of 173 – 0.5 to 173 + 0.5, which is 172.5 to 173.5 mm.

☐ **7** *(c)*
A number that is correct to the nearest 100 can vary by up to half of that value either side of the number. Therefore, the least number of schoolboys = 4500 – 50 = 4450.

☐ **8** *(d)*
The shortest time is 13.4 – ½(0.1) = 13.4 – 0.05 = 13.35 seconds.

☐ **9** *(a)*
The shortest length = 122 – ½(0.01) = 122 – 0.005 = 121.995 m.

☐ **10** *(b)*
The variation in mass = +½(0.1) = +0.05 kg. Therefore, the mass lies between 1.7 – 0.05 and 1.7 + 0.05, which equals 1.65 kg and 1.75 kg.

☐ **11** *(e)*
The variation in length = +½(0.01) = +0.005 m. Therefore, the length lies between 5.73 – 0.005 and 5.73 + 0.005, which equals 5.725 m and 5.735 m.

☐ **12** *(d)*
The minimum length of the room = 6.2 – ½(0.1) = 6.2 – 0.05 = 6.15 m. The minimum width of the room = 4.6 – ½(0.1) = 4.6 – 0.05 = 4.55 m. Therefore, the least perimeter = 2(6.15) + 2(4.55) = 12.3 + 9.1 = 21.4 m.

☐ **13** *(c)*
The upper bound of the weight of each parcel equals the given weight + 0.5 g. Therefore, the total weight is 325.5 + 407.5 + 494.5 + 509.5 + 362.5 = 2099.5 g.

☐ **14** *(a)*
The lower bound for the daily rainfall = 0.48 – ½(0.01) = 0.005 = 0.475 cm. The lower bound for 30 days = 30 × 0.475 = 14.25 cm.

☐ **15** *(b)*
Maximum weight loss = maximum original weight – minimum final weight = 101.8235 – 93.1675 = 8.656 kg.

☐ **16** *(d)*
Volume of cube = 16^3 = 4096 cm^3.
Volume of cone = $\frac{1}{3}\pi r^2 h$ = 4096 cm^3.
$r^2 = 4096 \times 3/\pi \times 21$ = 186.257. r = √186257 = 13.6 cm (1 d.p.).

Discrete and continuous measure

Higher Levels

☐ **17** *(a)*
The maximum length = 7.6 + ½(0.1) = 7.6 + 0.05 – 7.65 cm. The maximum width = 3.3 + ½(0.1) = 3.3 + 0.05 = 3.35 cm. The upper bound for the area is: 7.65 × 3.35 = 25.6275 cm^2 = 25.6 cm^2 (1 d.p.).

☐ **18** *(a)*
The minimum values of the given information are 59.5 m, 1.735 m, and 16.5°. h = 59.5 tan 16.5° + 1.735 = 17.6247 + 1.735 = 19.36 m (2 d.p.).

☐ **19** *(d)*
Area of a rectangle = maximum area/minimum length = $34.5/7.75$ = 4.45 cm (3 s.f.).

☐ **20** *(e)*
Volume of a cylinder = $\pi r^2 h$. h = $V/\pi r^2$ = $599.5/\pi \times 7.25^2$ = 3.6 cm (1 d. p.). Minimum height occurs when volume is a minimum and radius is a maximum.

☐ **21** *(e)*
Volume of a sphere = $\frac{4}{3}\pi r^3$. Maximum volume = $\frac{4}{3}\pi \times 5.85^3$ = 838.6 cm^3 (1 d.p.). Minimum volume = $\frac{4}{3}\pi \times 5.75^3$ = 796.3 cm^3 (1 d.p.).

☐ **22** *(a)*
Maximum rate of km/l = maximum distance/minimum capacity petrol = $895/42.45$ = 21.1 km/l (1 d.p.).

Compound measures

☐ **1** *(a)*
True. 18 km = 18 000 m. 1 hour = 60 ×

60 seconds = 3600 seconds. Therefore, 18 km/h = 18 000 ÷ 3600 = 5 m/s.

☐ **2** *(b)*
Density = $^{mass}/_{volume}$ = $^{800}/_{125}$ = 6.4 g/cm³.
☐ **3** *(b)*
Mass = density × volume = 8.5 × 120 = 1020 g.

☐ **4** *(d)*
Density = $^{mass}/_{volume}$ = $^{800}/_{600}$ = 1.3 g/cm³ (correct to 1 d.p.).

☐ **5** *(a)*
Convert mass into grams: 4 kg = 4000 g.
Volume = $^{mass}/_{density}$ = $^{4000}/_{1.4}$ = 2857.1 cm³ (correct to 1 d.p.).

☐ **6** *(a)*
Mass = density × volume = 0.25 × 40 = 10 g.

☐ **7** *(e)*
25 cm/min = 0.25 m/min = 0.25 × 60 mph = 15 mph.

☐ **8** *(c)*
Speed = distance ÷ time = 200 ÷ 2.5 = 80 km/h.

☐ **9** *(c)*
3 km = 3000 m. Speed = distance ÷ time = 3000 ÷ 48 = 62.5 m/min.

☐ **10** *(a)*
1 minute = $^{1}/_{60}$ hour. Distance = speed × time = 50 × 1 ÷ 60 = 0.83 km (correct to 3 s.f.).

☐ **11** *(b)*
30 seconds = 0.5 minutes. Speed = distance ÷ time = 5 ÷ 0.5 = 10 m/min.

☐ **12** *(b)*
Distance = speed × time = 15 × 3 = 45 m.

☐ **13** *(d)*
20 minutes = $^{20}/_{60}$ hour. Distance = speed × time = 30 × $^{20}/_{60}$ = 10 km.

☐ **14** *(c)*
From 11:00 to 11:15 = 15 minutes = 0.25 hours. Distance = speed × time = 140 × 0.25 = 35 km.

☐ **15** *(b)*
Time = distance ÷ speed = 500 ÷ 15 = 33.3 seconds.

☐ **16** *(c)*
One day = 24 hours. Distance = speed × time = 24 790 × 24 = 594 960 miles.

☐ **17** *(b)*
Time = distance ÷ speed. 81 ÷ 54 = 1.5 hours. One hour is 60 minutes, so

0.5 hours is 30 minutes. Therefore, the time is 1 hour 30 minutes.

☐ **18** *(b)*
The journey took 3 hours. Speed = distance ÷ time. 150 ÷ 3 = 50 mph.
☐ **19** *(e)*
Distance = speed × time. 50 × 4 = 200 miles. 200 ÷ 40 = 5 gallons.

☐ **20** *(a)*
24 minutes = 24 ÷ 60 = 0.4 hours. Speed = distance ÷ time = 19 ÷ 0.4 = 47.5 km/h.

☐ **21** *(d)*
1 hour 24 minutes = 60 + 24 = 84 minutes (1 hour = 60 minutes). 84 minutes = 84 ÷ 60 = 1.4 hours. Speed = distance ÷ time = 12 ÷ 1.4 = 8.6 km/h (correct to 1 d.p).

Compound measures

Higher Levels

☐ **22** *(a)*
Time = distance ÷ speed = 580 ÷ 145 = 4 hours, which is the time taken by the first cart to travel 580 km. In 4 hours, the second cart travels 4 × 124 = 496 km. Therefore, the first cart wins by 580 – 496 = 84 km.

☐ **23** *(c)*
$^{Mass}/_{volume}$ = density. So, $^{172.5}/_{volume}$ = 0.23. Hence, volume = $^{172.5}/_{0.23}$ = 750 cm³.

☐ **24** *(c)*
Distance = speed × time. Total distance travelled = (65 × 7) + (85 × 5) = 455 + 425 = 880 km. Total time = 12 hours. Average speed = $^{total\ distance}/_{total\ time}$ = $^{880}/_{12}$ = 73.3 km/h (1 d.p.).

Perimeter, area, and volume

☐ **1** *(a)*
True. Each term of the formula consists of two letters multiplied together. Therefore, the expression is of dimension 2 and is suitable to represent an area.

☐ **2** *(a)*
True. Volume of a cuboid is the length × breadth × height. The ten bricks have a volume of 10 × 5 × 10 × 20 cm³ = 10 000 cm³. This is equivalent to 100 × 100 × 1 cm³. Therefore, the water has risen by an additional 1 cm of depth spread over the whole surface of the water.

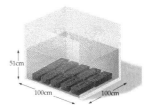

A2

☐ **3** *(a)*
True. Volume of a cuboid is the length × breadth × height. So, volume of the tea packet is 10 cm × 5 cm × 5 cm = 250 cm³. Surface area of the tea packet is 2 × (5 × 5) + 4 × (10 × 5) = 250 cm².

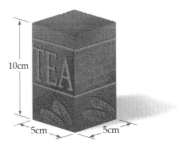

A3

☐ **4** *(a)*
True. The number of bricks in the tower is 24 × 6 × 4 = 576. If the base of the block is a square of side x, the number of bricks used is 9 × x × x or 9x². Therefore, 9x² = 576. x² = 64. So, x = 8.

☐ **5** *(d)*
Volume has dimension (length)³. 4r²h is number × length² × length, which has dimension (length)³. $^{πr²h}/_{2}$ is $^{number\ x\ length²\ ×\ length}/_{number}$, which has dimension (length)³. The other expressions do not have the correct dimensions for volume.

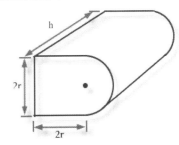

A5, A6, A7

☐ **6** *(b)*
Area has dimension (length)².
Both 4r² and $^{πr²}/_{2}$ have dimension (length)². The other expressions do not have the correct dimensions for area.

☐ **7** *(e)*
Perimeter is a dimension of length. Each of the terms in the expression 6r + πr is a length. The other expressions do not have the correct dimensions.

8 *(c)*
The perimeter of a shape is the distance around the edge of the shape. The perimeter = 3 + 5 + 3 + 5 = 16 cm. The area of a shape is a measure of the amount of space that it covers. The area of a rectangle is the product of the width and the length. The area = 3 × 5 = 15 cm².

9 *(a)*
The perimeter of a shape is the distance around the edge of the shape. The length of AB = 10 – 4 = 6 cm. The edge of BC = 12 – 2 = 10 cm. The perimeter = 12 + 4 + 10 + 6 + 2 + 10 = 44 cm.

10 *(c)*
The perimeter of a shape is the distance around the edge of the shape. The length of AB = 2 + 1.5 + 2 = 5.5 m. The perimeter = 1.5 + 3 + 2 + 1.5 + 5.5 + 1.5 + 2 + 3 = 20 m.

11 *(d)*
The area of a shape is a measure of the amount of space that it covers. The shape can be split into two parts, whose areas can be found. For A, area (rectangle) = 8 × 2 = 16 cm². Area (triangle) = ⁴ ˣ ⁸⁄₂ = ³²⁄₂ = 16 cm². Total area of A = 16 + 16 = 32 cm². Area of each rectangle = 6 × 3 = 18 cm². Total area of B = 18 + 18 = 36 cm².

12 *(e)*
The area of a shape is a measure of the amount of space that it covers. The shape can be split into three parts, each of which is a rectangle. Area A = 12 × 4 = 48 cm². B and C are the same size. Area B = 4 × 6 = 24 cm². Total area = 48 + 24 + 24 = 96 cm².

13 *(d)*
Area of circle = π × r² = π × 5² = π × 25 = 78.5 cm² (1 d.p.).

14 *(c)*
Circumference of a circle = π × diameter = π × 13 = 40.8 cm (1 d.p.).

15 *(d)*
The radius of the circle is 5.5 cm, so the diameter is 11 cm. The circumference of a circle = π × diameter = π × 11 = 34.6 cm (1 d.p.).

16 *(c)*
The two semicircles are equivalent to one circle. The circumference of a circle = π × diameter = π × 50 = 157.1 m. Therefore, the perimeter = 157.1 + 150 = 457.1 m (1 d.p.).

17 *(a)*
The parallelogram can be split into two

equal triangles, each of which has a height of 3.2 cm and a base of 8 cm. Area of triangle = ᵇᵃˢᵉ ˣ ʰᵉⁱᵍʰᵗ⁄₂ = 8 × ³·²⁄₂ = ²⁵·⁶⁄₂ = 12.8 cm². Therefore, the two triangles have a total area of 12.8 × 2 = 25.6 cm².

18 (e)
The radius of the ring is 35 m, so the diameter is equal to 70 m. The circumference of the ring = π × diameter = π × 70 = 219.9 m (1 d.p.).

19 *(a)*
Area of a circle = π × r². r² = A ÷ π = 20 ÷ π = 6.366. Therefore, r = √6.366 = 2.5 m (1 d.p.).

20 *(b)*
Circumference of a circle = π × diameter. Diameter = circumference ÷ π = 30 ÷ π = 9.5 m (1 d.p.).

21 *(b)*
The goat can graze over an area that is a quarter of a circle, of radius 20 m. Area of a circle = π × r² = π × 20 × 20 = 1256.6 m². Shaded area = ¹²⁵⁶·⁶⁄₄ = 314.2 m² (1 d.p.).

22 *(d)*
Area A = 12 × 3 = 36 cm²; area B = 12 × 5 = 60 cm²; area C = 12 × 4 = 48 cm². Area D = area E = 4 × ³⁄₂ = 6 cm². Total area = 36 + 60 + 48 + 6 + 6 = 156 cm².

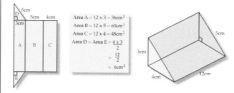

A22

23 *(d)*
The shape is split into a rectangle and two semicircles. The two semicircles make a circle. Area of a rectangle = 5.6 × 3.2 = 17.92 m². Since the diameter of the circle is 3.2 m, the radius is 1.6 m. Area of a circle = π × 1.6 × 1.6 = 8.04 m² (2 d.p.). Total area = 17.92 + 8.04 = 25.96 m².

24 *(c)*
The diagonals of a rhombus divide the shape into four identical right-angled triangles. The diagonals also bisect each other at right angles. Therefore, each triangle has a base of 8 cm and a height of 6 cm. Area of a triangle = 6 × ⁸⁄₂ = ⁴⁸⁄₂ = 24 cm². Area of four triangles = 4 × 24 = 96 cm².

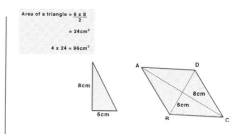

A24

25 *(e)*
The front layer contains 22 cubes and so does the back layer.

A25

26 *(c)*
Volume = length × width × height = 5 × 7 × 5 = 175 cm³.

A26

27 *(a)*
The dimensions of the cuboid are 4 cm by 7 cm by 10 cm. Volume = length × width × height = 4 × 7 × 10 = 280 cm³.

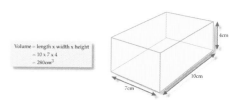

A27

28 *(b)*
Volume = length × width × height = 45 × 30 × 8 = 10 800 cm³. 1000 cm³ = 1 litre. 10 800 cm³ = 10 800 ÷ 1000 = 10.8 litres.

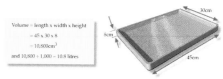

A28

29 *(a)*
Volume = length × width × height = 600 × 600 × 50 = 18 000 000 mm³. 18 000 000 ÷ 1000 = 18 000 cm³.

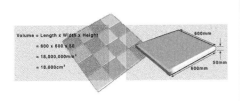

A29

☐ **30** *(c)*
Volume = length × width × height.
Therefore, 9 = 3 × 2 × h = 6h.
h = 9 ÷ 6 = 1.5 m.

A30

☐ **31** *(c)*
60 cm = 0.6 m. Volume = length × width × height = 12 × 7 × 0.6 = 50.4 m³.

A31

☐ **32** *(d)*
The solid can be split into two cuboids.
Volume A = 2 × 1 × 6 = 12 cm³.
Volume B = 1 × 1 × 6 = 6 cm³. Total volume = 12 + 6 = 18 cm³.

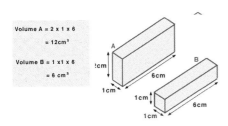

A32

☐ **33** *(e)*
Eight bricks fit along the length of the box, five rows fit the width, and three layers fit into the height. 8 × 5 × 3 = 120 bricks.

☐ **34** *(a)*
The dimensions of the tank are 200 cm by 300 cm by 400 cm (1 m = 100 cm).
Volume = 200 × 300 × 400 = 24 000 000 cm³. 1000 cm³ = 1 litre.
24 000 000 ÷ 1000 = 24 000 litres.

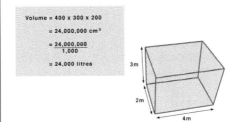

A34

☐ **35** *(d)*
Volume = length × width × height. 720 = width × 4 × 18 = width × 72. Width = 720 ÷ 72 = 10 cm.

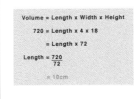

A35

☐ **36** *(c)*
Volume of a prism = area of cross-section × length = 30 × 18 = 540 cm³.

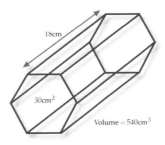

A36

☐ **37** *(d)*
The cross-section of the prism is a right-angled triangle. Area of cross-section = base × height/2 = 7 × 5.5/2 = 19.25 cm². Volume of a prism = area of cross-section × length = 19.25 × 12 = 231 cm³.

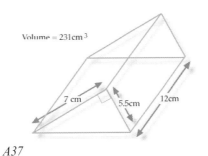

A37

☐ **38***(c)*
Volume of a cylinder = πr²h = π × 652 × 245 = 3 251 941 cm³. 1000 cm³ = 1 litre. So, the capacity in litres = 3 251 941 ÷ 1000 = 3251.9 litres (to 1 d.p.).

☐ **39** *(b)*
Volume of a cone = ⅓πr²h. Volume of oil = ⅓ × π × 324 × 30 = 10 178.76 cm³. 10 178.76 cm³ = 10 179 cm³ (to the nearest integer).

Perimeter, area, and volume

Higher Levels

☐ **40** *(a)*
True. Triangles AXY and ABC are similar in the linear ratio 2:3. So, their areas are in the ratio 4:9, and the ratio area of triangle AXY:area of trapezium XYCB = 4:5. Hence, the trapezium has a greater area than the triangle.

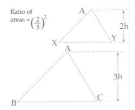

A40

☐ **41** *(b)*
False. If the length and breadth of a rectangle were originally a and b, the new length and breadth are a × 1.1 and b × 1.1. So the new area is (a × 1.1) × (b × 1.1) or 1.21 × ab. The original area was ab. Therefore, the increase is 21%.

☐ **42** *(e)*
Volume = length × width × height = 60 × 15 × 8 = 7200 cm³. Mass = 7200 × 6 = 43 200 g. 1000 g = 1 kg. Mass = 43 200 ÷ 1000 = 43.2 kg.

A42

☐ **43** *(b)*
Circumference of a circle = π × d = π × 12 = 37.699 cm. 130/360 = 13/36. Length of arc = 37.699 × 13/36 = 13.6 cm (1 d.p.).

111

☐ **44** *(e)*
Area of a triangle = ½bh = ½ × 4 × 2.5
= 5 m². Length AB = √(2² + 25²)
(Pythagoras' theorem). Therefore, AB =
3.202 m. Area of a rectangle = bh. Area
ABCD = 6 × AB = 19.21 m² (2 d.p.).
Total surface area = 2[5 + 12 + 18 +
19.21] = 108.4 m² (1 d.p.).

☐ **45** *(b)*
Volume of a cuboid = 60 × 25 × 12 =
18 000 mm³. Volume of a ball bearing =
$\frac{4}{3}πr^3$ = $\frac{4}{3}$ × π × 3³ = 113.097 mm³.
Number of ball bearings = $\frac{18\,000}{113\,097}$ =
159.15. Therefore, 159 ball bearings
are cast.

☐ **46** *(e)*
Volume of a sphere = $\frac{4}{3}πr^3$ = 600. r³ =
600 × $\frac{3}{4π}$ = 143.2395. r = $\sqrt[3]{143.2395}$ =
5.2322 cm. Therefore, d = 2 × r =
10.5 cm (1 d.p.).

☐ **47** *(d)*
Area of a sector = $\frac{50}{360}$ × πr² = 75.
r² = $\frac{75 × 360}{50 × π}$. r = √171.88734 =
13.11058 cm. Arc AB = $\frac{50}{360}$ × 2πr =
11.44114 cm. Therefore, the perimeter of
the sector = 2r + AB = 37.7 cm (1 d.p.).

Handling Data

With the current expansion in the ability to pass information electronically it has become more necessary to be able to handle data efficiently. Skills that are required include: gathering and presenting data in a way that can then be used effectively; undertaking purposeful enquiries based on analysing data; using computers as a source of large samples and graphical representations; looking critically at outcomes; and identifying where representations can be misleading.

Collecting data

KEY FACTS

• Data (information) can be collected from surveys, questionnaires, lists, charts, tables, computer databases etc.

• The data can be qualitative (i.e. descriptive – e.g. colour of car, type of blood group), or quantitative (i.e. numerical – e.g. heights, scores on dice).

• Quantitative data can be divided into two categories: discrete (or countable) data and continuous (or measurable) data. Scores on dice or number of pets you own are discrete data, while heights of plants or the time taken to run 400 m are examples of continuous data.

• Tally charts can be used to collect information in an efficient way.

• With large amounts of data, the information is often grouped into categories (or classes). For example, marks in a test out of 100 could be grouped into classes of 1-10, 11-20, 21-30, and so on. This makes the data more manageable.

QUESTIONS

1 "It is known that there are twice as many men employed in a factory as women. To take a sample of the employees, twice as many men should be selected to reflect this difference." Is this statement true or false?

☐ (a) True
☐ (b) False

2 The number of matches in 20 boxes was recorded and the data put into a frequency table, as shown in

the following diagram. What is the value of p?

☐ (a) 2
☐ (b) 11
☐ (c) 5
☐ (d) 12
☐ (e) 1

No. of matches	35-39	40-44	45-49	50-54
38	44	46	42	49
51	48	46	47	46
40	38	48	42	48
45	46	46	49	42
Frequency	(p)	(q)	(r)	(s)

Q2, Q3, Q4

3 The number of matches in 20 boxes was recorded and the data put into a frequency table, as shown in the diagram above. What is the value of r?

☐ (a) 2
☐ (b) 11
☐ (c) 5
☐ (d) 12
☐ (e) 1

4 The number of matches in 20 boxes was recorded and the data put into a frequency table, as shown in the previous diagram. How many boxes contain less than 50 matches?

☐ (a) 2
☐ (b) 11
☐ (c) 5
☐ (d) 12
☐ (e) 19

5 The number of pets owned by the 30 pupils in class 11P was recorded and the data put into a frequency table, as shown in the following diagram. What is the value of p?

☐ (a) 0
☐ (b) 1
☐ (c) 4
☐ (d) 7
☐ (e) 8

No. of pets	0	1	2	3	4	5	6
4	0	1	0	2	1		
3	6	2	1	3	2		
2	0	0	4	0	2		
1	0	1	1	0	3		
2	1	2	0	3	4		
Frequency	p	q	r	s	t	u	v

Q5, Q6, Q7, Q8

6 The number of pets owned by the 30 pupils in class 11P was recorded and the data put into a frequency table, as shown in the diagram above. What is the value of u?

☐ (a) 0
☐ (b) 1
☐ (c) 4
☐ (d) 7
☐ (e) 8

7 The number of pets owned by the 30 pupils in class 11P was recorded and the data put into a frequency table, as shown in the previous diagram. How many pupils own less than three pets?

☐ (a) 15
☐ (b) 22
☐ (c) 26
☐ (d) 4
☐ (e) 3

8 The number of pets owned by the 30 pupils in class 11P was recorded and the data put into a frequency table, as shown in the previous diagram. What is the total number of pets owned by the 30 pupils?

☐ (a) 30
☐ (b) 21
☐ (c) 40
☐ (d) 50
☐ (e) 51

9 The following diagram shows the tariff for hiring cars from an agency. How much would it cost to hire an automatic Rover 400 for five days?

☐ (a) £280
☐ (b) £56
☐ (c) £270

☐ (d) £380
☐ (e) £290

10 The diagram below shows the tariff for hiring cars from an agency. How much more would it cost to hire an automatic Rover 400 for five days than a Peugeot 106?

☐ (a) £56
☐ (b) £75
☐ (c) £15
☐ (d) £70
☐ (e) £205

	Model	Daily rate
Manual Gearbox	Vauxhall Corsa 1.2 3dr Peugeot 106 2dr	£41.00
	Vauxhall Astra 1.4 5dr Peugeot 306 1.4 5dr	£46.00
	Vauxhall Cavalier 1.8 Rover 400 Saloon Nissan Primera 1.6 Ford Mondeo 1.8	£54.00
	Vauxhall Cavalier 2.0 Nissan Primera 2.0	£57.00
Automatic Gearbox	Vauxhall Astra Saloon 1.6 Rover 400	£56.00
	Vauxhall Omega 2.0 GLS Rover 820	£76.00
	Vauxhall Omega 2.5CD	£91.00

Q9, Q10

11 The diagram opposite shows information on ferries and prices. How much would it cost for a car, three adults, and two children to cross from Dover to Calais on Friday 9th August?

☐ (a) £128
☐ (b) £152
☐ (c) £168
☐ (d) £142
☐ (e) £40

12 The diagram opposite shows a table with prices for villas in L'Estartit, Spain. How much would it cost for a family of seven to stay in Villa Trepuxtell the week beginning the 25th May?

☐ (a) £205
☐ (b) £255
☐ (c) £569
☐ (d) £295
☐ (e) £169

13 The diagram opposite shows the timetable for the Southampton tour. If Mary joins the first tour at the town quay at 1:50 pm, when will she arrive at the city centre?

☐ (a) 16:35
☐ (b) 12:20
☐ (c) 14:20
☐ (d) 13:20
☐ (e) 15:10

Routes	Crossing Time	Outward Time	Inward Time	Sailings	Standard Season 1 May-13 July 4 Sept-31 Oct			High Season 14 July-3 Sept		
SPEED FERRIES LINE					Car+2 Adults	Extra Adult	Child 3-14Yrs	Car+2 Adults	Extra Adult	Child 3-14Yrs
Newhaven Dieppe	4 hrs	0715,1015,1930 2230,0545,1115 1645,2300	0200,0530,1400 1730,0245,0930 1500,2030	Sun-Thurs	75	8	8	99	8	8
				Fri-Sat	75	8	8	122	8	8
Dover Calais	1.5 hrs	18 crosses daily	18 crosses daily	Sun-Thurs	81	8	8	106	8	8
				Fri-Sat	81	8	8	128	8	8
Southampton Cherbourg	5 hrs	1100,2300	0600,1800	Sun-Thurs	95	8	8	119	8	8
				Fri-Sat	101	8	8	152	8	8

Q11

L'Estartit	Sleeps	18th May and earlier	25 May 1, 8 15 22 June	29 June 6 July	13, 20, 27 July 3, 10, August	17, 24 Aug	31 Aug 7 Sept	14 Sept and later
Bell Raco	4	215	309	569	679	569	309	215
	6	235	365	599	725	599	365	235
Les Acacies	6	235	365	599	725	599	365	235
Les Oliveres	4/6	185	279	539	645	539	279	185
Les Palmeres	4/6	185	279	539	645	539	279	185
Val Gran	6	249	385	659	779	659	385	249
Trepuxtell	4	169	235	449	539	449	235	169
	4/5	190	255	479	569	479	255	190
	6/8	205	295	569	629	569	295	205
	2	119	169	325	385	325	169	119
(with double bedroom)	2/4	169	235	415	509	415	235	169

Q12

The Southampton Tour leaves every hour every day.

Join The Tour at:	First Tour:		Last Tour Bus:
City Centre	11:30am		3:30pm
Central Railway	11:40am	then every hour until	3:40pm
Town Quay	11:50am		3:50pm
Ocean Village	12:00noon		4:00pm
City Centre Arrive	12:20pm		4:35pm

Q13

Menorca: Type of Car	Citroen Ax 1.1 3dr	Citroen Ax 1.4 3dr	Citroen Ax 1.4 5dr	Citroen Ax 1.4 5dr	Minibus
No. of Seats	4	4	5	5	7/8
April, May, June Oct, Nov (£)	134	149	167	174	470
July,Aug,Sept (£)	155	167	184	198	513

Costa Blanca: Type of Car	Panda	VW Polo	Seat Ibiza 3dr	Seat Ibiza 5dr	Minibus
No. of Seats	4	4	5	5	7/8
April, May, June Oct, Nov (£)	105	119	141	162	367
July,Aug,Sept (£)	130	151	165	182	421

Lanzarote: Type of Car	Panda	Corsa 3dr	Fiesta 3dr	Corsa 5dr	Minibus
No. of Seats	4	4	5	5	7/8
April, May, June Oct, Nov (£)	112	118	127	144	357
July,Aug,Sept (£)	120	129	137	157	447

Malta/Gozo: Type of Car	Mazda 121 3dr	Fiesta 3dr	Mazda 121 4 dr	Escort	Minivan
No. of Seats	4	4	5	5	7/8
April, May, June Oct, Nov (£)	108	113	120	136	271
July,Aug,Sept (£)	127	132	140	151	302

Q14

14 Look at the information in the table above. Which is the cheapest five-seat car that can be hired for a week in July?

☐ (a) Citroen AX in Menorca
☐ (b) Mazda 121 in Malta/Gozo
☐ (c) Panda in the Costa Blanca
☐ (d) Panda in Lanzarote
☐ (e) Fiesta in Lanzarote

15 The following table gives the prices per person for staying in various villas in a Spanish holiday resort. Work out how much a fortnight in El Gecko for eight people would cost per person beginning 3rd July.

☐ (a) £555.80
☐ (b) £525
☐ (c) £527.20

Accommodation		FRANCESCA		EL GECKO		MIGUEL	
Number Sharing		8		9		9	
Number of Nights		7	14	7	14	7	14
24 APR - 14 MAY		305	355	299	385	299	339
15 MAY - 21 MAY		305	415	299	445	299	399
22 MAY - 04 JUN		419	465	409	495	415	449
05 JUN - 18 JUN		345	445	369	475	369	429
19 JUN - 02 JUL		405	479	399	509	399	465
03 JUL - 16 JUL		425	495	419	525	419	479
17 JUL - 20 AUG		495	599	489	629	489	585
21 AUG - 3 SEP		465	525	459	555	459	509
4 SEP - 17 SEP		399	469	389	499	395	455
18 SEP - 08 OCT		355	415	349	445	349	399
09 OCT - 15 OCT		305	375	299	405	299	359
16 OCT - 22 OCT		335	-	329	-	329	-

Supplements per person per night							
LOW - MAY,OCT	SEASON			LOW	MID	HIGH	
MID - JUN, SEPT	NUMBER SHARING	8	-	1.10	1.60	2.20	1.20
HIGH - JUL,AUG		7	1.40	2.40	3.60	4.80	2.80
		6	3.20	4.20	6.20	8.30	4.80
Prices in £'s per person		5	5.80	6.60	9.70	13.20	7.60

Q15

| (d) £7350 |
| (e) £540.40 |

16 The diagram below shows a table of prices for a hotel in Netley Abbey (the prices shown are per person). How much more would dinner, bed, and breakfast for two cost for four nights beginning on the 1st March as compared to three nights over a bank holiday?

- (a) £35
- (b) £50
- (c) £5
- (d) £20
- (e) £40

17 The table below shows the theatre sales for The Royal for the last week of their production of "An Evening with Gary Vinegar". Calculate how much money they made.

Netley Abbey Hotel

D/B&B	1/1-31/3	1/4-15/9	Bank Holidays	
2 nts	£65.00	£70.00	2 nts	£70.00
Ex nt	£30.00	£30.00	Ex nt	£35.00
7 nts	£200.00	£200.00	7 nts	£220.00

Q16

- (a) £1700
- (b) £7100
- (c) £11 044

Seat	Mon	Tues	Wed	Thur	Fri	Sat	Sun	Total
Stalls £12	25	26	32	28	36	40	0	?
Main Hall £10	101	104	110	120	140	135	0	?
Balcony £20	12	15	12	12	16	18	0	?

Q17

| (d) £11 032 |
| (e) £11 440 |

QUESTIONS

Higher Level only

18 "If you have to take a sample of something that you have no knowledge of, the best sampling method would be stratified sampling." Is this statement true or false?

- (a) True
- (b) False

19 A school roll consists of year groups of the sizes shown in the following table. If a stratified sample of 90 pupils were taken, how many pupils would be taken from Year 7?

- (a) 8
- (b) 13
- (c) 18
- (d) 20
- (e) 26

20 A school roll consists of year groups of the sizes shown in the following table. If a stratified sample of 90 pupils was taken, how many pupils would be taken from Year 8?

- (a) 11
- (b) 12
- (c) 13

- (d) 14
- (e) 15

Year	Number of pupils
7	130
8	85
9	160
10	120
11	90
	585

Q19, Q20, Q21

21 A school roll consists of year groups of the sizes shown in the previous table. If a stratified sample of 98 pupils was taken, how many pupils would be taken from Year 10?

- (a) 12
- (b) 13
- (c) 15
- (d) 18
- (e) 20

22 A stratified sample of 200 football fans is to be taken from four leagues, as shown in the following table. How many would be sampled from Division One?

- (a) 103
- (b) 105
- (c) 100
- (d) 95
- (e) 110

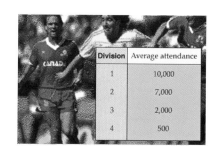

Division	Average attendance
1	10,000
2	7,000
3	2,000
4	500

Q22, Q23, Q24, Q25

23 A stratified sample of 200 football fans is to be taken from four leagues, as shown in the table above. How many would be sampled from Division Two?

- (a) 70
- (b) 72
- (c) 75
- (d) 85
- (e) 140

24 A stratified sample of 200 football fans is to be taken from four leagues, as shown in the previous table. How many would be sampled from Division Three?

☐ (a) 24
☐ (b) 23
☐ (c) 22
☐ (d) 21
☐ (e) 20

25 A stratified sample of 200 football fans is to be taken from four leagues, as shown in the previous table. How many would be sampled

from Division Four?

☐ (a) 25
☐ (b) 20
☐ (c) 15
☐ (d) 10
☐ (e) 5

Representing data

KEY FACTS

• Data (information) can be represented in a number of ways to make it easier to analyse and interpret.

• Bar charts, pictograms (where a symbol stands for a group of units), and frequency diagrams label the attribute (e.g. height, score on dice) on the horizontal axis, and the frequency is marked on the vertical axis. (Occasionally it is more convenient to change the axes.)

• Pie charts display information in a circle, in which the size of the sectors represent each attribute.

• When two attributes (e.g. height and weight of students in Class 10P) are being compared, a scatter diagram can be used. Height is drawn on one axis, and weight on the other. Each person is represented by the point on the diagram whose co-ordinates are their height and their weight.

• Using a cumulative frequency diagram is an efficient method of measuring how spread out a set of data is. Each point on the graph represents the frequency of all values of the data, up to the value chosen.

• All these methods of representing data make it easier to see the overall picture and to pick out general statistical information, than it would otherwise be if using figures in a list or a table.

QUESTIONS

1 "The graph below shows good negative correlation." Is this statement true or false?

☐ (a) True
☐ (b) False

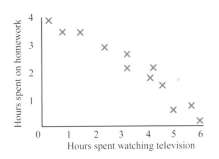

Q1

2 "Ten boys sat a maths test and a French test. Their scores are shown on the scatter graph below. The graph shows positive correlation. However, if the same scores had been plotted with the axes exchanged, the graph would have shown negative correlation." Is this statement true or false?

☐ (a) True
☐ (b) False

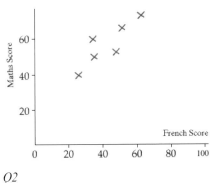

Q2

3 "The colour of the cars in the school car park was noted and the

results put into a bar chart, as shown in the following diagram. There are 16 cars altogether." Is this statement true or false?

☐ (a) True
☐ (b) False

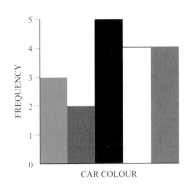

Q3

4 "The amount of pocket money that the pupils in class 10G were given was noted and the results put into a bar graph, as shown in the following diagram. Nine pupils received £5 or more." Is this statement true or false?

☐ (a) True
☐ (b) False

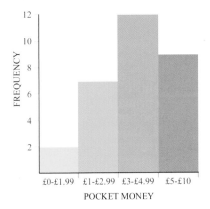

Q4, Q5, Q6

5 "The amount of pocket money that the pupils in class 10G were

117

given was noted and the results put into a bar graph, as shown in the previous diagram. There are 28 pupils in class 10G." Is this statement true or false?

☐ (a) True
☐ (b) False

6 The amount of pocket money that pupils in 10G were given was noted and the results put into a bar graph, as shown in the previous diagram. How many pupils received £2?

☐ (a) 2
☐ (b) 4
☐ (c) 6
☐ (d) 8
☐ (e) Cannot tell

7 "Ten students sat a maths test and a science test. Their scores were plotted on a scatter graph, as shown on the diagram below. The graph shows negative correlation." Is this statement true or false?

☐ (a) True
☐ (b) False

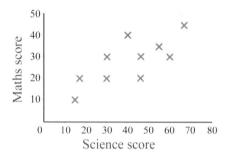

Q7, Q8

8 "Ten students sat a maths test and a science test. Their scores were plotted on a scatter graph, as shown on the diagram above. If another student scored 35 in science, her maths score is likely to be about 50." Is this statement true or false?

☐ (a) True
☐ (b) False

9 "The heights of sunflower plants grown by a primary school class were recorded and the results displayed, as shown in the following frequency diagram. There are eight plants under 1.2 m." Is this statement true or false?

☐ (a) True
☐ (b) False

10 "The heights of sunflower plants grown by a primary school class

were recorded and the results displayed, as shown in the following frequency diagram. There are 30 plants altogether." Is this statement true or false?

☐ (a) True
☐ (b) False

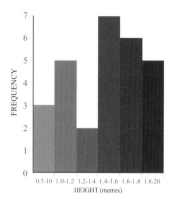

Q9, Q10, Q11, Q12

11 The heights of sunflower plants grown by a primary school class were recorded and the results displayed, as shown in the frequency diagram above. How many plants were at least 1.4 m tall?

☐ (a) 2
☐ (b) 7
☐ (c) 18
☐ (d) 20
☐ (e) 23

12 The heights of sunflower plants grown by a primary school class were recorded and the results displayed, as shown in the previous frequency diagram. Any plant taller than 1.7 m earned a prize. Estimate how many plants won a prize.

☐ (a) 28
☐ (b) 3
☐ (c) 5
☐ (d) 10
☐ (e) 8

13 The following bar chart shows the profit and loss of a bookshop during seven months of sales. What was the total profit that the book shop made over the seven months?

☐ (a) –£150
☐ (b) –£100
☐ (c) £150
☐ (d) £300
☐ (e) £1150

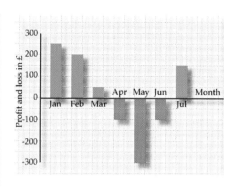

Q13

14 The following pie chart has eight evenly spaced sectors and shows how 240 workers in Sidley travelled to work. What fraction of workers travelled by bus?

☐ (a) $^1/_8$
☐ (b) $^1/_4$
☐ (c) $^1/_7$
☐ (d) $^1/_2$
☐ (e) $^3/_4$

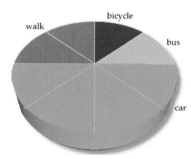

Q14, Q15, Q16, Q17

15 The pie chart above has eight evenly spaced sectors and shows how 240 workers in Sidley travelled to work. What fraction of workers walked to work?

☐ (a) $^1/_7$
☐ (b) $^1/_8$
☐ (c) $^1/_4$
☐ (d) $^1/_2$
☐ (e) $^2/_7$

16 The previous pie chart has eight evenly spaced sectors and shows how 240 workers in Sidley travelled to work. How many workers travelled to work by car?

☐ (a) 60
☐ (b) 100
☐ (c) 120
☐ (d) 150
☐ (e) 180

17 The previous pie chart has eight evenly spaced sectors and shows how 240 workers in Sidley travelled to work. How many workers travelled to work by bike?

☐ (a) 15
☐ (b) 30
☐ (c) 45
☐ (d) 60
☐ (e) 100

18 The following pie chart shows the time that Jennie spent on various activities during one evening. If the chart shows 5 hours of activities, how long did Jennie spend walking the dog?

☐ (a) 1 hour 25 minutes
☐ (b) 1 hour 22.5 minutes
☐ (c) 1 hour 10 minutes
☐ (d) 1 hour 20 minutes
☐ (e) 1 hour 15 minutes

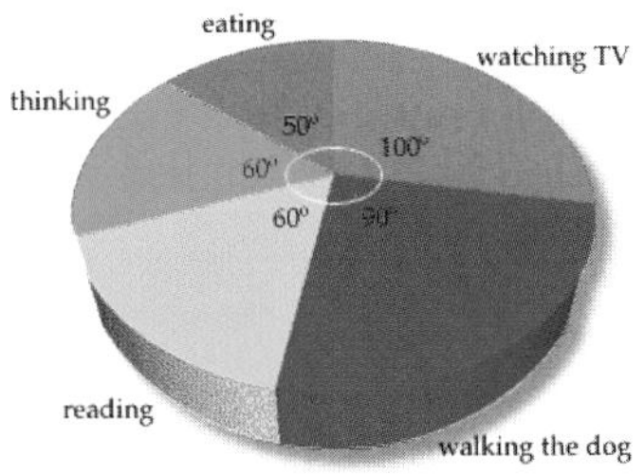

Q18, Q19, Q20, Q21

19 The pie chart above shows the time that Jennie spent on various activities during one evening. If the chart shows 4 hours of activities, how long did she spend reading?

☐ (a) 20 minutes
☐ (b) 40 minutes
☐ (c) 60 minutes
☐ (d) 80 minutes
☐ (e) 100 minutes

20 The previous pie chart shows the time Jenny spent on various activities during one evening. If the chart shows 4½ hours of activities, how much longer did she spend watching TV than thinking?

☐ (a) 15 minutes
☐ (b) 30 minutes
☐ (c) 45 minutes
☐ (d) 60 minutes
☐ (e) 90 minutes

21 The previous pie chart shows the time that Jennie spent on various activities during one evening. How much time did she spend eating if she walked the dog for 27 minutes?

☐ (a) 11 minutes
☐ (b) 12 minutes
☐ (c) 13 minutes
☐ (d) 14 minutes
☐ (e) 15 minutes

22 The following pie chart shows how a football supporter spent his money over a season. If he spent £160 in total, how much did he spend on programmes?

☐ (a) £40
☐ (b) £50
☐ (c) £60
☐ (d) £20
☐ (e) £30

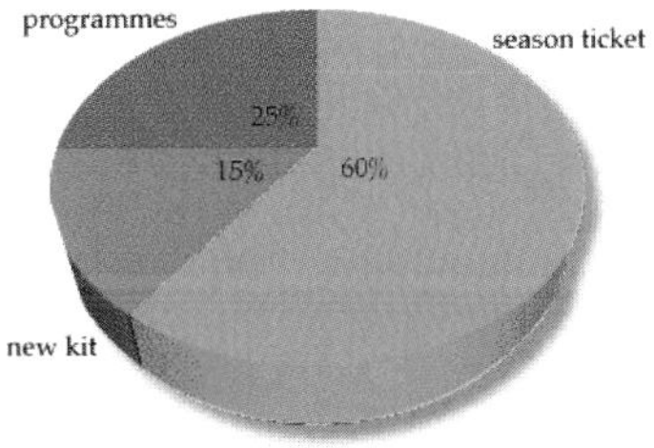

Q22

23 The data shown in the following diagram is to be displayed on a pie chart and shows the number of visitors to the rides of a fun fair during one afternoon. What size angle would be used to represent the people visiting the dodgems?

☐ (a) 15°
☐ (b) 30°
☐ (c) 45°
☐ (d) 60°
☐ (e) 90°

Ride	Dodgems	Rollercoaster	Ghost Train	Waltzer	Big Wheel
People	5	10	19	8	18

Q23, Q24, Q25, Q26

24 The data shown in the diagram above is to be displayed on a pie chart and shows the number of visitors to the rides of a fun fair during one afternoon. What size angle would be used to represent the people visiting the rollercoaster?

☐ (a) 60°
☐ (b) 45°
☐ (c) 30°
☐ (d) 90°
☐ (e) 15°

25 The data shown in the previous diagram is to be displayed on a pie chart and shows the number of visitors to the rides of a fun fair during one afternoon. What size angle would be used to represent the people visiting the waltzer?

☐ (a) 25°
☐ (b) 34°
☐ (c) 48°
☐ (d) 55°

☐ (e) 90°

26 The data shown in the previous diagram is to be displayed on a pie chart and shows the number of visitors to the rides of a fun fair during one afternoon. If the fun fair owners wanted to draw a pie chart just for the rollercoaster, waltzer, and big wheel, how many degrees would the waltzer require?

☐ (a) 48°
☐ (b) 60°
☐ (c) 70°
☐ (d) 80°
☐ (e) 90°

27 The following pie chart shows the favourite colour of 80 girls. What fraction of the girls like blue and how many of them is this?

☐ (a) ¼ and 20
☐ (b) ¼ and 10
☐ (c) ⅛ and 10
☐ (d) ½ and 40
☐ (e) ⅛ and 40

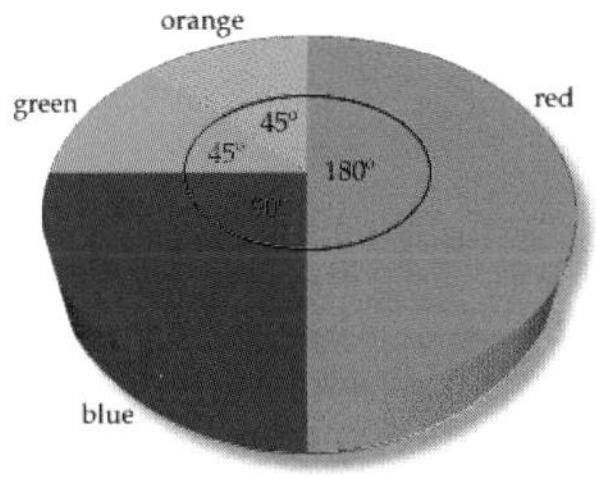

Q27, Q28, Q29

28 The pie chart above shows the favourite colour of 80 girls. What fraction of the girls like green and how many of them is this?

☐ (a) ⅛ and 20
☐ (b) ⅛ and 10
☐ (c) ¼ and 20
☐ (d) ¼ and 10
☐ (e) ½ and 40

29 The pie chart above shows the favourite colour of 80 girls. What percentage of the girls chose red and how many girls is this?

☐ (a) 30% and 30
☐ (b) 25% and 80
☐ (c) 40% and 40
☐ (d) 50% and 80
☐ (e) 50% and 40

30 "From an ordinary pack of 52 playing cards, 30 were dealt. The results are shown in the following diagram. Half of the cards were red and half were black." Is this statement true or false?

119

☐ (a) True
☐ (b) False

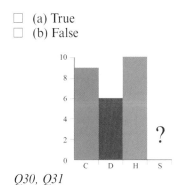

Q30, Q31

31 From an ordinary pack of 52 playing cards, 30 were dealt. The results are shown in the diagram above. How many of the playing cards were spades?

☐ (a) 7
☐ (b) 6
☐ (c) 90
☐ (d) 10
☐ (e) 5

32 What can be concluded from the following scatter graph, which shows the heights and weights of ten students?

☐ (a) The more a student weighs, the taller they will be
☐ (b) You cannot conclude anything from this graph
☐ (c) If a student doubles in height then their weight will also double
☐ (d) The taller a student, the lighter they will be
☐ (e) If a student loses weight then they will shrink in height proportionately

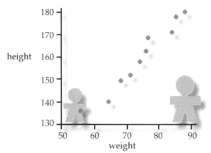

Q32

33 The following table shows the length and weight of 10 potatoes (to the nearest 10 g). If a best straight line was drawn, which point would it pass through?

L(cm)	6.0	7.2	10	6.8	6.3	6.5	8.0	5.8	6.0	6.7
W (g)	90	150	400	130	110	110	300	70	100	150

Q33

☐ (a) (6.93, 161)
☐ (b) (7.6, 180)
☐ (c) (6.5, 110)
☐ (d) (10, 400)
☐ (e) (6, 100)

34 The following scatter diagram shows values of p and m and the line of best fit. What is the value of p that corresponds to an m value of 30?

☐ (a) 25
☐ (b) 27
☐ (c) 30
☐ (d) 35
☐ (e) 40

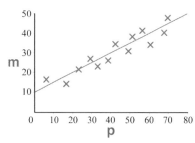

Q34, Q35

35 The scatter diagram above shows values of p and m and the line of best fit. What are the values of m that correspond to p = 20 and p = 70 respectively?

☐ (a) 30 and 100
☐ (b) 20 and 45
☐ (c) 24 and 57
☐ (d) 45 and 20
☐ (e) 60 and 70

36 "As each component comes off a production line it is weighed and the results recorded, as shown in the following frequency table. The cumulative frequency row is incomplete. The values of s and t are the same." Is this statement true or false?

☐ (a) True
☐ (b) False

Mass (kg)	10-	11-	12-	13-	14-	15-	16-
Frequency	14	22	27	30	16	11	0
C.F.	p	36	63	q	r	s	t

Q36, Q37, Q38

37 As each component comes off a production line it is weighed and the results recorded, as shown in the frequency table above. The cumulative frequency row is incomplete. What is the value of r?

☐ (a) 30
☐ (b) 120
☐ (c) 109
☐ (d) 16
☐ (e) 46

38 As each component comes off a production line it is weighed and the results recorded, as shown in the previous frequency table. The cumulative frequency row is incomplete. How many components weigh less than 14 kg?

☐ (a) 30
☐ (b) 57
☐ (c) 16
☐ (d) 93
☐ (e) 109

120

Analysing and interpreting data

KEY FACTS

• In order to have a general view of a large amount of data, it is convenient to have a measure of an average value, and a measure of how spread out the information is.

• The usual measures of central tendency are the mode (or most frequent value), the median (the middle value when the data are put in order of size), and the mean (calculated by adding all the values together, and dividing by the number of values you have added).

• There are techniques that make the calculation of the mean easier. Using a frequency table, for example, you can multiply each value by its own frequency, add up these figures, and divide by the total frequency. (In a grouped frequency table, you need to take the mid-interval value as a representative value of the group.)

• The other figures are used in the lower quartile and the upper quartile. The lower quartile is the median of the lower half of the values, and the upper quartile is the median of the upper half of the values.

• The commonly used measures of spread are the range (highest value – lowest value), the inter-quartile range (upper quartile – lower quartile, which contains the middle 50% of the values), and the standard deviation (the range containing the middle $^2/_3$, roughly, of the values).

• Once you have obtained some statistical information from your data, you can then evaluate it to see if it is what you had expected, whether it appears to be biased in some way, or whether you need to obtain more information.

• In particular, you can compare two sets of data to see if there are any similarities/differences, which may not be apparent from the original information. A scatter diagram can give a picture of the correlation, if any, between two sets of figures. A "line of best fit" can then be used to predict one characteristic from a knowledge of the other.

QUESTIONS

1 "A frequency polygon can be drawn by joining the mid-points of the tops of the lines on a bar chart or histogram." Is this statement true or false?

☐ (a) True
☐ (b) False

2 "If the bars of a histogram are all the same width, then the modal class is the tallest bar." Is this statement true or false?

☐ (a) True
☐ (b) False

3 "For any experiment, the sum of all the individual relative frequencies must add up to 1." Is this statement true or false?

☐ (a) True
☐ (b) False

4 "The mean value of the numbers 8, 10, 11, 14, and 17 is 11." Is this statement true or false?

☐ (a) True
☐ (b) False

5 "The mode of the numbers 14, 19, 14, 19, 23, 18, and 19 is 18." Is this statement true or false?

☐ (a) True
☐ (b) False

6 "The median value of the numbers 36, 38, 31, 31, 36, 31, 37, 35, and 32 is 36." Is this statement true or false?

☐ (a) True
☐ (b) False

7 "The range of the numbers 93, 97, 108, 102, and 100 is 7." Is this statement true or false?

☐ (a) True
☐ (b) False

8 "The mean value of the numbers 8, 10, 13, 14, and 15 is 12." Is this statement true or false?

☐ (a) True
☐ (b) False

9 "The median of 22, 24, 19, 16, 16, 24, and 23 is 22." Is this statement true or false?

☐ (a) True
☐ (b) False

10 "The mode of the numbers 12, 15, 13, 16, 15, 13, 18 and 15 is 15." Is this statement true or false?

☐ (a) True
☐ (b) False

11 "The following table shows the frequency of the values of T. The mean value is 25." Is this statement true or false?

☐ (a) True
☐ (b) False

T	10	20	30	40
x	3	6	3	4

Q11

12 "Ben has a set of coloured cubes The following frequency table shows how many of each colour he has. The modal colour is white." Is this statement true or false?

☐ (a) True
☐ (b) False

Red	Green	White	Blue	Yellow
23	16	20	26	19

Q12

13 "Zoe has six tomato plants in a greenhouse, which produced the following number of tomatoes: 17, 28, 32, 36, 36, and 43. The mean number of tomatoes per plant is 36." Is this statement true or false?

☐ (a) True
☐ (b) False

14 "Zoe has six tomato plants in a greenhouse, which produced the following number of tomatoes: 17,

121

28, 32, 36, 36, and 43. The range of the number of tomatoes per plant is 43 – 17." Is this statement true or false?

☐ (a) True
☐ (b) False

15 "The marks in a test taken by 50 students are shown in the following table. The median mark is in the range 40-59." Is this statement true or false?

☐ (a) True
☐ (b) False

Mark	0-19	20-39	40-59	60-79
Frequency	2	12	29	7

Q15

16 "The following diagram shows the cumulative frequency of the mass of 100 boxes of components. The median mass is 11 kg." Is this statement true or false?

☐ (a) True
☐ (b) False

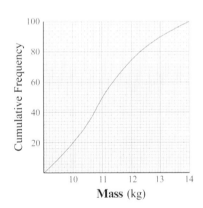

Q16, Q17, Q18

17 "The previous diagram shows the cumulative frequency of the mass of 100 boxes of components. The upper quartile mass is 75 kg." Is this statement true or false?

☐ (a) True
☐ (b) False

18 "The previous diagram shows the cumulative frequency of the mass of 100 boxes of components. The interquartile range is 1.8 kg." Is this statement true or false?

☐ (a) True
☐ (b) False

19 "The standard deviation of the numbers 11, 12, 13, 14, and 15 is 1.414, correct to 3 d.p." Is this statement true or false?

☐ (a) True
☐ (b) False

20 The highest afternoon temperature was recorded for a fortnight and the results plotted, as shown on the graph below. What was the range in temperatures?

☐ (a) 4°C
☐ (b) 8°C
☐ (c) 10°C
☐ (d) 12°C
☐ (e) 16°C

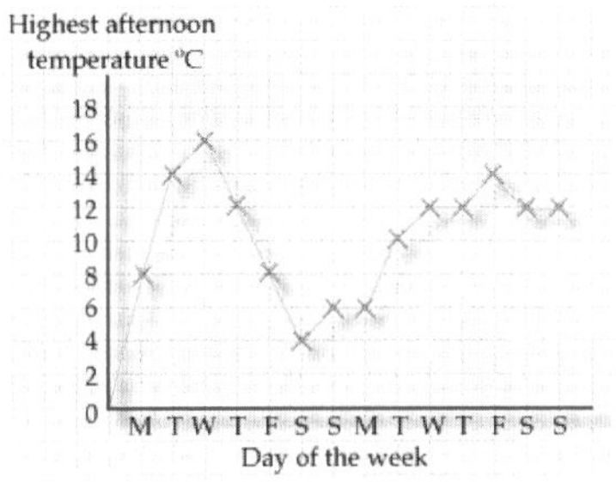

Highest afternoon temperature °C

Q20

21 The following grouped frequency table shows data on the ages of people who visited a certain doctor on a particular day. What is the modal class?

☐ (a) 1–9
☐ (b) 10–19
☐ (c) 20–29
☐ (d) 30–39
☐ (e) 40+

Number of People	8	17	28	13	6
Age	1 - 9	10 -19	20 - 29	30 - 39	40+

Q21

22 What is the mode of the numbers 38, 43, 43, 47, 41, 49, 41, 48, 38, 41, 46, and 44?

☐ (a) 38
☐ (b) 41
☐ (c) 6
☐ (d) 43
☐ (e) 11

23 What is the median of the

numbers 38, 43, 43, 47, 41, 49, 41, 48, 38, 41, 46, and 44?

☐ (a) 38
☐ (b) 41
☐ (c) 6
☐ (d) 43
☐ (e) 11

24 What is the mean of the numbers 48, 43, 43, 47, 41, 49, 40, 48, 38, 41, 46, and 44?

☐ (a) 41
☐ (b) 43
☐ (c) 44
☐ (d) 40.5
☐ (e) 42.7

25 What is the lower quartile of the numbers 19, 9, 12, 10, 14, 10, 11, 12, 9, 17, and 18?

☐ (a) 9
☐ (b) 10
☐ (c) 11
☐ (d) 15
☐ (e) 17

26 What is the upper quartile of the numbers 19, 9, 12, 10, 14, 10, 11, 12, 9, 17, and 18?

☐ (a) 9
☐ (b) 10
☐ (c) 11
☐ (d) 15
☐ (e) 17

27 What is the range of the numbers 19, 9, 12, 10, 14, 10, 11, 12, 9, 17, and 18?

☐ (a) 9
☐ (b) 10
☐ (c) 11
☐ (d) 15
☐ (e) 17

28 A die is thrown 40 times. The following table shows the results. What is the mean score?

Score	1	2	3	4	5	6
Frequency	7	8	10	6	4	5

Q28, Q29, Q30

☐ (a) 3.175
☐ (b) 6.67
☐ (c) 3.5

☐ (d) 3
☐ (e) 4.76

29 A die is thrown 40 times. The previous table shows the results. What is the modal score?

☐ (a) 3.175
☐ (b) 6.67
☐ (c) 3.5
☐ (d) 3
☐ (e) 4.76

30 A die is thrown 40 times. The previous table shows the results. What is the median score?

☐ (a) 3.175
☐ (b) 6.67
☐ (c) 3.5
☐ (d) 3
☐ (e) 4.76

31 The following diagram shows the cumulative frequency of scores in a test for two groups, 11P and 11Q, each of which has 200 pupils. What is the median score for group 11P?

☐ (a) 46
☐ (b) 40
☐ (c) 20
☐ (d) 13
☐ (e) 58

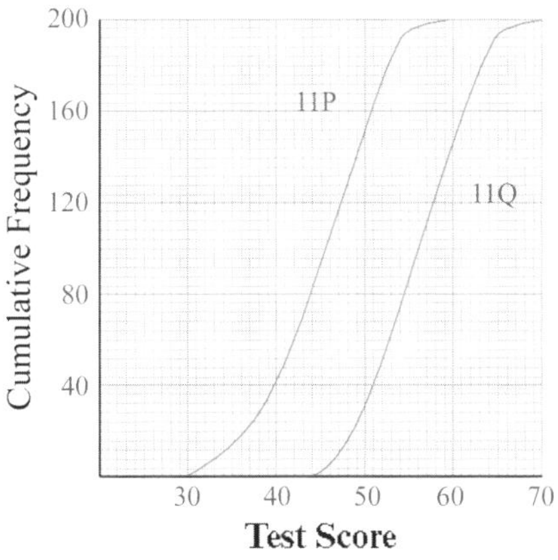

Q31, Q32, Q33, Q34, Q35

32 The diagram above shows the cumulative frequency of scores in a test for two groups, 11P and 11Q, each of which has 200 pupils. What is the interquartile range for group 11Q?

☐ (a) 61
☐ (b) 52
☐ (c) 9
☐ (d) 12
☐ (e) 150

33 The previous diagram shows the cumulative frequency of scores in a

test for two groups, 11P and 11Q, each of which has 200 pupils. By how many marks is the median score for 11Q greater than the median score for 11P?

☐ (a) 8
☐ (b) 18
☐ (c) 30
☐ (d) 11
☐ (e) 21

34 The previous diagram shows the cumulative frequency of scores in a test for two groups, 11P and 11Q, each of which has 200 pupils. How many of the 400 pupils scored more than 40 marks?

☐ (a) 44
☐ (b) 356
☐ (c) 202
☐ (d) 320
☐ (e) 80

35 The previous diagram shows the cumulative frequency of scores in a test for two groups, 11P and 11Q, each of which has 200 pupils. The mark for a credit is 50. How many pupils achieved a credit?

☐ (a) 170
☐ (b) 218
☐ (c) 30
☐ (d) 308
☐ (e) 250

36 "The mean of the two sets of numbers shown in the following diagram is the same. The value of d is 15." Is this statement true or false?

☐ (a) True
☐ (b) False

A	6	7	8	12	12	15
B	7	9	9	d		

Q36

37 "The two sets of numbers shown in the following diagram have the same mean and the same range." Is this statement true or false?

P	18	19	22	30	31
Q	28	29	32	40	41

Q37

☐ (a) True
☐ (b) False

38 "The following diagram shows two sets of numbers. The range of set R is twice the range of set S. The value of k is 12." Is this statement true or false?

☐ (a) True
☐ (b) False

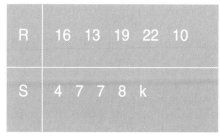

R	16	13	19	22	10
S	4	7	7	8	k

Q38

39 "The following diagram shows the scores of two classes. The mean mark for class 11HS is higher than the mean score for class 11PP." Is this statement true or false?

☐ (a) True
☐ (b) False

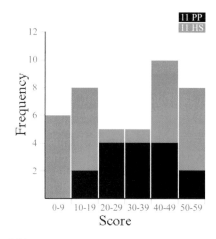

Q39

40 "On sports day, each of the 12 students in team F had a mean score of 16 points. Team G, with 10 students in it, had a mean score of 20 points each. Team G scored more points in total than team F." Is this statement true or false?

☐ (a) True
☐ (b) False

Probability

KEY FACTS

• Probability is a number, between 0 and 1, which estimates the likelihood of an event occurring.

• On a probability scale graduated from 0 (representing impossibility) to 1 (representing certainty), we can mark estimates of the probability of events, and see which are more likely to occur than others.

• We can also estimate probabilities by finding the relative frequency with which an event happens (e.g. if an event occurs 3 times out of 10 trials, its relative frequency is $^3/_{10}$, or 0.3, or 30%). The more trials, the more accurate the estimate of probability will be.

• If there are equally likely outcomes (e.g. coins, dice, playing cards, lottery numbers), we can work out expected probabilities without doing any trials.

• With two experiments (e.g. throwing two dice, two coins), we can use a table or a tree diagram in order to determine the probabilities of the possible outcomes.

• In any one experiment, if two outcomes can not occur simultaneously, then the two events are mutually exclusive. In this case, the probability of either event occurring is found by adding together the probabilities of the two separate events.

• If two experiments are conducted, one after the other, and the outcome of the first event does not alter the outcome of the second event, then the two events are said to be independent. The probability of both events occurring is found by multiplying the probabilities of the two separate events.

QUESTIONS

1 "Mike looked at all the past records of the National Lottery and found that the six most frequently drawn balls are 4, 5, 19, 24, 27, 38. He therefore concluded that he would increase his chances of winning if he selected those numbers the following week." Is this statement true or false?

☐ (a) True
☐ (b) False

Q1

2 "For the tree diagram shown below, the probability of event B occurring twice in a row is found by adding 0.2 + 0.2." Is this statement true or false?

☐ (a) True
☐ (b) False

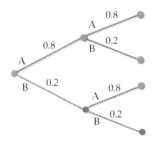

Q2

3 The line shown in the diagram below is a probability line. The point A stands for a probability of 0, and the point E stands for a probability of 1. What word could describe the probability of an event happening at point C?

☐ (a) Impossible
☐ (b) Unlikely
☐ (c) Evens
☐ (d) Likely
☐ (e) Certain

Q3, Q4, Q5

4 The line shown in the diagram above is a probability line. The point A stands for a probability of 0, and the point E stands for a probability of 1. What word could describe the probability of an event happening at point E?

☐ (a) Impossible
☐ (b) Unlikely
☐ (c) Evens
☐ (d) Likely
☐ (e) Certain

5 The line shown in the previous diagram is a probability line. The point A stands for a probability of 0, and the point E stands for a probability of 1. What word could describe the probability of an event happening at point A?

☐ (a) Impossible
☐ (b) Unlikely
☐ (c) Evens
☐ (d) Likely
☐ (e) Certain

6 The following results were obtained from rolling a biased die 40 times. On this evidence, what would you estimate the probability of rolling a 1 to be?

☐ (a) $^1/_6$
☐ (b) $^4/_{30}$
☐ (c) $^4/_6$
☐ (d) $^4/_{20}$
☐ (e) $^1/_{10}$

Score	1	2	3	4	5	6
Frequency	4	3	5	8	9	11

Q6

7 Which one of the following is not a mathematical way of writing the probability of spinning a head on a coin?

☐ (a) $^1/_2$
☐ (b) Evens
☐ (c) 50%
☐ (d) 0.5
☐ (e) 0.50

8 The letters of the word MATHEMATICAL are written on pieces of paper and put in a bag. One piece of paper is pulled out of the bag at random. What is the probability of getting a T?

- ☐ (a) $\frac{1}{6}$
- ☐ (b) $\frac{1}{12}$
- ☐ (c) $\frac{2}{10}$
- ☐ (d) $\frac{3}{12}$
- ☐ (e) $\frac{2}{6}$

M
       T   E
   A
       H   M
A
   T   C
     I   A   L

Q8, Q9

9 The letters of the word MATHEMATICAL are written on pieces of paper and put in a bag. One piece of paper is pulled out of the bag at random. What is the probability of getting an M or an L?

- ☐ (a) $\frac{1}{12}$
- ☐ (b) $\frac{5}{12}$
- ☐ (c) $\frac{2}{12}$
- ☐ (d) $\frac{1}{4}$
- ☐ (e) $\frac{1}{3}$

10 A bag contains three red, four blue, two black, and one green ball. If a ball is picked out at random, what is the probability of drawing a red ball?

- ☐ (a) $\frac{3}{7}$
- ☐ (b) $\frac{1}{3}$
- ☐ (c) $\frac{3}{10}$
- ☐ (d) $\frac{2}{5}$
- ☐ (e) 1

11 A bag contains three red, four blue, two black, and one green ball. If a ball is picked out at random, what is the probability of drawing a black ball?

- ☐ (a) $\frac{3}{10}$
- ☐ (b) $\frac{2}{5}$
- ☐ (c) $\frac{1}{4}$
- ☐ (d) $\frac{3}{11}$
- ☐ (e) $\frac{1}{5}$

12 The letters of the alphabet are written on 26 counters and one is drawn at random from the set of counters. What is the probability that it is not a letter of the word MISSISSIPPI?

- ☐ (a) $\frac{11}{13}$
- ☐ (b) $\frac{5}{26}$
- ☐ (c) $\frac{2}{13}$
- ☐ (d) $\frac{11}{26}$
- ☐ (e) $\frac{9}{13}$

13 Ten packets have the following numbers of sweets in them: 12, 13, 13, 13, 15, 16, 16, 12, 14, 16. If a bag is chosen at random, what is the probability of the bag containing an odd number of sweets?

- ☐ (a) $\frac{3}{10}$
- ☐ (b) $\frac{1}{2}$
- ☐ (c) $\frac{2}{5}$
- ☐ (d) $\frac{3}{5}$
- ☐ (e) $\frac{1}{3}$

14 Ten packets have the following numbers of sweets in them: 12, 13, 13, 13, 15, 16, 16, 12, 14, 16. If a bag is chosen at random, what is the probability of the bag containing more than 13 sweets?

- ☐ (a) $\frac{5}{13}$
- ☐ (b) $\frac{4}{5}$
- ☐ (c) $\frac{8}{13}$
- ☐ (d) $\frac{1}{5}$
- ☐ (e) $\frac{1}{2}$

15 A normal dice is rolled and the score is recorded. What is the probability that this number is a multiple of 3?

- ☐ (a) $\frac{1}{3}$
- ☐ (b) $\frac{1}{2}$
- ☐ (c) $\frac{5}{6}$
- ☐ (d) $\frac{2}{3}$
- ☐ (e) $\frac{1}{6}$

16 Paul has thrown a coin six times, and each time a head is the result of the throw. What is the probability that the result of the next throw will also be a head?

- ☐ (a) $\frac{1}{7}$
- ☐ (b) $\frac{1}{2}$
- ☐ (c) $\frac{1}{32}$
- ☐ (d) $\frac{1}{64}$
- ☐ (e) Depends what he calls

17 At Beezton Hockey Club, a tournament takes place with five teams in it – A, B, C, D, and E. If each team has an equal chance of winning, what is the probability that A does not win?

- ☐ (a) 0.5
- ☐ (b) $\frac{4}{5}$
- ☐ (c) $\frac{1}{5}$
- ☐ (d) $\frac{6}{10}$
- ☐ (e) $\frac{1}{10}$

18 A race takes part between Alice, Bruce, and Cecil, all of whom have an equal chance of winning. What is the probability of Cecil finishing first or second?

- ☐ (a) $\frac{1}{2}$
- ☐ (b) $\frac{1}{3}$
- ☐ (c) $\frac{2}{3}$
- ☐ (d) $\frac{5}{6}$
- ☐ (e) $\frac{1}{6}$

19 A raffle sells all of its tickets labelled 11 to 99 and has one prize. If Brian buys two of the tickets, what is the probability he will win?

- ☐ (a) $\frac{2}{89}$
- ☐ (b) $\frac{2}{99}$
- ☐ (c) $\frac{1}{50}$
- ☐ (d) $\frac{1}{49}$
- ☐ (e) 0

20 How many outcomes are there when two dice are thrown?

- ☐ (a) 6
- ☐ (b) 8
- ☐ (c) 10
- ☐ (d) 12
- ☐ (e) 36

21 If two dice are thrown, what is the probability of the two numbers being the same?

- ☐ (a) $\frac{1}{2}$
- ☐ (b) $\frac{3}{12}$
- ☐ (c) $\frac{5}{6}$
- ☐ (d) $\frac{5}{36}$
- ☐ (e) $\frac{1}{6}$

22 If two dice are thrown, what is the probability of getting a total that is divisible by 3?

- ☐ (a) $\frac{1}{3}$
- ☐ (b) $\frac{2}{9}$
- ☐ (c) $\frac{7}{36}$
- ☐ (d) $\frac{1}{6}$
- ☐ (e) $\frac{1}{4}$

23 A die is thrown and a coin is spun. Their results are noted. How many outcomes are there?

Q23

☐ (a) 10
☐ (b) 12
☐ (c) 8
☐ (d) 36
☐ (e) 6

24 The two spinners shown in the diagram below are spun and their totals are added together. What is the probability of getting a total of over 6?

☐ (a) $5/12$
☐ (b) $6/12$
☐ (c) $5/10$
☐ (d) $7/12$
☐ (e) $5/14$

Q24

25 Work out the probability of drawing a red ball from a bag that contains three red, two blue, and four black balls.

☐ (a) $1/3$
☐ (b) $2/9$
☐ (c) $1/9$
☐ (d) $4/9$
☐ (e) $1/2$

26 A bag contains a large number of coloured balls. The probabilities of drawing any particular ball from the bag are given below. What is the probability of drawing a blue ball?

☐ (a) 0.5
☐ (b) 0.59
☐ (c) 0.6
☐ (d) 0.41
☐ (e) 0.47

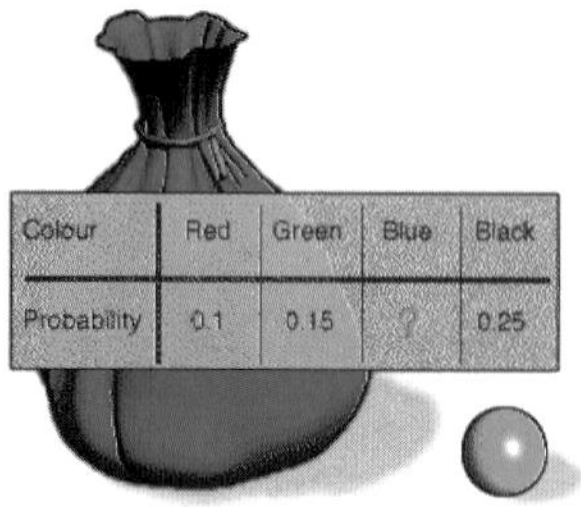

Colour	Red	Green	Blue	Black
Probability	0.1	0.15	?	0.25

Q26

27 A bag contains a large number of coloured balls. The probabilities of drawing any particular ball from the bag are given below. What is the probability of drawing any colour apart from green?

☐ (a) 0.15
☐ (b) 0.5
☐ (c) 0.66
☐ (d) 0.75
☐ (e) 0.80

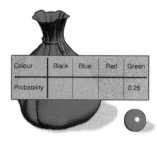

Colour	Black	Blue	Red	Green
Probability				0.25

Q27

28 A certain game of chance (win or lose) is played and, at the end of a round, points are scored if a win occurs. The scores and probabilities are shown on the diagram below. What is the probability, X, of losing (i.e. scoring no points)?

☐ (a) 0.08
☐ (b) 0.22
☐ (c) 0.4
☐ (d) 0.6
☐ (e) 0.78

Points	10	5	3	1	Lose
Probability	0.01	0.07	0.12	0.2	X

Q28

29 A certain game of chance (win or lose) is played and, at the end of a round, points are scored. The scores and probabilities are shown on the diagram below. What is the probability of scoring either 3 points or 10 points?

☐ (a) 0.13
☐ (b) 0.22
☐ (c) 0.08
☐ (d) 0.065
☐ (e) 0.0012

Points	10	5	3	1	Lose
Probability	0.01	0.07	0.12	0.2	0.6

Q29

30 Two coins are spun. What is the probability of getting two heads or two tails?

☐ (a) $1/4$
☐ (b) $1/2$
☐ (c) $4/6$
☐ (d) $1/6$
☐ (e) $2/3$

31 The following spinner is used in a game. It has eight equal sectors. The probability of landing on red is $2/8$ and the probability of landing on an odd number is $4/8$. What is the probability of landing on a red or an odd number?

☐ (a) $3/8$
☐ (b) $4/8$
☐ (c) $5/8$
☐ (d) $6/8$
☐ (e) $7/8$

Q31, Q32

32 The spinner above is used in a game. It has eight equal sectors. The probability of landing on red is $2/8$ and the probability of landing on orange is $4/8$. What is the probability of landing on a red or orange?

☐ (a) $8/64$
☐ (b) $6/16$
☐ (c) $2/3$
☐ (d) $3/4$
☐ (e) $6/7$

33 A toy manufacturer makes cuddly toys. Twelve out of every 50 have a fault. What is the probability that if two toys are selected at random, both have a fault?

☐ (a) 0.480
☐ (b) 0.144
☐ (c) 0.0576
☐ (d) 0.2400
☐ (e) 0.0212

34 A toy manufacturer makes cuddly toys. Twelve out of every 50 have a fault. What is the probability that if two toys are selected at random, neither have a fault?

☐ (a) 0.5776
☐ (b) 0.057
☐ (c) 0.1444
☐ (d) 0.7600
☐ (e) 0.3458

35 A bag contains five balls – three red, and two blue. Robert picks out one ball at a time at random and doesn't replace it. If the first two draws give a red followed by a blue, what is the probability that the next draw is a red?

- ☐ (a) $\frac{1}{3}$
- ☐ (b) $\frac{3}{5}$
- ☐ (c) $\frac{18}{125}$
- ☐ (d) $\frac{3}{10}$
- ☐ (e) $\frac{2}{3}$

36 The numbers 1, 2, 3, and 4 are put into a hat and one number is drawn out at random, noted down, and replaced. The results of 98 trials are shown in the table below. What is the relative frequency of drawing a 3?

- ☐ (a) 0.28
- ☐ (b) 0.25
- ☐ (c) 0.27
- ☐ (d) $\frac{27}{98}$
- ☐ (e) $\frac{1}{4}$

Number	1	2	3	4
Frequency	23	20	27	28

Q36, Q37

37 The numbers 1, 2, 3, and 4 are put into a hat and one number is drawn out at random, noted down, and replaced. The results of 98 trials are shown in the previous table. What is the relative frequency of drawing a 2?

- ☐ (a) 0.28
- ☐ (b) 0.25
- ☐ (c) 0.27
- ☐ (d) $\frac{1}{4}$
- ☐ (e) $\frac{20}{98}$

38 Two dice were rolled repeatedly and the sum of the spots was noted each time, as shown in the following table. Estimate the probability of rolling more than 7 on the two dice.

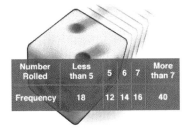

Number Rolled	Less than 5	5	6	7	More than 7
Frequency	18	12	14	16	40

Q38, Q39

- ☐ (a) 0.4
- ☐ (b) 0.8

- ☐ (c) 0.4166
- ☐ (d) 0.6
- ☐ (e) $\frac{15}{36}$

39 Two dice were rolled repeatedly and the sum of the spots was noted each time, as shown in the previous table. Estimate the probability of rolling less than 6 on the two dice.

- ☐ (a) $\frac{10}{36}$
- ☐ (b) $\frac{1}{6}$
- ☐ (c) 0.3
- ☐ (d) 0.18
- ☐ (e) 0.2

40 A game consists of drawing a counter at random from a bag, then replacing it and drawing another counter. There are 10 counters of different colours, including three red counters. One of the players is only interested in the red counters and draws the following tree diagram for all the events and their probabilities. What should be written in the black boxes?

- ☐ (a) Blue
- ☐ (b) Black
- ☐ (c) Not blue
- ☐ (d) Not red
- ☐ (e) Difficult to tell

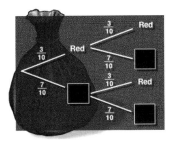

Q40

41 A game consists of drawing a counter at random from a bag, then replacing it and drawing another counter. There are 10 counters of different colours, including three red counters. One of the players is only interested in the red counters and draws the tree diagram below for all the events and their probabilities. What number should be written in the blue boxes?

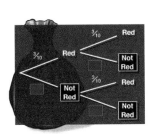

Q41

- ☐ (a) $\frac{7}{10}$ and $\frac{49}{100}$
- ☐ (b) $\frac{7}{10}$
- ☐ (c) $\frac{3}{10}$
- ☐ (d) $\frac{3}{7}$
- ☐ (e) Difficult to tell

42 A game consists of drawing a counter at random from a bag, then replacing it and drawing another counter. There are 10 counters of different colours, including three red counters. One of the players is only interested in the red counters and draws the tree diagram below for all the events and their probabilities. What is the probability of drawing two red counters?

- ☐ (a) $\frac{6}{10}$
- ☐ (b) $\frac{9}{100}$
- ☐ (c) $\frac{9}{10}$
- ☐ (d) $\frac{21}{100}$
- ☐ (e) $\frac{6}{20}$

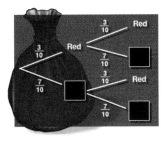

Q42

43 A game consists of drawing a counter at random from a bag, then replacing it and drawing another counter. There are 10 counters of different colours including three red counters. One of the players is only interested in the red counters and draws the tree diagram below for all the events and their probabilities. What is the probability of drawing at least one red counter?

- ☐ (a) $\frac{25}{40}$
- ☐ (b) $\frac{26}{40}$
- ☐ (c) $\frac{27}{40}$
- ☐ (d) $\frac{51}{100}$
- ☐ (e) Difficult to tell

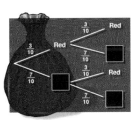

Q43

44 Mr Cooke goes fishing in the local pond. The pond is stocked with carp and tench. The probability

127

that he catches a carp is $^3/_5$. Draw a tree diagram for the outcomes for the first two fish that he catches and use this to work out the probability that he catches exactly one carp and one tench in any order.

- [ ] (a) $^6/_{20}$
- [ ] (b) $^{12}/_{20}$
- [ ] (c) $^{12}/_{50}$
- [ ] (d) $^6/_{25}$
- [ ] (e) $^{12}/_{25}$

45 Mr Cooke goes fishing in the local pond. The pond is stocked with carp and tench. The probability that he catches a carp is $^3/_5$. Draw a tree diagram for the outcomes for the first two fish that he catches and use this to work out the probability that he catches at least one tench from the first two fish he catches.

- [ ] (a) $^3/_4$
- [ ] (b) $^2/_5$
- [ ] (c) $^{16}/_{25}$
- [ ] (d) $^{21}/_{25}$
- [ ] (e) $^6/_{10}$

46 A bag contains three blue balls, four red balls, and two green balls. A ball is removed at random, its colour noted down, and then replaced. A second ball is then drawn from the bag at random. Draw a tree diagram for the two draws. What is the probability of drawing one green and one red ball in any order?

- [ ] (a) $^2/_3$
- [ ] (b) $^{16}/_{18}$
- [ ] (c) $^{12}/_{81}$
- [ ] (d) $^{16}/_{81}$
- [ ] (e) $^{12}/_{18}$

47 A bag contains three blue balls, four red balls, and two green balls. A ball is removed at random, its colour noted down, and then replaced. A second ball is then drawn from the bag at random. Draw a tree diagram for the two draws. What is the probability of drawing two different colours?

- [ ] (a) $^{29}/_{18}$
- [ ] (b) $^{25}/_{81}$
- [ ] (c) $^{52}/_{81}$
- [ ] (d) $^2/_3$
- [ ] (e) $^{11}/_{18}$

48 A normal six-sided die has had its sides changed to read 1, 1, 1, 1, 2, 3. The die is rolled twice and the total score recorded. Draw a table and use it to find the probability of rolling a score of at least 3. What is this probability?

- [ ] (a) $^1/_2$
- [ ] (b) $^5/_9$
- [ ] (c) $^7/_{36}$
- [ ] (d) $^8/_{12}$
- [ ] (e) $^7/_{12}$

49 A normal six-sided die has had its sides changed to read 1, 1, 1, 1, 2, 3. The die is rolled twice and the total score recorded. Draw a table and use it to find the probability of rolling a score of 4. What is this probability?

- [ ] (a) $^1/_2$
- [ ] (b) $^1/_3$
- [ ] (c) $^1/_4$
- [ ] (d) $^1/_5$
- [ ] (e) $^1/_6$

50 If two coins are spun together 360 times, how many times would you expect two heads to turn up?

- [ ] (a) 120
- [ ] (b) 270
- [ ] (c) 45
- [ ] (d) 180
- [ ] (e) 90

⬤ QUESTIONS

Higher Level only

51 A bag contains seven counters; three are green and the rest are red. Two counters are drawn out of the bag at random, one after the other. Using the following tree diagram, what is the probability of drawing two counters of different colours?

- [ ] (a) $^4/_7$
- [ ] (b) $^{20}/_{42}$
- [ ] (c) $^{24}/_{49}$
- [ ] (d) $^{20}/_{49}$
- [ ] (e) $^1/_2$

Q51, Q52, Q53

52 A bag contains seven counters; three are green and the rest are red. Two counters are drawn out of the bag at random, one after the other. Using the previous tree diagram, what is the probability of drawing two counters of the same colour?

- [ ] (a) $^{25}/_{49}$
- [ ] (b) $^{18}/_{49}$

- [ ] (c) $^{24}/_{49}$
- [ ] (d) $^3/_7$
- [ ] (e) $^4/_7$

53 A bag contains seven counters; three are green and the rest are red. Two counters are drawn out of the bag at random, one after the other. Using the previous tree diagram, what is the probability of drawing a red counter followed by a green one?

- [ ] (a) $^{13}/_{49}$
- [ ] (b) $^2/_7$
- [ ] (c) $^{12}/_{49}$
- [ ] (d) $^3/_7$
- [ ] (e) $^{23}/_{49}$

54 A game uses 10 coloured cards – seven green and three red. Three cards are dealt at random. Draw a tree diagram and use this to work out the probability of being dealt two or more red cards. What is this probability?

- [ ] (a) $^{11}/_{60}$
- [ ] (b) $^{23}/_{720}$
- [ ] (c) $^{23}/_{120}$
- [ ] (d) $^{32}/_{720}$
- [ ] (e) $^2/_3$

55 A game uses 10 coloured cards – seven green and three red. Three cards are dealt at random. What is the probability of being dealt at least one green card?

- [ ] (a) $^{125}/_{134}$
- [ ] (b) 0.7
- [ ] (c) $^{119}/_{120}$
- [ ] (d) $^{710}/_{720}$
- [ ] (e) $^7/_8$

56 Two bags contain counters; the first has three red and two blue counters and the other has four red and five blue counters. A counter is taken at random from the first bag and placed into the second bag, then a counter is taken at random from the second bag. What is the probability that this counter is blue?

- [ ] (a) $^{12}/_{25}$
- [ ] (b) $^{15}/_{50}$
- [ ] (c) $^2/_5$
- [ ] (d) $^{27}/_{50}$
- [ ] (e) $^5/_9$

Q56

ANSWERS

Collecting data

☐ **1** *(a)*
True. This is an example of stratified sampling. Since some prior knowledge of the population (all the employees) is known, then the men and women can be sampled proportionally.

☐ **2** *(a)*
The diagram below shows that there are two numbers in the 35-39 group.

35-39	I I	2
40-44	⊺⊦⊦⊦	5
45-49	⊺⊦⊦⊦ ⊺⊦⊦⊦ I I	12
50-54	I	1

A2, A3, A4

☐ **3** *(d)*
The diagram above shows that there are 12 numbers in the 45-49 group.

☐ **4** *(e)*
The diagram above shows that there is only one value of 50 or greater. Hence, 19 boxes have less than 50 matches.

☐ **5** *(e)*
The diagram below shows a tally chart of the number of pets owned. From this, it can be seen that the number of pupils who do not own any pets is eight.

No. of Pets	0	1	2	3	4	5	6
Tally	⊺⊦⊦⊦ III	⊺⊦⊦⊦ II	⊺⊦⊦⊦ II	⊺⊦⊦⊦ II	IIII	III		I
Frequency	8	7	7	4	3	0	1

A5, A6, A7, A8

☐ **6** *(a)*
The diagram above shows that there are no pupils who own five pets.

☐ **7** *(b)*
The previous diagram shows that there are 8 + 7 + 7 = 22 pupils who own less than three pets.

☐ **8** *(e)*
The previous diagram shows that there are (0 × 8) + (1 × 7) + (2 × 7) + (3 × 4) + (4 × 3) + (5 × 0) + (6 × 1) = 0 + 7 + 14 + 12 + 12 + 0 + 6 = 51 pets owned altogether.

☐ **9** *(a)*
An automatic Rover 400 costs £56 daily. Five days will cost 5 × 56 = £280.

☐ **10** *(b)*
An automatic Rover 400 costs £56 daily, so five days will cost 5 × 56 = £280. A Peugeot costs £41 daily, so five days will cost 5 × 41 = £205. The difference in five days will be 5 × £15 = £75.

☐ **11** *(b)*
Friday 9th August is high season. A car and two adults cost £128 on a Friday night, an extra adult costs £8, and two children £8 each also. Total = 128 + (3 × 8) = 128 + 24 = £152.

☐ **12** *(d)*
Looking at the appropriate part of the table it shows the cost to be £295.

☐ **13** *(c)*
The first tour shows that the trip from the town quay to the city centre takes from 11:50 to 12:20 – i.e. 30 minutes. Therefore, a tour leaving the town quay at 1:50 pm will arrive at the city centre 30 minutes later, at 2:20 pm or 14:20.

☐ **14** *(e)*
The highlighted area on the following diagram shows the cheapest five-seat hire car in July, which is the Fiesta in Lanzarote.

☐ **15** *(a)*
The highlighted area on the following diagram shows that the initial price is £525. However there is a supplement of £2.20 (highlighted) per person per night. Over 14 days this is £30.80. Therefore, £525 + £30.80 = £555.80.

☐ **16** *(e)*
Per person in March = 65 + 30 + 30 = 125. Two people = £250. Per person over a bank holiday = 70 + 35 = 105. Two people = £210. Therefore, the difference = 250 – 210 = £40.

☐ **17** *(c)*
The appropriate totals have been filled in on the previous table: (187 × 12) + (710 × 10) + (85 × 20) = £11 044.

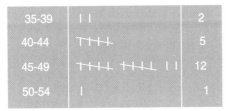

Type of Car	Citroen Ax 1.1 3dr	Citroen Ax 1.4 3dr	Citroen Ax 1.4 5dr	Citroen Ax 1.4 5dr	Minibus	Panda	VW Polo	Seat Ibiza 3dr	Seat Ibiza 5dr	Minibus	Panda	Corsa 3dr	Fiesta 3dr	Corsa 5dr	Minibus	Mazda 121 3dr	Fiesta 3dr	Mazda 121 4 dr	Escort	Minivan
No. of Seats	4	4	5	5	7/8	4	4	5	5	7/8	4	4	5	5	7/8	4	4	5	5	7/8
April, May, June Oct, Nov (£)	134	149	167	174	470	105	119	141	162	367	112	118	127	144	357	108	113	120	136	271
July, Aug, Sept (£)	155	167	184	198	513	130	151	165	182	421	120	129	137	157	447	127	132	140	151	302
	Menorca					Costa Blanca					Lanzarote					Malta/Gozo				

A14

Accommodation		FRANCESCA		EL GECKO		MIGUEL	
Number Sharing		8		9		9	
Number of Nights		7	14	7	14	7	14
24 APR - 14 MAY		305	355	299	385	299	339
15 MAY - 21 MAY		305	415	299	445	299	399
22 MAY - 04 JUN		419	465	409	495	415	449
05 JUN - 18 JUN		345	445	369	475	369	429
19 JUN - 02 JUL		405	479	399	509	399	465
03 JUL - 16 JUL		425	495	419	525	419	479
17 JUL - 20 AUG		495	599	489	629	489	585
21 AUG - 3 SEP		465	525	459	555	459	509
4 SEP - 17 SEP		399	469	389	499	395	455
18 SEP - 08 OCT		355	415	349	445	349	399
09 OCT - 15 OCT		305	375	299	405	299	359
16 OCT - 22 OCT		335	-	329	-	329	-

Supplements per person per night						
LOW - MAY, OCT	SEASON		LOW	MID	HIGH	
MID - JUN, SEPT	NUMBER SHARING	8	1.10	1.60	2.20	1.20
HIGH - JUL, AUG		7	1.40	2.40	3.60	4.80	2.80
		6	3.20	4.20	6.20	8.30	4.80
Prices in £'s per person		5	5.80	6.60	9.70	13.20	7.60

A15

Seat	Mon	Tues	Wed	Thur	Fri	Sat	Sun	Total
Stalls £12	25	26	32	28	36	40	0	2244
Main Hall £10	101	104	110	120	140	135	0	7100
Balcony £20	12	15	12	12	16	18	0	1700

A17

Collecting data

Higher Levels

18 *(b)*
False. If you have no information about the population, then the best method is random sampling.

19 *(d)*
The sample taken depends on the size of the year group compared to the size of the school as a whole. The calculation proceeds as shown on the diagram below, with a school size of 585.

Year	Number of pupils	Sample size
7	130	130 / 585 x 90 = 20
8	85	–
9	160	–
10	120	–
11	90	–
	585	

A19

20 *(c)*
The sample taken depends on the size of the year group compared to the size of the school as a whole. The calculation proceeds as shown on the diagram below, with a school size of 585.

Year	Number of pupils	Sample size
7	130	–
8	85	85 / 585 x 90 = 13
9	160	–
10	120	–
11	90	–
	585	

A20

21 *(e)*
The sample taken depends on the size of the year group compared to the size of the school as a whole. The calculation proceeds as shown on the diagram below, with a school size of 585.

Year	Number of pupils	Sample size
7	130	–
8	85	–
9	160	–
10	120	120/585 x 98 = 20
11	90	–
	585	

A21

22 *(a)*
To find the proportion out of 200, the calculations proceed as shown on the table below (note that, because of the

need to round each calculation to the nearest whole number, the actual number of fans that need to be sampled totals 201).

League	Average attendance	
1	10,000	$\frac{10,000}{19,500}$ x 200 = 103
2	7,000	$\frac{7000}{19,500}$ x 200 = 72
3	2,000	$\frac{2,000}{19,500}$ x 200 = 21
4	500	$\frac{500}{19,500}$ x 200 = 5

A22, A23, A24, A25

23 *(b)*
To find the proportion out of 200, the calculations proceed as shown on the above table (note that, because of the need to round each calculation to the nearest whole number, the actual number of fans that need to be sampled totals 201).

24 *(d)*
To find the proportion out of 200, the calculations proceed as shown on the previous table (note that, because of the need to round each calculation to the nearest whole number, the actual number of fans that need to be sampled totals 201).

25 *(e)*
To find the proportion out of 200, the calculations proceed as shown on the previous diagram (note that, because of the need to round each calculation to the nearest whole number, the actual number of fans that need to be sampled totals 201).

Representing data

1 *(a)*
True. The points very nearly lie on a straight line with a negative gradient. Hence, the graph shows good negative correlation.

2 *(b)*
False. It would make no difference on which axes the French marks and the maths marks were plotted. The graph would still show positive correlation, as shown on the following diagram.

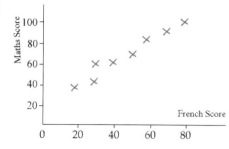

A2

3 *(b)*
False. There are 3 + 2 + 5 + 4 + 4 = 18 cars altogether.

4 *(a)*
True. The £5-£10 column has a frequency of 9.

5 *(b)*
False. Adding the height of each bar, then the total frequency (i.e. number of pupils in 10G) is 2 + 7 + 12 + 9 = 30.

6 *(e)*
From the information given, seven pupils received between £1-£2.99 but you cannot tell the exact amount that any one pupil received.

7 *(b)*
False. Negative correlation would give a downwards trend. The scatter diagram in the question represents positive correlation since there is an upwards trend (i.e. the higher the science score, the higher the maths score).

8 *(b)*
False. In general, science scores are higher than maths scores. A score of 35 in science corresponds to a score of about 27 in maths.

9 *(a)*
True. Three plants are between 0.5-1.0 m and five plants are between 1.0-1.2 m.

10 *(b)*
False. There are 3 + 5 + 2 + 7 + 6 + 5 = 28 plants altogether.

11 *(c)*
7 (1.4-1.6 m) + 6 (1.6-1.8 m) + 5 (1.8-2.0 m) = 18 plants.

12 *(e)*
We can estimate that half of the plants in the 1.6-1.8 m group are taller than 1.7 m. Half of six is three, plus the five that are 1.8-2.0 m, making eight plants. (N.B. This is only a "best guess" – there may be no plants between 1.6-1.7 m, or all six could be between 1.6-1.7 m. It is not possible to tell from the diagram.)

☐ **13** *(c)*
Adding up the profits for each individual month gives 250 + 200 + 50 − 100 − 300 − 100 + 150 = £150.

☐ **14** *(a)*
The pie chart is split into eight equal sectors and the area of the pie chart for bus travel is covering one of these sectors, so the fraction is $^1/_8$.

☐ **15** *(c)*
The pie chart is split into eight equal sectors and the area of the pie chart for walking is covering two of these sectors, so the fraction is $^2/_8 = ^1/_4$.

☐ **16** *(c)*
The section of the pie chart that shows car users covers $^1/_2$ of the total. As the whole pie chart represents 240 people, half of this is 120 people.

☐ **17** *(b)*
The section of the pie chart that shows bike users covers $^1/_8$ of the total. As the whole pie chart represents 240 people, $^1/_8$ of this is 30 people.

☐ **18** *(e)*
Walking the dog is represented by 90° on the pie chart. As a fraction of the chart this is $^{90}/_{360} = ^1/_4$. So, to find the time taken you need to find $^1/_4$ of 5 hours (5 × 60 minutes). Therefore, $^1/_4$ × 300 = 75, which is 1 hour 15 minutes.

☐ **19** *(b)*
Reading is represented by 60° on the pie chart. As a fraction of the chart this is $^{60}/_{360} = ^1/_6$. So, to find the time taken you need to find $^1/_6$ of 4 hours (4 × 60 minutes). Therefore, $^1/_6$ × 240 = 40 minutes.

☐ **20** *(b)*
Thinking is represented by 60° and watching TV is represented by 100°, so the difference is 40°. This as a fraction is $^{40}/_{360} = ^1/_9$ so you need to find $^1/_9$ of the total time. The total time is $4^1/_2$ hours. Therefore $4^1/_2$ × 60 = 240 + 30 = 270 minutes, so $^1/_9$ × 270 = 30 minutes.

☐ **21** *(e)*
Walking the dog is represented by 90°, which is equivalent to 27 minutes. Each degree therefore represents $^{27}/_{90}$ minutes = 0.3 minutes. Thus, 50° of eating represents 50 × 0.3 = 15 minutes.

☐ **22** *(a)*
Programmes represent 25% of the chart and 25% of £160 is £40. This can be worked out by the sum $^{25}/_{100}$ × £160 = £40.

☐ **23** *(b)*
Firstly add all the visitors: 5 + 10 + 19 + 8 + 18 = 60. Each person is represented by $^{360}/_{60}$ = 6°. The dodgems has five visitors so is therefore represented by 5 × 6 = 30°.

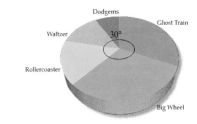

A23

☐ **24** *(a)*
Firstly add all the visitors: 5 + 10 + 19 + 8 + 18 = 60. Each person is represented by $^{360}/_{60}$ = 6°. The rollercoaster has 10 visitors, so is therefore represented by 10 × 6 = 60°.

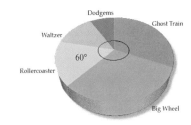

A24

☐ **25** *(c)*
Firstly add all the visitors: 5 + 10 + 19 + 8 + 18 = 60. Each person is represented represented by $^{360}/_{60}$ = 6°. The waltzer has eight visitors, so is therefore represented by 8 × 6 = 48°.

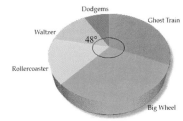

A25

☐ **26** *(d)*
The new total amount of visitors is 10 + 8 + 18 = 36, so each person is represented by $^{360}/_{36}$ = 10°. The number of people visiting the waltzer is eight, and therefore the amount of degrees is 8 × 10 = 80°.

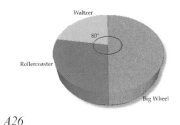

A26

☐ **27** *(a)*
The fraction of girls who like blue is represented by 90°, which is $^1/_4$ of 360°. The total number of girls is 80 and so $^1/_4$ of 80 is 20.

☐ **28** *(b)*
The fraction of girls who like green is represented by 45°, which is $^1/_8$ of 360°. The total number of girls is 80 and so $^1/_8$ of 80 is 10.

☐ **29** *(e)*
Red represents $^1/_2$ of the chart which is 50%. The total number of girls is 80 and so $^1/_2$ of this is 40.

☐ **30** *(b)*
False. There are six diamonds and 10 hearts = 16 red. Therefore, there must have been 14 black cards dealt.

☐ **31** *(e)*
There are nine clubs, six diamonds, and 10 hearts, making 25 altogether. Therefore, there must have been 30 − 25 = 5 spades.

☐ **32** *(a)*
The points on the scatter graph slope upwards and to the right indicating that there is a connection between height and weight. The heavier the student (i.e. the further to the right), the taller the student will be (i.e. the further upwards on the graph). This is known as a positive correlation.

☐ **33** *(a)*
The best straight line passes through the point ($\bar{x}$, $\bar{y}$), where x is the mean of one set (L in this case) and y is the mean of the other set (W in this case).

☐ **34** *(e)*
You need to go along from 30 on the y-axis (m) to the line of best fit, then down to the x-axis (p), as shown on the following diagram.

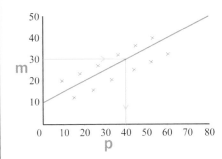

A34

☐ **35** *(b)*
You need to go up from 20 and 70 on the x-axis (p) to the line of best fit, then across to the y-axis (m), as shown on the following diagram.

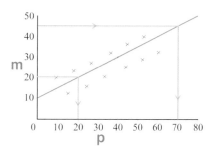

A35

☐ **36** *(a)*
True. The diagram below shows that both values are 120.

Mass (kg)	10–	11–	12–	13–	14–	15–	16–
Frequency	14	22	27	30	16	11	0
C. F.		43	36	63	93	109	120	120

A36, A37, A38

☐ **37** *(c)*
The diagram above shows that the value of r is 109.

☐ **38** *(d)*
The diagram above shows that the cumulative frequency of all masses up to and including "13- kg" are 93.

Analysing and interpreting data

☐ **1** *(a)*
True. This is the correct way to draw a frequency polygon.

☐ **2** *(a)*
True. It is the area of a bar in a histogram that represents the frequency of the class. However, if the bars of the histogram are all of the same width, then the most frequent class is given by the highest bar.

☐ **3** *(a)*
True. The relative frequencies are an estimate of the probabilities of an experiment. When added up, they must total to 1 because this represents the probabilities of all the possible outcomes.

☐ **4** *(b)*
False. The mean is not the middle number. It is the median that is 11.

☐ **5** *(b)*
False. The mode is the most frequently occurring number, which is 19. (It occurs three times.)

☐ **6** *(b)*
False. The median is the middle value when the numbers are written in order. In this case, the median is 35 since the order is 31, 31, 31, 32, 35, 36, 36, 37, 38.

☐ **7** *(b)*
False. The range is highest – lowest, which is 108 – 93 = 15.

☐ **8** *(a)*
True. (8 + 10 + 13 + 14 + 15) ÷ 5 = 60 ÷ 5 = 12.

☐ **9** *(a)*
True. Putting the numbers in order gives 16, 16, 19, 22, 23, 24, 24. The middle number is 22.

☐ **10** *(a)*
True. The most frequently occurring number is 15.

☐ **11** *(a)*
True. (10 × 3) + (20 × 6) + (30 × 3) + (40 × 4) = 30 + 120 + 90 + 160 = 400. Mean = 400 ÷ 16 = 25.

☐ **12** *(b)*
False. The mode (or modal colour) is the colour that occurs the most frequently. In this case, blue is the modal colour as it occurs the most often.

☐ **13** *(b)*
False. The mean number is (17 + 28 + 32 + 36 + 36 + 43) ÷ 6 = 192 ÷ 6 = 32. (The mode is 36 since 36 occurs twice and the other numbers occur once only.)

☐ **14** *(b)*
False. The range is a single number, which is 43 – 17 = 26.

☐ **15** *(a)*
True. The median mark is the mark scored by the middle student when the marks have been arranged in order. (Because there is an even number of students, the median is halfway between the 25th and 26th students). The first 14 students scored less than 40 marks, the next 29 scored between 40 and 59. However, this range includes the 25th and 26th student – hence, the median mark must be in the range 40-59.

☐ **16** *(a)*
True. The median value is obtained by drawing a line from halfway up the cumulative frequency axis (50 in this case) horizontally to the curve, then down to the mass axis.

☐ **17** *(b)*
False. The upper quartile is obtained by drawing a line from ³/₄ the way up the cumulative frequency axis across to the curve, then down to the mass axis.

☐ **18** *(a)*
True. The interquartile range is the range between the quartiles.

☐ **19** *(a)*
True. The mean value is (11 + 12 + 13 + 14 + 15) ÷ 5 = 13. $(11 – 13)^2 + (12 – 13)^2 + (13 – 13)^2 + (14 – 13)^2 + (15 – 13)^2 = 4 + 1 + 0 + 1 + 4 = 10$. Hence the variance is $^{10}/_5 = 2$, and the standard deviation is $\sqrt{2} = 1.414$ (3 d.p.).

☐ **20** *(d)*
The highest temperature was 16°C on Wednesday of the first week and the lowest temperature was 4°C on Saturday of the first week, so the difference between the two is 16 – 4 = 12°C.

☐ **21** *(c)*
The modal class is the class with the highest frequency. 20-29 occurs more often than any other class.

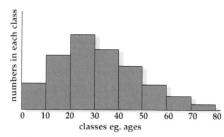

A21

☐ **22** *(b)*
The number 41 occurs more often than any other number.

☐ **23** *(d)*
In order the numbers are 38, 38, 41, 41, 41, 43, 43, 44, 46, 47, 48, 49. The median is the middle number (or halfway between the two middle numbers if there is an even number of values). As both middle numbers are 43, then this is the median.

☐ **24** *(c)*
The sum of the 12 numbers is 528. The mean is therefore 528 ÷ 12 = 44.

☐ **25** *(b)*
In order the numbers are 9, 9, 10, 10, 11,

12, 12, 14, 17, 18, 19. The median is the 6th number, which is 12. The lower quartile is the middle number of the remaining lower half (9, 9, 10, 10, 11), which is 10.

☐ **26** *(e)*
In order the numbers are 9, 9, 10, 10, 11, 12, 12, 14, 17, 18, 19. The median is the 6th number, which is 12. The upper quartile is the middle number of the remaining upper half (12, 14, 17, 18, 19), which is 17.

☐ **27** *(b)*
Highest – lowest = 19 – 9 = 10.

☐ **28** *(a)*
The total number of spots is $(1 \times 7) + (2 \times 8) + (3 \times 10) + (4 \times 6) + (5 \times 4) + (6 \times 5) = 127$. The mean number is $127 \div 40 = 3.175$.

☐ **29** *(d)*
The score that occurred more often than any other was 3.

☐ **30** *(d)*
The lowest seven scores were 1 and the next eight scores were 2 (i.e. a total of 15 scores). As the next 10 scores were 3, then the 20th and 21st scores must have been 3. Therefore, the median is 3.

☐ **31** *(a)*
A line drawn across from 100 on the cumulative frequency axis to the curve, and then drawn down to the test score axis gives a score of 46.

☐ **32** *(c)*
The upper quartile is 61 and the lower quartile is 52. Hence, the interquartile range is 61 – 52 = 9.

☐ **33** *(d)*
11Q has a median of 57 and 11P has a median of 46. Hence the difference is 57 – 46 = 11 marks.

☐ **34** *(b)*
All 200 of 11Q plus all but 44 of 11P scored over 40 marks. 200 + 156 = 356.

☐ **35** *(b)*
For 11P, 200 – 152 = 48 scored 50 marks or more. For 11Q, 200 – 30 = 170 scored 50 marks or more. Therefore, 170 + 48 = 218 scored 50 or more marks.

☐ **36** *(a)*
True. The mean of set A is $(6 + 7 + 8 + 12 + 12 + 15) \div 6 = 60 \div 6 = 10$. The four numbers in set B must add up to $4 \times 10 = 40$. Therefore, d must be $40 - (7 + 9 + 9) = 40 - 25 = 15$.

☐ **37** *(b)*
False. The range is the same (31 – 18 = 13 for P and 41 – 28 = 13 for Q), but the mean is $(18 + 19 + 22 + 30 + 31) \div 5 = 24$ for P and $(28 + 29 + 32 + 40 + 41) \div 5 = 34$ for Q.

☐ **38** *(b)*
False. The range of R is 22 – 10 = 12, so the range of set S is 6. If 4 is the lowest value, then k would be 4 + 6 = 10. If, however, 8 was the highest value, then k would be 8 – 6 = 2. Therefore, there are two possible answers for k in this case.

☐ **39** *(b)*
False. Class 11PP had more students scoring the higher marks and less scoring the lower marks than class 11HS. The mean for 11PP will therefore be higher than the mean of class 11HS.

☐ **40** *(a)*
True. Team F had a total points score of $12 \times 16 = 192$, whereas team G's total points score was $10 \times 20 = 200$.

Probability

☐ **1** *(b)*
False. The National Lottery draws are totally independent from one draw to the next. The previous draws have no effect on the next draw.

☐ **2** *(b)*
False. You have to multiply along the branches. So, the probability (B, B) = $0.2 \times 0.2 = 0.04$.

☐ **3** *(c)*
Point C is in the centre of the scale and has a probability of 0.5. The event has an equally likely chance of happening as it has of not happening so it can be said that it has an even chance of happening.

☐ **4** *(e)*
Point E has a probability of 1, meaning that the event is certain to happen.

☐ **5** *(a)*
Point A has a probability of 0, meaning that it is impossible for the event to happen.

☐ **6** *(e)*
On this evidence, 4 out of the 40 trials scored 1, so the expected probability would be $^4/_{40} = ^1/_{10}$.

☐ **7** *(b)*
A probability must be a number – either a decimal, fraction, or a percentage, and not any word or phrase.

☐ **8** *(a)*
There are 12 letters in the word MATHEMATICAL and there are two T's, so the probability is $^2/_{12} = ^1/_6$.

☐ **9** *(d)*
There are 12 letters in the word MATHEMATICAL and there are two M's and one L, so the probability of an M or an L is $^3/_{12} = ^1/_4$.

☐ **10** *(c)*
The total number of balls is 3 + 4 + 2 + 1 = 10. There are three red balls so the probability is $^3/_{10}$.

☐ **11** *(e)*
The total number of balls is 3 + 4 + 2 + 1 = 10. There are two blacks so the probability is $^2/_{10} = ^1/_5$.

☐ **12** *(a)*
The word MISSISSIPPI has four different letters – M, I, S, P, so the number of letters that can be drawn are 26 – 4 = 22. The probability of not getting one of them is $^{22}/_{26} = ^{11}/_{13}$.

☐ **13** *(c)*
There are four bags containing an odd number of sweets. So, the probability will be $^4/_{10}$ or $^2/_5$.

☐ **14** *(e)*
There are five bags containing more than 13 sweets (15, 16, 16, 14, 16), so the probability will be $^5/_{10}$ or $^1/_2$.

☐ **15** *(a)*
Multiples of 3 are 3 and 6, so the probability of this happening is $^2/_6 = ^1/_3$.

☐ **16** *(b)*
The probability of calling correctly is $^1/_2$. This is the same even if he had lost the last 1000 times because the coin has no memory of what the previous spin was.

☐ **17** *(b)*
There are five teams so each one has a probability of $^1/_5$ of winning. Therefore, the probability of A not winning is $^4/_5$.

☐ **18** *(c)*
Cecil could finish first, second, or third. The probability of him finishing first or second is therefore $^1/_3 + ^1/_3 = ^2/_3$.

☐ **19** *(a)*
There are 89 numbers from 11 to 99 and Brian has two of these, so the probability is $^2/_{89}$.

☐ **20** *(e)*
As there are two dice, each with six outcomes, the total number is $6 \times 6 = 36$, as shown in the table below.

133

	1	2	3	4	5	6
1	2	3	4	5	6	7
2	3	4	5	6	7	8
3	4	5	6	7	8	9
4	5	6	7	8	9	10
5	6	7	8	9	10	11
6	7	8	9	10	11	12

A20

□ **21** *(e)*
There are 36 outcomes for two dice, as shown in the table below. Out of these, there are six that are doubles, so the probability is $^6/_{36} = ^1/_6$.

	1	2	3	4	5	6
1	2	3	4	5	6	7
2	3	4	5	6	7	8
3	4	5	6	7	8	9
4	5	6	7	8	9	10
5	6	7	8	9	10	11
6	7	8	9	10	11	12

A21

□ **22** *(a)*
There are 36 possible outcomes for two dice, as shown in the following table. The multiples of 3 are 3 (1, 2; 2, 1); 6 (1, 5; 5, 1; 2, 4; 4, 2; 3, 3); 9 (4, 5; 5, 4; 6, 3; 3, 6) and 12 (6, 6). This adds up to 12 ways out of 36, so the probability is $^{12}/_{36} = ^1/_3$.

	1	2	3	4	5	6
1	2	3	4	5	6	7
2	3	4	5	6	7	8
3	4	5	6	7	8	9
4	5	6	7	8	9	10
5	6	7	8	9	10	11
6	7	8	9	10	11	12

A22

□ **23** *(b)*
The die has six outcomes and the coin has two outcomes so the combined outcome is 2 × 6 = 12, as shown in the table below.

Die	Coin	Die	Coin
1	H	1	T
2	H	2	T
3	H	3	T
4	H	4	T
5	H	5	T
6	H	6	T

A23

□ **24** *(a)*
The table below shows that there are five totals over 6. The probability is therefore $^5/_{12}$.

1st Spinner	2nd Spinner	Total
1	1	2
1	2	3
1	5	6
1	6	7
3	1	4
3	2	5
3	5	8
3	6	9
4	1	5
4	2	6
4	5	9
4	6	10

A24

□ **25** *(a)*
Each ball is equally likely to be drawn so the probability of drawing a red ball from the bag is $^3/_9 = ^1/_3$.

□ **26** *(a)*
All the probabilities have to add up to 1 as these are the only events that can happen, so 0.1 + 0.15 + P(Blue) + 0.25 = 1. P(Blue) + 0.5 = 1. P(Blue) = 0.5.

Colour	Red	Green	Blue	Black
Probability	0.1	0.15	0.5	0.25

A26

□ **27** *(d)*
All the probabilities have to add up to 1 as these are the only events that can happen, so the probability of any colour except green is the number needed to add to 0.25 in order to get 1. This number is 1 – 0.25 = 0.75.

Colour	Not Green	Green
Probability	0.75	0.25

A27

□ **28** *(d)*
The combined probabilities for winning are 0.01 + 0.07 + 0.12 + 0.2 = 0.4. If a win doesn't occur, then the result must be a loss. Therefore, the probability of a loss is 1 – 0.4 = 0.6.

Points	10	5	3	1	Lose
Probability	0.01	0.07	0.12	0.2	0.6

A28

□ **29** *(a)*
You can't win one game with both 3 and 10 points, so use the "or" rule to add the probabilities, which gives 0.01 + 0.12 = 0.13.

□ **30** *(b)*
The probability of two heads is $^1/_4$ and the probability of two tails is also $^1/_4$. The probability of one or the other is $^1/_4 + ^1/_4 = ^1/_2$. As the probabilities are mutually exclusive (i.e. you cannot throw two heads and two tails at the same time), use the "or" rule to add the probabilities together.

□ **31** *(c)*
The events "landing on red" or "landing on an odd number" are not mutually exclusive as they can happen at the same time (i.e. when it lands on red 1). Therefore, the answer must be read from the board instead, which gives five out of the eight sections, or a probability of $^5/_8$.

□ **32** *(d)*
The two events are mutually exclusive (i.e. they cannot happen at the same time). So, to find the probability, add the two separate probabilities together, which gives $^2/_8 + ^4/_8 = ^6/_8 = ^3/_4$.

□ **33** *(c)*
The probability of fault is $^{12}/_{50} = 0.24$, so the probability of fault and fault = 0.24 × 0.24 = 0.0576.

□ **34** *(a)*
The probability of fault is $^{12}/_{50} = 0.24$, so the probability of not having a fault is 0.76. Therefore, the probability of not fault and not fault = 0.76 × 0.76 = 0.5776.

□ **35** *(e)*
The problem is equivalent to drawing a red from a bag that has two reds and one blue ball in it. This is because the balls have already been removed and they do not figure in the probability of the next draw.

□ **36** *(d)*
The relative frequency is the number of times the event happens divided by the total number of trials. This is $^{27}/_{98}$.

□ **37** *(e)*
The relative frequency is the number of times the event happens divided by the total number of trials. This is $^{20}/_{98}$.

□ **38** *(a)*
The relative frequency of an event is an estimation of the probability of that event. The relative frequency is the

number of times the event happens divided by the total number of trials. In this case it is $^{40}/_{100} = 0.4$.

☐ 39 (c)
The relative frequency is the number of times the event happens divided by the total number of trials. Here it is a probability of less than 6, i.e. 5 or less that gives a relative frequency of $^{12}/_{100} + ^{18}/_{100} = 0.3$.

☐ 40 (d)
The two branches must cover all possible outcomes. Therefore, if one branch is red the other is everything else, i.e. not red.

☐ 41 (b)
The probabilities are written along the branches, and the probability of a red counter is $^3/_{10}$, so the probability of not getting a red is $^7/_{10}$.

☐ 42 (b)
Multiply along the red branches, which gives a probability of $^3/_{10} \times ^3/_{10} = ^9/_{100}$.

☐ 43 (d)
The probability of at least one red counter is 1 – probability of no red counters. This is $1 - (^7/_{10} \times ^7/_{10}) = 1 - ^{49}/_{100} = ^{51}/_{100}$. Alternatively, you could add up the probabilities at the ends of all the other branches.

☐ 44 (e)
The probabilities are shown on the diagram below. The two probabilities are highlighted and added together: $^6/_{25} + ^6/_{25} = ^{12}/_{25}$.

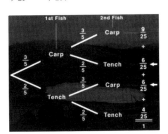

A44

☐ 45 (c)
The only probability not wanted is the branch that is carp, carp. The other probabilities add up to $^{16}/_{25}$.

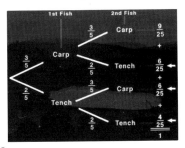

A45

☐ 46 (d)
Add the probabilities of the GR and RG branches together, which gives $^8/_{81} + ^8/_{81} = ^{16}/_{81}$.

☐ 47 (c)
The branches not wanted are RR, GG, and BB, so the probability is $1 - (^{16}/_{81} + ^4/_{81} + ^9/_{81}) = 1 - ^{29}/_{81} = ^{52}/_{81}$.

☐ 48 (b)
The only combination that does not yield a total of at least 3 is 1 + 1 = 2. So, the probabilities wanted are all the others, i.e. $1 - ^{16}/_{36} = ^{20}/_{36}$, which can be simplified to $^5/_9$.

	1	1	1	1	2	3
1	2	2	2	2	3	4
1	2	2	2	2	3	4
1	2	2	2	2	3	4
1	2	2	2	2	3	4
2	3	3	3	3	4	5
3	4	4	4	4	5	6

A48

☐ 49 (c)
The numbers needed are highlighted on the following diagram.

	1	1	1	1	2	3
1	2	2	2	2	3	4
1	2	2	2	2	3	4
1	2	2	2	2	3	4
1	2	2	2	2	3	4
2	3	3	3	3	4	5
3	4	4	4	4	5	6

A49

☐ 50 (e)
The expected number of times two heads turn up is equal to the probability ($^1/_4$) multiplied by the number of trials (360), which gives $^1/_4 \times 360 = 90$.

Probability
Higher Levels

☐ 51 (a)
If a red counter is drawn then there is one less counter in the bag. The possible combinations are shown on the tree diagram below.

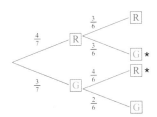

A51

☐ 52 (d)
If a red counter is drawn then there is one less counter in the bag. The possible combinations are shown on the tree diagram below.

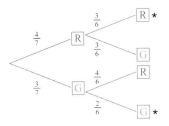

A52

☐ 53 (b)
A red counter has a probability of $^4/_7$ and if that is drawn, a green counter has a $^3/_6$ chance of being drawn, as the red counter has been removed. The combined probability is therefore $^4/_7 \times ^3/_6 = ^2/_7$.

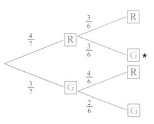

A53

☐ 54 (a)
The following tree diagram shows the branches wanted are GRR, RGR, RRG, and RRR, which gives a probability of $^{42}/_{720} + ^{42}/_{720} + ^{42}/_{720} + ^6/_{720} = ^{130}/_{720} = ^{11}/_{60}$.

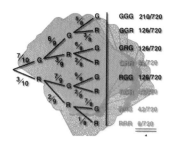

A54

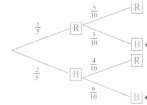

GGG 210/720
GGR 126/720
GRG 126/720
GRR 36/720
RGG 126/720
RGR 42/720
RRG 42/720
RRR 6/720

□ **55** *(c)*

The probability of at least one green card is equivalent to 1 – P (all red) = $1 - (^3/_{10} \times {}^2/_9 \times {}^1/_8) = {}^{119}/_{120}$.

□ **56** *(d)*

The probability depends on the draw from the first bag, i.e. if it is blue or red. The combinations shown on the diagram below are either red, blue or blue, blue.

A56